A TREATMENT IMPROVEMENT PROTOCOL

Addressing Fetal Alcohol Spectrum Disorders (FASD)

TIP 58

U.S. DEPARTMENT OF HEALTH AND HUMAN SERVICES
Substance Abuse and Mental Health Services Administration
Center for Substance Abuse Prevention

1 Choke Cherry Road
Rockville, MD 20857

Acknowledgments

This publication was produced by Northrop Grumman under the FASD Center for Excellence contract number HHSS283201200017I/HHSS28342002T with the Substance Abuse and Mental Health Services Administration (SAMHSA), U.S. Department of Health and Human Services (HHS). Patricia B. Getty, Ph.D., Jon Dunbar-Cooper, M.A., C.P.P., CDR Josefine Haynes-Battle, R.N., B.S.N., M.S.N., and LCDR Daniel A. Bailey, M.S., M.B.A., served as the Center for Substance Abuse Prevention (CSAP) FASD Center for Excellence Contracting Officer Representatives, with Dr. Getty providing guidance, comments, and contributions throughout the development and review of this publication.

Disclaimer

Public Domain Notice

Electronic Access and Copies of Publication

This publication may be ordered from SAMHSA's Publications Ordering Web page at http://store.samhsa.gov/home. Or, please call SAMHSA at 1-877-SAMHSA-7 (1-877-726-4727) (English and Español).

Recommended Citation

Substance Abuse and Mental Health Services Administration. *Addressing Fetal Alcohol Spectrum Disorders (FASD)*. Treatment Improvement Protocol (TIP) Series 58. HHS Publication No. (SMA) 13-4803. Rockville, MD: Substance Abuse and Mental Health Services Administration, 2014.

Originating Office

Quality Improvement and Workforce Development Branch, Division of Services Improvement, Center for Substance Abuse Treatment, Substance Abuse and Mental Health Services Administration, 1 Choke Cherry Road, Rockville, MD 20857.

HHS Publication No. (SMA) 13-4803
Printed 2014

Contents

Consensus Panel

Chairs, Part 1 and Part 2 Consensus Panels

Sterling K. Clarren, M.D., FAAP
Chief Executive Officer and Scientific
    Director
Canada NW FASD Research Network,
    Vancouver, British Columbia
Clinical Professor of Pediatrics
University of British Columbia, Vancouver,
    British Columbia
Clinical Professor of Pediatrics
University of Washington, Seattle, Washington

Melinda Ohlemiller, M.A.
Chief Executive Officer
Nurses for Newborns Foundation
St. Louis, Missouri

Part 1 Consensus Panel Members

Susan Adubato, Ph.D.
Director
Northern New Jersey FAS Diagnostic Center,
    Newark, New Jersey
Director
New Jersey/North East FASD Education and
    Research Center
University of Medicine and Dentistry of New
    Jersey
New Jersey Medical School, Newark, New
    Jersey

Mercedes Alejandro
FASD Prevention Advocate
The Arc of Greater Houston
Houston, Texas

Mary C. DeJoseph, D.O.
Adjunct Faculty
Philadelphia College of Osteopathic Medicine
Palmyra, New Jersey

Norma Finkelstein, Ph.D., LICSW
Executive Director
Institute for Health and Recovery
Cambridge, Massachusetts

Therese Grant, Ph.D.
Ann Streissguth Endowed Professor in Fetal
    Alcohol Spectrum Disorders
University of Washington School of Medicine
Director, Washington State Parent-Child
    Assistance Program
Seattle, Washington

Patricia Moran
Program Manager
White Earth Substance Abuse Program
Ponsford, Minnesota

Mark B. Sobell, Ph.D., ABPP
Professor /& Co-Director
Healthy Lifestyles Guided Self-Change
    Program
Center for Psychological Studies
Nova Southeastern University
Fort Lauderdale, Florida

Jasmine Suarez-O'Connor
Network Coordinator
Self Advocates with FASD in Action (SAFA)
Scotia, New York

Diane L. O'Connor
FASD Prevention Initiative
Research Foundation of Mental Hygiene
Support Person
Self Advocates with FASD in Action
Albany, New York

Part 2 Consensus Panel Members

Hortensia Amaro, Ph.D.
Hortensia Amaro, Ph.D.
Associate Dean and Distinguished Professor
Bouve College of Health Sciences
Director, Institute on Urban Health Research
Northeastern University
Boston, Massachusetts

L. Diane Casto, M.P.A.
Manager
Behavioral Health, Prevention & Early
    Intervention Services
Alaska Department of Health and Social
    Services
Juneau, Alaska

Deborah E. Cohen, Ph.D.
Director
Office for Prevention of Mental Retardation
    and Developmental Disabilities
State of New Jersey (Retired)

Norma Finkelstein, Ph.D., LICSW
Executive Director
Institute for Health and Recovery
Cambridge, Massachusetts

Sidney L. Gardner, M.P.A.
President
Children and Family Futures
Irvine, California

Pamela Gillen, N.D., R.N., CACIII
Director
Colorado FASD/ATOD Substances
    Prevention Outreach Project (COFAS)
University of Colorado at Denver
Aurora, Colorado

Logan Lewis, LMSW, CASAC
Clinical Director
Camelot Counseling
Jamaica, New York

Donna N. McNelis, Ph.D.
Director, Behavioral Healthcare Education
Vice-Chair, Program Development &
    Administration
Professor of Psychiatry
Drexel University College of Medicine
Philadelphia, Pennsylvania

Sara Messelt
Executive Director
Minnesota Organization on Fetal Alcohol
    Syndrome (MOFAS)
St. Paul, Minnesota

Heather Carmichael Olson, Ph.D.
Department of Psychiatry and Behavioral
    Sciences
University of Washington School of Medicine
Seattle Children's Hospital Child Psychiatry
    Outpatient Clinic
Fetal Alcohol Syndrome Diagnostic and
    Prevention Network
Seattle Children's Hospital Research Institute
Families Moving Forward Program
Seattle, Washington

Deborah Stone, Ph.D.
Social Science Analyst
Center for Mental Health Services (CMHS)
Rockville, Maryland (Retired)

What Is a TIP?

The Treatment Improvement Protocol (TIP) series, which has been published by the Substance Abuse and Mental Health Services Administration (SAMHSA) within the U.S. Department of Health and Human Services (HHS) since 1993, has generally offered best-practices guidelines for the treatment of substance use disorders. For this TIP, the Center for Substance Abuse Prevention (CSAP), a sub-agency within SAMHSA, has drawn on the experience and knowledge of clinical, research, and administrative experts. As behavioral health disorders are increasingly recognized as a major problem, the audience for the TIPs is expanding beyond public and private treatment facilities to include practitioners in mental health, criminal justice, primary care, public health, and other healthcare and social service settings.

The recommendations contained in each TIP are grounded in an evidence base. Evidence includes scientific research findings and the opinion of the TIP consensus panel of experts that a particular practice will produce a specific clinical outcome (measurable change in client status). In making recommendations, the consensus panel engages in a process of "evidence-based thinking" in which they consider scientific research, clinical practice theory, practice principles, and practice guidelines, as well as their own individual clinical experiences. Based on this thinking, they arrive at recommendations for optimal clinical approaches for given clinical situations. Relevant citations (to research outcome reports, theoretic formulations, and practice principles and guidelines) are provided.

TIP Format

This TIP is organized into three parts:
- Part 1 for behavioral health practitioners focuses on providing appropriate counseling methods and frameworks.
- Part 2 for program administrators focuses on providing administrative support to implement adoption of the counseling recommendations made in Part 1.
- Part 3 for clinical supervisors, program administrators, and interested practitioners is an online literature review that provides an in-depth look at relevant published resources. Part 3 will be updated regularly following publication of the TIP.

Ideally, it is envisioned that a supervisor might assemble a small group of counselors, distribute copies of this TIP (which are free), and begin a series of six or so meetings where the materials in the TIP would be reviewed, discussed, and in other ways used as an educational and training vehicle for the improvement of treatment skills (with the particulars of how this training would be done determined by the individual supervisor, based upon her or his unique situation, needs, and preferences). Thus, after a relatively short period of time and with only limited additional resources, this TIP could help to meet the challenge of fostering a specific kind of improvement in service delivery.

Development Process

The need for this TIP was identified through a collaborative discussion with leadership from each of SAMHSA's three Centers; CSAP, the Center for Substance Abuse Treatment (CSAT), and the Center for Mental Health Services (CMHS). Two consensus panels of experts were convened; one for clinical issues, and the other for administrative guidelines. The TIP was then field reviewed by an external group of subject matter experts, who provided suggestions for further refining the document (see appendix J).

TIPs Online

TIPs can be accessed via the Internet at **http://store.samhsa.gov/home**. The online *Addressing Fetal Alcohol Spectrum Disorders: Part 3, A Review of the Literature*, which will be updated periodically, is available at **http://store.samhsa.gov/home**.

Terminology

Throughout the TIP, the term "behavioral health" is used to refer to both substance abuse treatment and mental health settings. (The term can, in fact, refer to many types of health settings, but the primary audiences for this TIP are substance abuse treatment and mental health providers.) The term "substance abuse" has been used to refer to both substance abuse and substance dependence (as defined by the *Diagnostic and Statistical Manual of Mental Disorders, 5th edition* [DSM-5] [American Psychiatric Association 2013]). This term was chosen partly because substance abuse treatment professionals commonly use the term "substance abuse" to describe any excessive use of addictive substances. In this TIP, the term refers to the use of alcohol as well as other substances of abuse. Readers should note the context in which the term occurs in order to determine what possible range of meanings it covers; in most cases, however, the term refers to all varieties of substance use disorders described by the DSM-V.

Foreword

The Treatment Improvement Protocol (TIP) series supports SAMHSA's mission of building resilience and facilitating recovery for people with or at risk for mental or substance use disorders by providing best practices guidance to clinicians, program administrators, and payors to improve the quality and effectiveness of service delivery and, thereby, promote recovery. TIPs are the result of careful consideration of all relevant clinical and health services research findings, demonstrated experience, and implementation requirements. Clinical researchers, clinicians, and program administrators meet to debate and discuss their particular areas of expertise until they reach a consensus on best practices. This panel's work is then reviewed and critiqued by field reviewers.

The talent, dedication, and hard work that TIP panelists and reviewers bring to this highly participatory process have helped bridge the gap between the promise of research and the needs of practicing clinicians and administrators to serve, in the most scientifically sound and effective ways, people who abuse substances. We are grateful to all who have joined with us to contribute to advances in the substance abuse treatment field.

Pamela S. Hyde, J.D.
Administrator, Substance Abuse and Mental Health Services Administration

Dr. H. Westley Clark, M.D., J.D., M.P.H., CAS, FASAM
Director
Center for Substance Abuse Treatment
Substance Abuse and Mental Health Services Administration

Frances M. Harding
Director
Center for Substance Abuse Prevention
Substance Abuse and Mental Health Services Administration

A. Kathryn Power, M.Ed.
Director
Center for Mental Health Services
Substance Abuse and Mental Health Services Administration

How This TIP Is Organized

This TIP is divided into three parts:
- *Addressing Fetal Alcohol Spectrum Disorders, Part 1: Background and Clinical Strategies for FASD Prevention and Intervention*
- *Addressing Fetal Alcohol Spectrum Disorders, Part 2: Administrator's Guide to Implementing FASD Prevention and Intervention*
- *Addressing Fetal Alcohol Spectrum Disorders, Part 3: Literature Review*

Parts 1 and 2 are presented in this publication; Part 3 is available only online, at **http://store.samhsa.gov/home**. Each part is described below.

Part 1 of the TIP is for behavioral health providers and consists of three chapters:
- Chapter 1 discusses approaches to preventing FASD; that is, assisting women who are in treatment settings and are pregnant or may become pregnant to remain abstinent from alcohol. In providing these guidelines, this TIP adopts the Institute of Medicine (IOM) model for prevention, which sees prevention as a step along a continuum that also incorporates treatment and maintenance.
- Chapter 2 discusses methods for identifying individuals in treatment who have or may have an FASD, referring them for diagnosis where possible, and providing appropriate interventions to meet their needs.
- Chapter 3 provides clinical vignettes designed to realistically portray the provider–client interactions that might take place when providing FASD prevention or interventions.

Part 2 is an implementation guide for program administrators and consists of two chapters.
- Chapter 1 lays out the rationale for the approach taken in chapter 2 and will help readers understand how administrators can provide support for programs and counselors as they address FASD. It is hoped that this knowledge will enhance the ability of treatment programs to address FASD concurrently with other behavioral health needs; addiction, mental health issues, etc.
- Chapter 2 provides detailed information on how to achieve high-quality implementation of the recommendations in *Part 1*.

Part 3 of this TIP is a literature review on the topic of FASD and is available for use by clinical supervisors, interested counselors, and administrators. *Part 3* includes literature that addresses both clinical and administrative concerns. To facilitate ongoing updates, the literature review will only be available online at **http://store.samhsa.gov/home**.

Preface

Giving Voice to a Hidden Population

- A woman gives birth to a child with a Fetal Alcohol Spectrum Disorder (FASD); no one told her that alcohol consumption during pregnancy could harm the baby.

- A man is repeatedly kicked out of various forms of treatment for noncompliance; he never means to be noncompliant, his special needs and lack of understanding are simply never recognized.

- A teen-aged girl doesn't receive appropriate screening for alcohol use during her pregnancy; her child is removed when she's identified with a substance use disorder, and her child is later found to have an FASD.

- A man repeatedly loses jobs because he can't "follow orders;" he ends up homeless and cycles repeatedly through the social service system.

These stories are not unusual. They are not "worst case scenarios." They are the all-too-common realities of people with an FASD, or women who wanted to have a healthy child but weren't given the basic help they needed before and during pregnancy. And sometimes these realities overlap.

Addressing Fetal Alcohol Spectrum Disorders was written to help you offer hope to these individuals when they present in your setting. This TIP will not ask you to implement a whole new way of treating clients, although you may discover alternative approaches that you want to explore. Rather, it asks you to see people who have or may have an FASD as you see any individual in your care with a significant co-occurring life issue that should be recognized and incorporated into treatment planning. This TIP also asks you to see pregnant women who consume alcohol not through a lens of judgment but as women in need, for whom even a few minutes of information and education can make a lifetime of difference for their health and the health of their babies.

This TIP is also about hope for you as a substance abuse or mental health treatment professional because it gives you another way to view the clients who "just don't get it" or who seem to want to succeed in treatment but can't follow directions, don't make it to appointments, grow restless in group sessions, or generally seem "resistant" with no clear explanation. You can "reframe" your thinking about these clients. Not all of these cases will be explained by FASD, obviously, but making FASD awareness a part of the culture of your agency widens the net of understanding that you can offer to your clients and increases your staff's capabilities for achieving positive outcomes with a higher percentage of them.

Ultimately, SAMHSA's goal is to provide knowledge and assistance to help substance abuse and mental health treatment programs better serve their clients. Providing FASD-informed services is a part of that mission, and is the guiding principle behind the publication of this TIP. Thank you for taking the time to read this publication, and for potentially making a difference for a population that should not remain hidden any longer.

Executive Summary

Introduction

About FASD

Overview

Fetal Alcohol Spectrum Disorders (FASD) is a non-diagnostic umbrella term describing the range of effects that can occur in an individual whose mother consumed alcohol during pregnancy. These effects may include physical, mental, behavioral, and/or learning disabilities with possible lifelong implications. As is discussed in greater detail later in this TIP, these disorders often co-occur with substance abuse and mental health issues, and generally require treatment modifications for successful outcomes. They are 100 percent preventable, however, if those at risk of consuming alcohol during pregnancy are identified and effective prevention strategies are used.

Possible diagnoses within the spectrum include Fetal Alcohol Syndrome (FAS), Partial Fetal Alcohol Syndrome (pFAS), Alcohol-Related Neurodevelopmental Disorder (ARND), Static Encephalopathy/Alcohol-Exposed (SE/AE), and Neurobehavioral Disorder/Alcohol Exposed (ND/AE). (See box, *FASD: Key Terms*, for a fuller description of the disorders within the spectrum and related terminology.)

FASD: Key Terms

- *Fetal Alcohol Spectrum Disorders (FASD)*: Umbrella term referring to a group of disorders caused by prenatal exposure to alcohol; a particular condition on the fetal alcohol spectrum is referred to as "an FASD." Now generally considered to refer to Fetal Alcohol Syndrome (FAS), partial FAS (pFAS), Alcohol-Related Neurodevelopmental Disorders (ARND), Static Encephalopathy/Alcohol-Exposed (SE/AE), and Neurobehavioral Disorder/Alcohol Exposed (ND/AE). See below for all. A variety of diagnostic approaches exist for the disorders within the spectrum; the five most commonly used approaches are included in the key terms below, and are summarized/compared in Appendix E.

Disorders currently or previously described as forms of FASD (in alphabetical order):

- *Alcohol-Related Birth Defects (ARBD)*: Term used to describe individuals who present with congenital defects (including malformations and dysplasia), but not the growth or cognitive/behavioral impairments typically seen in FAS (see definition below). Now less used, although diagnostic guidelines still exist through the Institute of Medicine (IOM; see *Fetal Alcohol Syndrome: Diagnosis, Epidemiology, Prevention, and Treatment,* below in this box).

- *Alcohol-Related Neurodevelopmental Disorder (ARND)*: Term created by the IOM to describe individuals with prenatal alcohol exposure and neurodevelopmental abnormalities, but no

FAS facial phenotype. The neurodevelopmental abnormalities are characterized by a complex pattern of behavioral or cognitive conditions inconsistent with developmental level and not explained by genetic background or environment. Problems may include learning disabilities; school performance deficits; inadequate impulse control; social perceptual problems; language dysfunction; abstraction difficulties; mathematics deficiencies; and judgment, memory, and attention problems. The term ARND presents with the same limitations as the discontinued term Fetal Alcohol Effects (see definition below), as one cannot confirm that the neurodevelopmental disorder present in a child with prenatal alcohol exposure was caused by the alcohol exposure in the absence of the FAS facial phenotype. Some diagnostic systems replace the term ARND with Static Encephalopathy/Alcohol-Exposed and Neurobehavioral Disorder/Alcohol Exposed (SE/AE and ND/AE; see definitions below).

- *Fetal Alcohol Effects (FAE)*: Term introduced in the late 1970's to describe less complete partial expressions of FAS (see definition below) in individuals with prenatal alcohol exposure (Clarren & Smith, 1978). Aase, Jones, and Clarren (1995) expressed concern about the validity of the term FAE and proposed abandoning its clinical use, as it implied a causal association (between prenatal alcohol exposure and abnormalities observed in an individual patient) that could not actually be confirmed.

- *Fetal Alcohol Syndrome (FAS)*: Term for what is generally considered to be the most recognizable form of FASD. These individuals exhibit the FAS facial phenotype, impaired growth, and cognitive and behavioral abnormalities.

- *Neurobehavioral Disorder/Alcohol Exposed (ND/AE)*: Term used to describe individuals with prenatal alcohol exposure, moderate cognitive/behavioral impairment (equivalent to moderate ARND), and no FAS facial phenotype.

- *Partial FAS (pFAS)*: Term applied to individuals who exhibit FAS without growth deficiency, or exhibit FAS with most but not all of the facial features.

- *Static Encephalopathy/Alcohol Exposed (SE/AE)*: Term used to describe individuals with prenatal alcohol exposure and severe cognitive/behavioral impairment (equivalent to severe ARND), but no FAS facial phenotype.

Additional terms are presented in alphabetical order:

- *Alcohol-Exposed Pregnancy (AEP)*: Any pregnancy during which the woman drinks any amount of alcohol at any time during the pregnancy. This exposure does not mean the offspring has been affected in any way, but it does place the offspring at some degree of risk for an array of developmental difficulties, including damage to the brain and central nervous system, retardation of growth and other physical effects, and cognitive and behavioral impairments.

- *Diagnosis*: In the context of this TIP, "diagnosis" refers to the formal identification of an FASD by a qualified team and/or dysmorphologist (someone who specializes in structural, or birth, defects). When the TIP discusses the primary diagnosis that brought the client into your substance abuse or mental health setting, or for which your setting is primarily assessing or treating the client, it will be referred to as the "primary treatment issue."

- *Diffuse Brain Damage*: Damage to the brain that is not localized or necessarily the result of a specific traumatic incident to one part of the brain. Such damage can arise from other sources besides alcohol or occur from multiple sources including alcohol. As an AEP (see definition above) can impair the development of multiple parts of the brain of the fetus over the period of pregnancy, an FASD can be considered a manifestation of diffuse brain damage. However, not all diffuse brain damage is the result of alcohol and its expression does not always qualify as an FASD.

- *FASD 4-Digit Diagnostic Code* (Astley, 2004b): Comprehensive, reproducible method for diagnosing the full spectrum of outcomes of patients with prenatal alcohol exposure. First developed in 1997 by the Washington State FAS Diagnostic and Prevention Network (FAS DPN), the Code was revised in 1999 and again in 2004. Summarized in Appendix E.

- *Fetal Alcohol Spectrum Disorder: Canadian Guidelines for Diagnosis* (Chudley et al., 2005): Canadian guidelines for the diagnosis of FAS, pFAS, and ARND. Summarized in Appendix E.

- *Fetal Alcohol Syndrome: Diagnosis, Epidemiology, Prevention, and Treatment* (Stratton, Howe, Battaglia, & the Committee to Study Fetal Alcohol Syndrome, 1996): Diagnosis and treatment guidelines developed by the IOM and published in 1996. These guidelines would be revised by Hoyme, May, and Kalberg (2005) in *A Practical and Clinical Approach to the Diagnosis of Fetal Alcohol Spectrum Disorders: Clarification of the Institute of Medicine Criteria*. Each is summarized in Appendix E.

- *Fetal Alcohol Syndrome: Guidelines for Referral and Diagnosis* (Bertrand et al., 2004): FAS diagnosis and referral guidelines developed by the Centers for Disease Control and Prevention (CDC). Summarized in Appendix E.

- *Intervention*: In the context of this TIP, 'intervention' describes 1) a brief methodology for informing women of childbearing age about the results of alcohol screening and the dangers of alcohol use during pregnancy, or 2) the selection of an appropriate treatment methodology to best meet the needs of a client who has or may have an FASD, and any accompanying modifications or accommodations in treatment planning.

- *Screening*: 'Screening' is a familiar term in mental health and substance abuse treatment settings. Validated screening instruments for identifying alcohol use among women are available, and no modification to the basic understanding of screening is necessary for their use. To accomplish the important goal of screening for an individual with an FASD in your setting, formalized tools are limited. However, this TIP does provide indicators to look for, and screening may need to be done more informally through guided observation and/or diagnostic interviewing. In most cases, screening for an FASD will need to occur over time, rather than being a process that can be completed through the use of a simple, brief instrument administered once (e.g., at intake).

- *Static Encephalopathy*: Permanent or unchanging brain damage. Effects on development depend on the part(s) of the brain involved and the severity of the damage.

- *Teratogen*: Any substance that can damage a developing fetus. Common teratogens include alcohol, tobacco, lead, radiation, and exposure to infectious disease.

Prevalence

The prevalence of FAS in the United States has been estimated at 1–3 per 1,000 live births among the general population (Stratton et al., 1996) and 10–15 per 1,000 in some higher-risk populations, such as children residing in foster care (Astley, Stachowiak, Clarren, & Clausen, 2002; Astley, 2004a). The prevalence of the full spectrum of FASD in the general population is estimated at 9.1 per 1,000 live births, though a review of in-school screening and diagnosis studies suggest that the national rate could potentially be closer to 50 per 1,000 (May et al., 2009). In addition, recent retrospective analyses of hospital admissions data indicate that under-reporting of alcohol misuse by women may further disguise true prevalence (Morleo et al., 2011).

Although prenatal alcohol exposure has been clearly established as a causal factor for FASD in animal models, the amount of alcohol required to cause damage to the fetus remains in question, and may differ based on the individual. Factors such as dose of alcohol, pattern and timing of exposure, genetics, whether the mother also smoked and/or used other drugs, general health and nutrition of the mother, her level of stress and/or trauma, and her age all may play a role in the impact that alcohol has on the developing fetus (Guerri, Bazinet, & Riley, 2009). Animal studies do suggest that binge drinking (four or more drinks on one occasion) is associated with more severe effects (Bonthius & West, 1988; Clarren, Astley, Gunderson, & Spellman, 1992), and it is generally asserted that there is no known 'safe' level of alcohol consumption during pregnancy (Office of the Surgeon General, 2005; Hicks & Tough, 2009; Feldman et al., 2012).

> **Not every woman who consumes alcohol during pregnancy will give birth to a child with an FASD. However, because science has not determined a safe level of alcohol that may be consumed during pregnancy, the possibility of an FASD is created any time a woman consumes alcohol while pregnant.**

Due to the range of deficits—and variability in degree of severity of each deficit—within the diffusely damaged brain, FASD can present as functionally different in each individual that is affected. However, certain cognitive, behavioral, and adaptive functioning problems are common across the spectrum, including lower IQ, impaired learning ability, and difficulty processing information (such as not being able to remember or follow instructions, or poor verbal receptive skills) (Streissguth, Barr, & Bookstein, 1996; Bertrand et al., 2004; Streissguth et al., 2004; Astley et al., 2009a; Astley, 2010). Physical abnormalities and facial dysmorphology (i.e., congenital malformation) are only common with FAS. Other functional issues regularly observed include attention deficit (Nanson & Hiscock, 1990; Lee, Mattson, & Riley, 2004), decreased proficiency in cognitive planning (Kodituwakku, Handmaker, Cutler, Weathersby, & Handmaker, 1995; Kodituwakku, Kalberg, & May, 2001; Rasmussen, 2005), reduced working memory (Burden, Jacobson, Sokol, & Jacobson, 2005; Astley et al., 2009b; Green et al., 2009),

reduced response inhibition (Noland et al., 2003; Mattson, Crocker, & Nguyen, 2011), socially inappropriate behaviors (Bishop, Gahagan, & Lord, 2007; Jirikowic, Kartin, & Olson, 2008; Mattson, Crocker, & Nguyen, 2011), and deficits in fine motor (Kalberg et al., 2006; Jirikowic et al., 2008) and visual-spatial functions (Chiodo, Janisse, Delaney-Black, Sokol, & Hannigan, 2009; Mattson et al., 2010).

Cost Factors

Estimates of the cost to raise a child with an FASD vary depending on the source and the factors included in the analysis, and detailed cost estimates are generally only available in relation to the specific condition of FAS. Nonetheless, these costs are significant. In an analysis of medical expenditures for pediatric Medicaid enrollees, Amendah, Grosse, and Bertrand (2010) found that, for a child with identified FAS, incurred health costs were nine times higher than for children without an FASD. Astley, Bailey, Talbot, and Clarren (2000a) further isolated cost factors in a demonstration of primary FAS prevention in an FASD diagnostic clinic that targeted high-risk women; using this approach, the cost of raising a child with FAS was found to be roughly 30 times higher than the cost of preventing FAS in the child.

The most widely acknowledged estimate of the lifetime cost of care for an individual with an FAS is that of Lupton, Burd, and Harwood (2004), who adjusted figures originating with Harwood and Napolitano (1985) for 2002 dollars to suggest that the figure was roughly $2 million (including medical treatment, special education, residential care for persons with mental retardation, and productivity losses; in 2012 dollars, this would be over $2.5 million). The overall annual cost of FAS to the U.S. healthcare system (based on an assumption of 2 cases per 1,000 live births) is estimated at $5 billion (Lupton et al., 2004).

Part 3 of this TIP, the online Literature Review, contains additional information on FASD surveillance and cost factors, as well as the impact of alcohol on the brain and behavior.

Historical Background

FASD is often described as a 'new' or 'recent' discovery. In fact, references to the harmful effects of maternal drinking on infant outcome date back to biblical times: "Behold, thou shalt conceive, and bear a son; and now drink no wine or strong drink" (Judges 13:7, as noted in Clarren & Smith, 1978). In addition, several comprehensive descriptions were compiled by physician groups in the 18th and 19th centuries (Royal College, 1726; Sullivan, 1899; Goodacre & Mercer, 1965). The more recent history commonly referred to begins in 1968, when Lemoine, Harousseau, Borteyni, and Menuet from France published an article describing children with distinctive facial features and other symptoms related to prenatal alcohol exposure. In 1970, unaware of the Lemoine publication, Ulleland and colleagues published similar observations describing a small group of alcohol-exposed infants admitted to several high-risk maternal-child health clinics at the University of Washington (Ulleland, Wennberg, Igo, & Smith, 1970; Ulleland, 1972). This work would eventually lead to a seminal, collaborative article describing the pattern of outcomes associated with prenatal alcohol exposure (Jones, Smith, Ulleland, & Streissguth, 1973), as well as the publication that coined the term FAS (Jones & Smith, 1973).

In the roughly 40 years that have followed, extensive study has been conducted on alcohol's teratogenic effects, as well as on interventions for women of childbearing age who consume alcohol, leading to several significant federal milestones in addressing FASD. In 1996, the Institute of Medicine (IOM) published *Fetal Alcohol Syndrome: Diagnosis, Epidemiology, Prevention, and Treatment* (Stratton et al., 1996), leading the National Institute on Alcohol Abuse and Alcoholism (NIAAA) to establish the Interagency Coordinating Committee on FASD (originally Interagency Coordinating Committee on FAS) to address that publication's recommendations. Then, in 2000, Congress set forth mandates related to children's health, including FASD, leading the Centers for Disease Control and Prevention (CDC) to establish the National Task Force on FAS and FAE (completed in 2007), and SAMHSA to establish the FASD Center for Excellence in 2001.

In the decade since the Congressional mandates, the research and knowledge base around FASD has expanded greatly. According to Goodlett (2010), a PubMed search of FAS-, FASD-, or fetal alcohol-specific terminology at the end of 2010 returned nearly 3,900 articles published since 1973, of which more than 38 percent had been published since 2000. This growth is translating to practice: Since 2001, the FASD Center for Excellence alone has funded more than 70 subcontractors across the United States to carry out pilot efforts to implement FASD-related services into existing programs, including substance abuse and mental health treatment settings.

This body of work has revealed an unfortunate paradox: Individuals with an FASD require more intensive and personalized services, and early diagnosis and intervention have been identified as critical to improved outcomes and minimized secondary disabilities (Streissguth et al., 2004; Astley, 2010). Yet, individuals with an FASD often go undiagnosed or are misdiagnosed (Greenbaum, Stevens, Nash, Koren, & Rovet, 2009), are difficult to identify early and may not receive appropriate early intervention (Olson, Jirikowic, Kartin, & Astley, 2007), and often receive services that do not account for their disabilities and thus may result in poor outcomes.

Audience: Who Should Read This TIP?

This TIP is designed for use by behavioral health providers, particularly substance abuse and mental health treatment professionals, not only because these are the primary constituencies of SAMHSA but also because individuals with FASD experience higher rates than the general population of both substance abuse and mental health issues (Streissguth et al., 1996; O'Connor et al., 2002; Streissguth et al., 2004; Clark, Lutke, Minnes, & Quellette-Kuntz, 2004; Astley, 2010). In addition, individuals with an FASD exhibit higher rates of life problems commonly encountered in substance abuse and mental health treatment populations, including higher risk of suicide (Huggins, Grant, O'Malley, & Streissguth, 2008), exposure to multiple traumas throughout the lifespan (Henry, Sloane, & Black-Pond, 2007; Greenbaum et al., 2009), homelessness (Fryer, McGee, Matt, Riley, & Mattson, 2007), and increased interaction with the criminal justice system (Streissguth et al., 1996; Streissguth et al., 2004).

This TIP is also important because there are great opportunities for FASD prevention in mental health and substance abuse treatment settings. According to the 2009 *National Survey on Drug Use and Health* (NSDUH), 17.1 percent of women age 18 or over in the U.S. received mental health treatment or counseling in 2009, compared to only 9.2 of men in the same age group (Center for Behavioral Health Statistics and Quality [CBHSQ], 2010), while the *Treatment Episode Data Set* (TEDS) indicates that 33.0 percent of admissions to substance abuse treatment facilities in 2011 were female, more than half of whom (50.5 percent) indicated alcohol as a primary, secondary, or tertiary substance of abuse (CBHSQ, 2013). Thus, these settings provide ideal opportunities to implement brief, effective approaches to preventing an AEP.

Part 1 of this TIP is for frontline personnel and consists of three chapters:

- *Chapter 1* discusses approaches to FASD prevention; that is, assisting women who are in treatment settings and are pregnant or may become pregnant to remain abstinent from alcohol. In providing these guidelines, this TIP adopts the IOM model for prevention, which sees prevention as a step along a continuum that also incorporates treatment and maintenance.

- *Chapter 2* discusses methods for identifying individuals in treatment who have or may have an FASD, referring them for diagnosis where possible, and providing appropriate interventions to meet their needs. These clients are assumed to be adolescent or older, as they would need to be capable of presenting in treatment on their own (although the TIP strongly recommends including the family in treatment, when possible).

- *Chapter 3* provides clinical vignettes designed to realistically portray the provider–client interactions that might take place when providing FASD prevention or interventions.

Part 2 provides administrators with strategies and tools for undertaking the activities that will support treatment professionals and clients and for making the changes required to incorporate FASD prevention and/or intervention in daily practice. Part 2 also includes methods, materials, resources, and examples to assist administrators with quality improvement and ongoing evaluation of the necessary programmatic changes.

At the same time, the clinical and administrative guidance set forth in this TIP has strong applicability across healthcare and social service settings. While the client interactions described generally involve substance abuse and mental health treatment, any provider assisting women at risk of an AEP or assisting individuals who may have an FASD can implement the majority of these recommendations if they adapt them for that professional's setting. This is particularly the case if the setting in question overlaps with the life issues that more frequently occur among individuals with an FASD, as discussed above (i.e., criminal justice, housing, primary care).

Barriers to Treatment: The Need for the TIP

For a variety of reasons, including the somewhat hidden nature of many of the symptoms, individuals with an FASD are frequently misdiagnosed or their condition is not recognized (Olson et al., 2007; Greenbaum et al., 2009). This, in turn, leads to care that is not matched to the patient's needs and strengths, increasing the risk for secondary disabilities (Streissguth et al., 2004).

Added to this, recent statistics on drinking among pregnant women show that AEP prevention is as serious an issue as appropriate services for individuals who have an FASD (see box, *Drinking Rates Among Pregnant Women*, in the next chapter). AEP prevention may not be a familiar goal in mental health and substance abuse treatment settings. Yet these are ideal settings in which to prevent prenatal alcohol exposure, as behavioral health professionals routinely work with women of childbearing age (age 10–49 years). Treatment can then have a positive affect not only on the client, but on his or her family and generations to come.

Ideally, this TIP will help to alleviate many barriers to providing successful treatment for these two populations, including:

- The application of treatment approaches that, while effective with general

populations, may not be ideally suited to the needs of individuals with an FASD;

- A lack of awareness among treatment professionals of the rapid developments in the field of FASD services over the last decade; and

- Helping clients deal with feelings of shame, loss, or fear of discrimination.

Lack of Success With Typical Treatment Approaches

Prenatal exposure to alcohol has many teratogenic effects, among them that it can alter brain structure and function, meaning that people with an FASD do not process information in the same ways that those without an FASD do. These effects are permanent; an FASD cannot be 'cured.' Processing differences that may affect treatment can take many forms, including:

- Poor receptive language skills (difficulty with complex language and multiple instructions);

- Difficulty with social cognition and accurately understanding social cues;

- Difficulty taking in new information, and in generalizing learning to new settings; and

- Not always connecting cause and effect (particularly if the effect is delayed).

Expert consensus suggests that treatment approaches that rely on an assumption of 'normal' functioning of these cognitive processes are likely to be less effective with individuals with an FASD. This appears to be true for both mental health and substance abuse treatment settings.

Cognitive–Behavioral Therapy (CBT) models, for instance, are verbally based insight therapies designed to reduce target symptoms, and are based on the idea that inaccurate thoughts are linked to maladaptive feelings and behaviors. However, CBT approaches do not fit well given that individuals with an FASD have biologically based cognitive deficits (O'Connor et al., 2002). Behaviors of individuals with an FASD may result from errors in thinking that are difficult to change because of underlying diffuse brain damage. Modification to CBT, and adding other approaches, will be needed to maximize treatment efficiency and success.

The disease model of substance abuse treatment, which advocates lifelong abstinence from alcohol, also relies on the assumption that a client has normative function. Behavioral health professionals assume that the client can comprehend that he or she has a 'disease' and also that he or she can plan ahead to recognize why it is important to achieve abstinence. For an individual with an FASD, this link may be difficult to make, and so his or her substance abuse or mental health target symptoms may be harder to change (and change harder to maintain) because of the underlying diffuse brain damage.

Rapid Developments in the Field

The tremendous growth in FASD-related research and the establishment of the SAMHSA FASD Center for Excellence have practical implications for behavioral health professionals, in that the field of FASD-related practices is growing dynamically. Much of the practical guidance in this TIP has emerged only over the last 5 to 10 years. Even professionals who have had some form of FASD training in the past are likely to discover new and useful strategies in this TIP that can be effectively applied in their programs.

Treatment Barriers

Despite their unique treatment needs, clients with an FASD or pregnant women at risk of an AEP still share with any other client a significant, common barrier to treatment success: The impact of negative self-perception. An individual with an FASD or a woman who has consumed alcohol during pregnancy may perceive themselves negatively, either because of internal feelings of shame, a sense of not belonging, or due to experiencing external shaming or judgment. These internal feelings and external experiences can each become a barrier to treatment (Astley, Bailey, Talbot, & Clarren, 2000b; Salmon, 2008).

When implementing the practices recommended in this TIP, behavioral health professionals are urged to keep sight of the importance of addressing the client's feelings and experiences, as well as the need for sensitivity to issues such as gender, ethnicity, cultural background, and sexuality, as these factors impact treatment success among individuals with an FASD and women of childbearing age as significantly as any other treatment population.

> "We must move from viewing the individual as failing if s/he does not do well in a program to viewing the program as not providing what the individual needs in order to succeed."
> Dubovsky, 2000

1 Prevention of Alcohol-Exposed Pregnancies Among Women of Childbearing Age

Introduction

This TIP adopts the IOM continuum of care model, which sees prevention as a step along a continuum that also incorporates treatment and

One act of AEP prevention can positively impact the life of the mother and the life of the unborn child. One change in how services are provided can multiply that impact many times over.

maintenance (see Figure 1.1, below). The IOM model defines three types of prevention: universal, selective, and indicated.

- *Universal prevention* "[a]ddresses [the] general public or [a] segment of [the] entire population with average probability, risk or condition of developing [a] disorder" (Springer & Phillips, 2007). Universal prevention can take a variety of forms, including media campaigns, large-scale health initiatives (e.g., immunization), point-of purchase signage, and warning labels on products.

- *Selective prevention* is designed for a "[s]pecific sub-population with risk significantly above average, either imminently or over [his or her] lifetime" (Springer & Phillips, 2007), and can include "screening women for alcohol use, training healthcare professionals, working with family members of pregnant women who abuse alcohol, developing biomarkers, brief interventions, and referrals" (Grant, 2011).

- *Indicated prevention* "[a]ddresses identified individuals with minimal but detectable signs or symptoms suggesting a disorder" (Springer & Phillips, 2007), such as pregnant women who drink heavily, or women who have already given birth to a

Figure 1.1: The IOM Continuum of Care Model

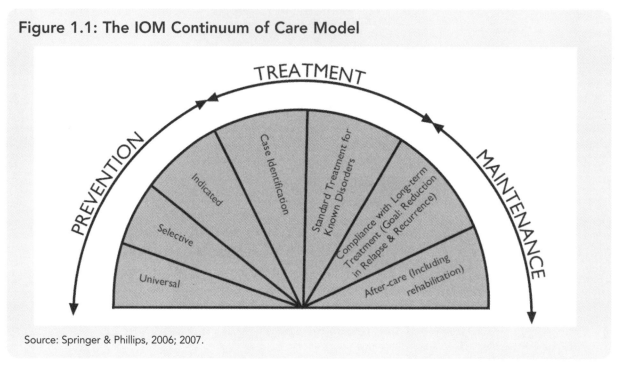

Source: Springer & Phillips, 2006; 2007.

child with FASD and continue to drink. Indicated prevention can include some of the same methods applied in selective prevention, but applied more intensively based on the severity of the alcohol-related problem.

For the purposes of the AEP prevention discussion in this chapter, women of childbearing age (i.e., females age 10–49) in your treatment setting should receive AEP prevention based on the following:

- *Universal prevention*: A woman who is not pregnant, and either reports no alcohol use or does not screen positive for at-risk alcohol use;

- *Selective prevention*: A woman of childbearing age who reports alcohol use but has only one of the two indicators for an indicated intervention; she is either pregnant but does not screen positive for at-risk alcohol use, or she screens positive for at-risk alcohol use but is not pregnant; or

- *Indicated prevention*: A woman of childbearing age who screens positive for at-risk alcohol use and is pregnant.

This chapter will first discuss screening, then appropriate brief interventions for AEP prevention in each of the three categories, before discussing treatment issues and referral. In each category, screening is a vital starting point before moving on to appropriate prevention, treatment, or referral.

Professional Responsibility to Screen

As the box "Risk Factors for an AEP" (next page) makes clear, a variety of factors can impact a woman's consumption of alcohol during pregnancy. These and other factors make it critical to inquire about alcohol use among *all* women of childbearing age in behavioral health settings for alcohol consumption:

- There is *no* known safe level of alcohol consumption during pregnancy, and even low levels of prenatal alcohol exposure have been shown to negatively impact a fetus (Chang, 2001).

- Screening facilitates the implementation of appropriate interventions, at the earliest possible point (Leonardson, Loudenburg, & Struck, 2007).

- Prevented AEP can result in significant cost savings through prevented cases of FASD and reduced use of the health and social services systems (Abel & Sokol, 1991; Astley et al., 2000a; Lupton et al., 2004; Astley, 2004a).

- Screening is an ethical obligation, one that should be conducted equally of men and women regardless of race and economic status, and which should be performed with women using instruments that are designed for women (Committee on Ethics of the American College of Obstetricians and Gynecologists [ACOG], 2008). Additionally, in an FASD prevention study assessing the feasibility of identifying high-risk women through the FASD diagnostic evaluation of their children, Astley and colleagues (2000a) concluded that these women are not only at high risk for producing more children damaged by alcohol exposure, but they themselves often face serious adverse social, mental, and physical health issues, as well. Thus, one could argue that it would be unethical to ignore their existence and ignore opportunities to provide them with advocacy support and primary prevention intervention.

- Awareness *does* create change: Statistics from SAMHSA's NSDUH (May 21, 2009) suggest that drinking rates among women drop considerably during pregnancy, particularly in the second and third trimesters when there is a much higher awareness of pregnancy status.

In addition, screening:
- Gives the client permission to talk about drinking;
- Helps to identify and or clarify co-occurring issues;
- Minimizes surprises in the treatment process; and
- Can mean more effective treatment.

Risk Factors for an AEP

Substance Abuse/Mental Health Factors

- *History of alcohol consumption (NIAAA, 2000; Bobo, Klepinger, & Dong, 2007)*
- *Family background of alcohol use (Stratton et al., 1996; Leonardson et al., 2007)*
- *History of inpatient treatment for drugs or alcohol and/or history of inpatient mental health treatment (Project CHOICES Research Group, 2002)*

Personal/Sexual/Family Factors

- *Previous birth to a child with an FASD (Kvigne et al., 2003; Leonardson et al., 2007)*
- *Lack of contraception use/unplanned pregnancy (Astley et al., 2000b)*
- *Physical/emotional/sexual abuse (Astley et al., 2000b)*
- *Partner substance use/abuse (Stratton et al., 1996; Leonardson et al., 2007)*
- *Multiple sex partners (Project CHOICES Research Group, 2002)*
- *Smoking (CDC, 2002; Leonardson et al., 2007)*
- *Never having been tested for HIV (Anderson, Ebrahim, Floyd, & Atrash, 2006)*
- *Lack of education, income, and/or access to care (Astley et al., 2000a)*

Drinking Rates Among Pregnant Women

According to SAMHSA's 2010 NSDUH, "Among pregnant women aged 15 to 44, an estimated 10.8 percent reported current alcohol use, 3.7 percent reported binge drinking, and 1.0 percent reported heavy drinking. These rates were significantly lower than the rates for non-pregnant women in the same age group (54.7, 24.6, and 5.4 percent, respectively). Binge drinking during the first trimester of pregnancy was reported by 10.1 percent of pregnant women aged 15 to 44" (Office of Applied Studies [OAS], 2011). All of these estimates are based on data averaged over 2009 and 2010. (Binge drinking for women has been defined by NIAAA as four or more drinks on one occasion [2004]).

In telephone interviews with 4,088 randomly selected control mothers from the CDC's National Birth Defects Prevention Study who delivered live born infants without birth defects during 1997–2002, Ethen and colleagues (2009) found even higher numbers: 30.3 percent of respondents reported alcohol use during pregnancy, with 8.3 percent reporting binge drinking during pregnancy (approximately 97 percent of those indicating binge drinking stating that it was during the first trimester).

In addition, one study of stool and hair samples of neonates who had been prenatally exposed to heavy ethanol use suggested that these children were also 3.3 times more likely to have been exposed to amphetamines and twice as likely to have been exposed to opiates, both of which can also impair long-term child development (Shor, Nulman, Kulaga, & Koren, 2010). Another recent study found that, among 1,400 patients with prenatal alcohol exposure attending an FASD diagnostic clinic in Washington state, 62 percent were prenatally exposed to tobacco, 37 percent were prenatally exposed to marijuana, and 38 percent were prenatally exposed to crack cocaine (Astley, 2010).

Statistics from SAMHSA's TEDS and from SAMHSA's NSDUH indicate a potentially greater need to address the FASD issue specifically in substance abuse treatment settings: More than 22 percent of pregnant women admitted into treatment from 1992 to 2006 indicated alcohol as their primary substance of abuse (OAS, 2006).

Lastly, 49 percent of all pregnancies in the United States are unintended (Finer & Henshaw, 2006). As a result, many women will consume alcohol without knowing that they are pregnant.

Procedures for Screening

Behavioral health settings are busy, and screening procedures must be efficient. Figure 1.2, *Screening Decision Tree for AEP Prevention*, provides a procedure for an opening question about alcohol use, moving on to screening (if necessary), suggested instruments for screening, and next steps. The goal of screening is to determine, as quickly and as accurately as possible, whether a client is at risk and therefore brief intervention and treatment or referral is warranted.

The screening instruments recommended in Figure 1.2 are not the only options available

for determining client alcohol use, but are validated as indicated in the decision tree (Sokol & Clarren, 1989; Russell, 1994; Chang, 2001). Nonetheless, if your agency does not use these instruments or does not have a 'perfect' alternative, it is better to screen with what is available to your program than to not screen women of childbearing age at all.

Part 3 of this TIP, the online Literature Review, includes further discussion of these and other alcohol screening instruments for use with women.

Screening should be done with sensitivity to the client's level of health literacy, or, "the degree to which people have the capacity to

Figure 1.2: A Screening Decision Tree for AEP Prevention

AEP prevention can be simple and brief. The TIP consensus panel developed the following Screening Decision Tree for AEP Prevention to help behavioral health providers quickly touch upon the topic of alcohol use with all women of childbearing age, and then provide brief but effective prevention or intervention.

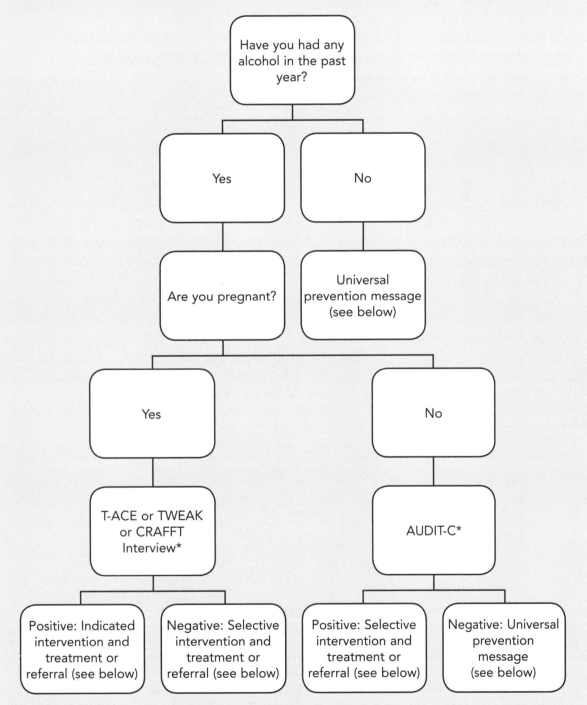

* The T-ACE and TWEAK are validated for use with pregnant women. The CRAFFT Interview may be more helpful when assisting adolescent clients. The AUDIT-C is validated for use with non-pregnant women. All of these instruments are reprinted in Appendix B of this TIP.

obtain, process, and understand basic health information and services needed to make appropriate health decisions" (Parker, Ratzan, & Lurie, 2003; Liechty, 2011). More than a third of adults in the United States do not have adequate health literacy (Kutner, 2006; Liechty, 2011), so the prevention message may need to be simplified and reinforced by asking the client on several occasions and in a variety of ways. This means that your agency will likely need to screen at several different points in time.

In addition, talking about alcohol use or seeking help for an alcohol-related problem can be potentially embarrassing or difficult for the client (NIAAA, 2005). Counselors should be conscious of this risk, and be respectful when raising the issue of alcohol use. Additional sources of information that can help to identify alcohol use include collateral reports from

family and friends of the client, and client medical/court records.

Vignette #2 in Part 1, Chapter 3 incorporates discussion of drink size and the use of a visual aid with a client.

Selecting an Appropriate Prevention Approach

Based on the results of your client screening, the next step is to decide on an appropriate brief approach: Universal prevention message or selective or indicated brief intervention. Brief interventions are associated with sustained reduction in alcohol consumption by women of childbearing age, and those discussed have shown promise for being adaptable to various settings and needs (Fleming, Barry, Manwell, Johnson, & London, 1997; Manwell, Fleming, Mundt, Stauffacher, & Barry, 2000; Burke, Arkowitz, & Menchola,

What Is a Standard Drink?

All clients being screened for alcohol consumption should be given a clear indication of what constitutes a 'standard drink.' A standard drink in the United States is any drink that contains about 14 grams of pure alcohol (about 0.6 fluid ounces or 1.2 tablespoons). Below are U.S. standard drink equivalents. These are approximate, since different brands and types of beverages vary in their actual alcohol content.

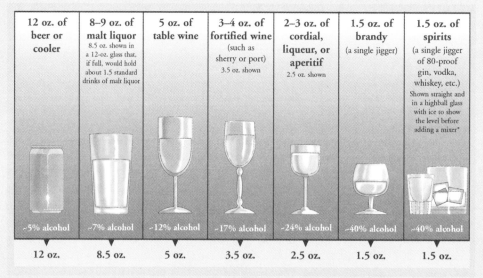

12 oz. of beer or cooler	8–9 oz. of malt liquor 8.5 oz. shown in a 12-oz. glass that, if full, would hold about 1.5 standard drinks of malt liquor	5 oz. of table wine	3–4 oz. of fortified wine (such as sherry or port) 3.5 oz. shown	2–3 oz. of cordial, liqueur, or aperitif 2.5 oz. shown	1.5 oz. of brandy (a single jigger)	1.5 oz. of spirits (a single jigger of 80-proof gin, vodka, whiskey, etc.) Shown straight and in a highball glass with ice to show the level before adding a mixer*
~5% alcohol	~7% alcohol	~12% alcohol	~17% alcohol	~24% alcohol	~40% alcohol	~40% alcohol
12 oz.	8.5 oz.	5 oz.	3.5 oz.	2.5 oz.	1.5 oz.	1.5 oz.

Source: *Helping Patients Who Drink Too Much: A Clinicians Guide* (Updated 2005 Edition), NIAAA, p. 24. NIH Publication No. 07-3769.

2003; Project CHOICES Intervention Research Group, 2003; Chang et al., 2005; Grant, Ernst, Streissguth, & Stark, 2005; O'Connor & Whaley, 2007).

When using these prevention approaches, counselors should remember that no intervention constitutes full treatment of a woman's alcohol use. Each is designed simply to encourage a dialogue about alcohol and begin a process of change. Each should be the basis for ongoing evaluation and an informed approach to treatment or referral. For

programs that do not have existing approaches to substance abuse treatment, procedures for appropriate referral are discussed after the brief interventions.

Universal Prevention

As indicated in Figure 1.2, *Screening Decision Tree for AEP Prevention*, a woman who is not pregnant, and either reports no alcohol use or does not screen positive for at-risk alcohol use, can receive a simple universal prevention message. Consider the following scripted messages.

Universal AEP Prevention Statement and Possible Follow-Up Questions

"It's great that you're choosing not to drink alcohol. I know you aren't currently pregnant or planning to become pregnant, but you are in the primary childbearing years right now. If you change your mind about pregnancy or discover in the future that you are pregnant, or you do begin to drink, please keep in mind that research has shown a link between drinking during pregnancy and the baby having an FASD. A child with an FASD can have physical and behavior problems, as well as cognitive problems (or, problems with the brain). These effects are caused by the alcohol, and they don't go away, although they can be treated. There is no known safe amount of alcohol to consume during pregnancy, and any type of alcohol can cause FASD.

Can I give you a brochure [or Web address, such as **www.fasdcenter.samhsa.gov**] *to take with you? This will explain more about FASD and how to have a healthy baby. Even if you aren't planning to become pregnant, you could share it with a friend or family member who is."*

*****

If asked: Why is there no known safe amount of alcohol that a woman can have during pregnancy?

Answer: The amount of alcohol required to damage an unborn baby differs based on the individual. Things like how much alcohol a woman drinks, how often she drinks during pregnancy, and which trimesters she drinks in all play a part. It also depends on genetics, whether the woman smokes or uses other drugs, her general health and nutrition, her age, and her levels of stress or trauma. That's why the Surgeon General recommends that pregnant women not drink any alcohol at all.

If asked: What kinds of alcohol should I avoid?

Answer: All alcohol can harm a baby while you're pregnant, not just beer, wine, and hard liquor. Wine coolers and 'alco-pops' also count. Anything with alcohol. Even some over-the-counter medications have a lot of alcohol in them; if you're pregnant or thinking of becoming pregnant, you should be careful about those, too.

If asked: Where can I find more information about FASD?

Answer: In addition to the SAMHSA FASD Center for Excellence (**www.fasdcenter.samhsa.gov**), the CDC (**http://www.cdc.gov/ncbddd/fasd/index.html**) provides extensive information about FASD.

Whether asked for more information or not, the universal AEP prevention message should be accompanied by appropriate awareness materials, either in print or via a Web address. The SAMHSA FASD Center for Excellence provides a series of consumer fact sheets called *What You Need to Know* that provides helpful information about how to have a healthy baby. Appendix C, *Public and Professional Resources on FASD*, has links to additional information resources.

At the same time, counselors should keep in mind with universal AEP prevention that, in some situations, women may deny using alcohol, but a combination of signs and symptoms suggest otherwise. In such cases, it may be prudent to re-screen frequently (Taylor, Bailey, Peters, & Stein, 2009).

Selective Prevention

The following section discusses two brief interventions for AEP prevention that are appropriate with women of childbearing age who report alcohol use but have only one of the two indicators for an indicated intervention; they are either pregnant but do not screen positive for at-risk alcohol use, or they screen positive for at-risk alcohol use but are not pregnant. These are organized in terms of the time required to perform the intervention effectively. As with universal prevention, each of these approaches should be accompanied by appropriate FASD information material, such as the *What You Need to Know* fact sheets, either in hard copy or through a Web link.

The first selective intervention, called 'FLO' for short, is a simple, three-step approach (see box below). An example of using the FLO approach with a client is illustrated in Vignette #1 in Part 1, Chapter 3 of this TIP.

The second selective intervention, FRAMES, is a more established and slightly more detailed method for motivating a client toward change, and has demonstrated positive results in brief intervention situations (Miller & Sanchez, 1994; Miller & Rollnick, 2002). See the box on the following page.

Each of these brief interventions discusses 'action plans' or strategies for changing alcohol-related behaviors. For counselors who are not already well-versed in substance use-related change strategies, NIAAA has provided a brief guide to simple change strategies in the publication *Helping Patients Who Drink Too Much* (2007). Basic strategies to discuss with the client can include:

- What specific steps the client will take (e.g., not go to a bar after work, measure all drinks at home, alternate alcoholic and non-alcoholic beverages);
- How drinking will be tracked (diary, kitchen calendar);
- How the patient will manage high-risk situations; and

FLO (Feedback, Listen, Options)

1. Provide **F**eedback about screening results. If possible, confirm the results with additional screening and provide information about recommended drinking limits. (For women who are— or are planning to become— pregnant, the ideal goal is abstinence.)

2. Ask clients for their views about their own drinking and **L**isten carefully to encourage their thinking and decision-making process.

3. Provide medical advice, and negotiate a decision about **O**ptions clients can pursue, including establishing a goal and developing an action plan.

Source: Higgins-Biddle, J., Hungerford, D., & Cates-Wessel, K. (2009). *Screening and brief interventions (SBI) for unhealthy alcohol use: A step-by-step implementation guide for trauma centers.* Atlanta: Centers for Disease Control and Prevention, National Center for Injury Prevention and Control. [Parenthetical in #1 added.]

FRAMES

F	**Feedback**	Compare the patient's level of drinking with drinking patterns that are not risky. She may not be aware that what she considers normal is actually risky (*or that **any** consumption during pregnancy creates risk*).
R	**Responsibility**	Stress that it is her responsibility to make a change.
A	**Advice**	Give direct advice (not insistence) to change her drinking behavior.
M	**Menu**	Identify risky drinking situations and offer options for coping.
E	**Empathy**	Use a style of interaction that is understanding, non-judgmental, and involved.
S	**Self-efficacy**	Elicit and reinforce self-motivating statements such as, "I am confident that I can stop drinking." Encourage the patient to develop strategies, implement them, and commit to change.

Source: Miller, W. R., & Rollnick, S. (2002). *Motivational interviewing: Preparing people for change.* (2nd ed.) New York, NY: Guildford Press. [Italics in "Feedback" added.]

- Who might be willing to help the client avoid alcohol use, such as a significant other or a non-drinking friend.

Indicated Prevention: Alcohol Screening and Brief Intervention (SBI)

Alcohol Screening and Brief Intervention (SBI) is a workbook-based brief intervention that is appropriate with women of childbearing age who screen positive for at-risk alcohol use and are pregnant. SBI generally takes 10 to 15 minutes to complete, and has been shown to positively impact abstinence rates and key subsequent health factors in the newborn, including higher birth weight/length and lower mortality (O'Connor & Whaley, 2007).

The WIC Project Care: Health and Behavior Workbook was originally developed for Women, Infants and Children (WIC) programs, which provide support to current and expecting mothers, but the workbook can be used across settings. It is crafted in very simple language and uses traditional brief intervention

techniques, including education and feedback, cognitive–behavioral procedures, goal-setting, and contracting. The care provider should go through the workbook *with* the client. As with both universal and selective prevention, the SBI approach should be accompanied by appropriate FASD print materials or a relevant and reliable Web link for further information.

The workbook can be downloaded for free in multiple languages from the WIC Web site: **http://www.phfewic.org/Projects/Care.aspx**

Providing Intervention/Treatment: Additional Factors to Consider

The following are factors to keep in mind when delivering a brief intervention for AEP prevention, as well as when delivering full substance abuse treatment (for agencies that are able to offer such care).

- Selective and indicated prevention services should be delivered by someone with motivational interviewing (MI) skills if at all possible. While a detailed discussion of MI techniques is outside the scope of this TIP, SAMHSA provides a Web site (**http://www.motivationalinterview. org/**) that contains extensive materials and training resources for providers looking to develop their MI skills. See also TIP 35, *Enhancing Motivation for Change in Substance Abuse Treatment* (SAMHSA, 1999).

- Consider the woman's age and circumstances, and how these impact intervention/treatment. For example, life factors and obstacles to abstinence (family responsibilities, work, other children, etc.) will probably be very different for a teen vs. an older woman.

- Consider cultural context, as well; the cultural factors that impact treatment may be very different for an African-American, Hispanic/Latina, Asian-American, or Native-American woman (or a woman of any other minority) than for a Caucasian woman.

- Be willing to make modifications (e.g., frequency, duration) to maximize opportunities for prevention and recovery.

- Include and engage families in treatment, including significant others, grandparents, guardians, and custodians.

- Include relapse prevention.

- Include family support skills.

- Consider additional counseling factors:
  - Parenting skills (that work for both the parent and the child)
  - Trauma and abuse
  - Co-occurring mental health issues

- Using a calendar with a client who is already pregnant may help her differentiate when she found out she was pregnant from when she actually became pregnant. She may have consumed alcohol for some time before knowing of the pregnancy, and showing that the drinking occurred even before she knew she was pregnant can help her feel less pressured and alleviate feelings of guilt. Clients may feel guilty and not tell the whole truth (or even withhold the truth). This means that getting an accurate picture of alcohol use may require multiple screenings. It is critical to build trust over several sessions. [Vignette #4 in Part 1, Chapter 3 demonstrates the use of a calendar with a client.]

- Watch for clients who 'shut down' on the topic of alcohol, and be understanding if the client experiences a sense of panic

Ensuring Effective Contraception

A woman who drinks alcohol at risky levels may not always follow prescribed procedures for effective contraception (Astley et al., 2000b). Review contraception use with her to ensure that she has full contraceptive coverage every time she has sexual intercourse. This might include providing secondary, back-up, or emergency contraception methods. For example, along with oral contraceptives, advise her to use condoms, which have the added benefit of reducing sexually transmitted diseases.

Source: *Division of Women's Health Issues. (2006). Drinking and reproductive health: A Fetal Alcohol Spectrum Disorders prevention tool kit. Washington, DC: American College of Obstetricians and Gynecologists.*

about what she may have unintentionally done to her baby.

- If the client is not pregnant but is drinking, and is not resistant to talking about contraception, qualified professionals can consider adding a discussion of effective contraception (see box, "Ensuring Effective Contraception") to discussions about drinking reduction.

Approaches to Resistance

With any approach to AEP prevention, counselors should keep in mind that, while a female client may feel safe enough to share about her alcohol use, she may not be ready to take the next step of comprehensive assessment and treatment (Astley et al., 2000b). A woman may present as resistant, reluctant, resigned, or rationalizing. The publication *Substance Abuse During Pregnancy: Guidelines for Screening* (Taylor et al., 2009) provides guidance on meeting these various forms of resistance. In addition, see the box below.

Procedures for Referral

If you believe, based on screening and interaction during intervention, that your client requires assistance that is best delivered in another care setting (or treatment in another setting becomes necessary due to factors such as criminal justice or social service involvement), you should discuss the benefits of treatment with the client and offer to provide her with a referral to a local substance abuse treatment center or other appropriate provider. A general list of treatment facilities can be searched through The SAMHSA Treatment Locator (**http://findtreatment.samhsa.gov**). Additional referral possibilities include the following:

- County substance abuse services;

Resistant, Reluctant, Resigned, or Rationalizing

• Resistant: "Don't tell me what to do."

Provider Response: Work with the resistance. Avoid confrontation and try to solicit the woman's view of her situation. Ask her what concerns her about her use and ask permission to share what you know, and then ask her opinion of the information. Accept that the process of change is a gradual one and it may require several conversations before she feels safe about discussing her real fears. This often leads to a reduced level of resistance and allows for a more open dialogue. Try to accept her autonomy but make it clear that you would like to help her quit or reduce her use if she is willing.

• Reluctant: "I don't want to change; there are reasons."

Provider Response: Empathize with the real or possible results of changing (for example, her partner may leave). It is possible to give strong medical advice to change and still be empathetic to possible negative outcomes to changing. Guide her problem-solving.

• Resigned: "I can't change; I've tried."

Provider Response: Instill hope, explore barriers to change.

• Rationalizing: "I don't use that much."

Provider Response: Decrease discussion. Listen, rather than responding to the rationalization. Respond to her by empathizing and reframing her comments to address the conflict between wanting a healthy baby and not knowing whether "using" is really causing harm.

Sources: Taylor, P., Bailey, D., Peters, R., & Stein, B. (2009). *Substance abuse during pregnancy: Guidelines for screening.* Olympia, WA: Washington State Department of Health.
DiClemente, C. C. (1991). Motivational interviewing and stages of change. In W. R. Miller & S. Rollnick (Eds.), *Motivational Interviewing: Preparing People to Change Addictive Behaviors* (pp. 191- 206). New York: Guilford.

Targeted Referral Options

Non-Pregnant Women: Project CHOICES

Project CHOICES is an evidence-based intervention (Project CHOICES Intervention Research Group, 2003; Floyd et al., 2007) that targets women at risk of having an AEP *before* they become pregnant. The goal is to reduce drinking and/or prevent pregnancy through contraception.

The target population for Project CHOICES is women ages 18 to 44 who are sexually active and drinking alcohol at risk levels. The model uses a four-session intervention approach based in MI methods, and discussions in each session are tailored to the client's self-rated readiness to change and interest in discussing alcohol use or contraception.

Project CHOICES programs exist in multiple settings, including residential and outpatient substance abuse treatment, community mental health treatment, jails, and community-based teen programs for girls. Eligibility criteria include 1) self-report of being sexually active, 2) being non-pregnant (but able to conceive), 3) high-risk drinking (8 or more drinks per week or 4 or more drinks in one occasion) in the past 30 days, 4) ineffective use of or no contraception, and 5) not currently trying to become pregnant or planning to try in the next 6 months.

Intervention Components:

- Four MI-based counseling sessions, including personalized feedback of risk, motivation to change one or both risk behaviors, decreasing temptation to engage in risk behaviors and increasing confidence to avoid them, goal-setting, and change planning; and
- One contraceptive counseling visit.

The CDC provides additional information about Project CHOICES at **http://www.cdc.gov/ncbddd/fasd/research-preventing.html**.

Pregnant Women: Parent-Child Assistance Program (PCAP)

The Parent-Child Assistance Program (PCAP) is a scientifically validated (Grant et al., 2005) paraprofessional case management model that provides support and linkages to needed services to women for 3 years following enrollment. The goal is to reduce future AEP by increasing abstinence from alcohol and drug use and/or improving regular use of reliable contraception among enrollees.

The target population for PCAP is pregnant or post-partum women (up to 6 months) who have had an AEP and will self-report drug and/or alcohol use during the target pregnancy. The model is based in Relational Theory, the Stages of Change, and harm reduction.

PCAP programs exist in a variety of settings, including substance abuse treatment and family support centers. Eligibility criteria include self-report of heavy alcohol or illicit drug use during pregnancy and ineffective or non-engagement with community social services.

Intervention Components:

- Paraprofessional home visitation;
- Goal-setting;
- Case management targeting alcohol use and contraception use; and
- Linkages to community services and programs.

Case management is provided at least twice monthly for up to 3 years following initial entry into the program.

To learn more about PCAP, including contact information, background materials, an implementation guide, and relevant forms and materials, visit **http://depts.washington.edu/pcapuw/**.

- 12-Step programs;
- Hospital treatment programs;
- Mental health programs; and
- Special pregnancy-related programs, which can be identified through your state health department by calling 800-311-BABY (2229), or 800-504-7081 for Spanish.

Programs throughout the United States have worked and are working directly with the SAMHSA FASD Center for Excellence to implement SBI (summarized above), Project CHOICES, or the Parent-Child Assistance Program (PCAP) (both summarized in the box "Targeted Referral Options," previous page). A program near you can be considered a source for possible referral or for guidance on locating a similar program. Please contact the FASD Center for Excellence for current program contact information (**www.fasdcenter.samhsa.gov**). Your local FASD State Coordinator may also be able to provide guidance on appropriate referrals. The National Association of FASD State Coordinators can be con¬tacted via the SAMHSA FASD Center for Excellence Web site: **http://fasdcenter.samhsa.gov/statesys temsofcare/nafsc.aspx**.

The feasibility of fully implementing SBI, Project CHOICES, or PCAP in your agency will depend on your staff skill set, your collaborative network, your funding, and a variety of other factors that are examined in greater detail in the Administrative section (Part 2) of this TIP.

Providing a Referral: Additional Factors to Consider

- Discuss possible strategies for the client to stop consuming alcohol; for example, individual counseling, 12-Step programs, and other treatment programs. Studies have shown that people given choices are more successful in treatment (Taylor et al., 2009).

- Use an advocate or special outreach services, if available, such as PCAP or Maternity Support Services (Taylor et al., 2009). Refer to Appendix C, *Public and Professional Resources on FASD*, for additional sources of information on community supports.

- Obtain information about costs, which health plans cover alcohol services (e.g., Medicaid, Medicare, state assistance, and public programs), who to contact to refer a patient, the phone numbers, and the necessary procedures for enrollment. This will allow you to tailor the referral to the client's needs and health insurance coverage (Higgins-Biddle, Hungerford, & Cates-Wessel, 2009).

- Identify the types of services available in your area (e.g., cognitive–behavioral, 12-Step, Motivational Enhancement Therapy) and the types of modalities (e.g., in-patient, outpatient), and prepare short descriptions of the available options so patients can understand the differences among alternative approaches (Higgins-Biddle et al., 2009).

- If possible, help the client make an appointment while she is in your office. If the woman is unwilling to make that commitment, ask if she would like some information to take with her if she should change her mind. Schedule the next visit, continue to maintain interest in her progress, and support her efforts to change. Monitor and follow up on any

Helping Your Clients Receive Culturally Competent Services

This TIP, like all others in the TIP series, recognizes the importance of delivering culturally competent care. Cultural competency, as defined by HHS, is…

"A set of values, behaviors, attitudes, and practices within a system, organization, program, or among individuals that enables people to work effectively across cultures. It refers to the ability to honor and respect the beliefs, language, interpersonal styles, and behaviors of individuals and families receiving services, as well as staff who are providing such services. Cultural competence is a dynamic, ongoing, developmental process that requires a long-term commitment and is achieved over time" (U.S. Department of Health and Human Services, 2003, p. 12).

This section discusses national information resources that are available on the topic of cultural competence or for providing care to specific cultural groups (listed alphabetically). However, the absence of a specific cultural group from this section is not meant to suggest that cultural competency is not an issue for that population. Individuals from all cultural backgrounds deserve respect and attention in a treatment environment, and the significance of culture needs to be recognized in relation to many different areas of a person's life; race, ethnicity, gender, sexual orientation, age, socioeconomic status, language, etc.

Chapter 3 of this TP, *Clinical Vignettes*, contains additional information on the essential elements of culturally competent counseling.

Hispanic/Latin Populations

If your agency is not fully capable in serving Hispanic/Latin clients or a Hispanic/Latin client requests culturally specific services, the National Council of La Raza provides a search tool (**http://www.nclr.org/index.php/nclr_affiliates/affiliate_network/**) that can direct clients to over 300 community-based organizations that provide a variety of health and general services for Hispanic/Latin populations.

In addition, SAMHSA's National Hispanic & Latino Addiction Technology Transfer Center (ATTC) offers a variety of products and resources focused on the health needs of Hispanics and Latinos. Visit their Web site at **http://www.attcnetwork.org/regcenters/index_nfa_hispaniclatino.asp**.

Native Populations

If your agency is not fully capable in serving native clients or a native client requests culturally specific services, the Indian Health Service (IHS) provides an interactive search map (**http://www.ihs.gov/findhealthcare/**) that can be used to find an IHS, Tribal, or Urban Indian Health Program (UIHP) facility. This search engine scans a variety of settings, including hospitals, behavioral health settings, village clinics, and school health facilities.

If you are unable to locate services through the map, the Health Resources and Services Administration (HRSA) provides the HRSA Health Center locator (**http://findahealthcenter.hrsa.gov/Search_HCC.aspx**) to determine if there are other culturally specific services available in your area.

Cultural Competency Training/Learning

The SAMHSA FASD Center for Excellence can provide training or technical assistance (TA) on cultural competency topics, or can put your agency in touch with a nearby specialist. Training and TA request forms can be accessed online (**http://www.fasdcenter.samhsa.gov**). Chapter 3 of this part of the TIP, Clinical Vignettes, also contains a checklist of core competencies for the culturally sensitive counselor.

In addition, the HRSA's Culture, Language and Health Literacy page (**http://www.hrsa.gov/culturalcompetence/index.html**) provides links to a range of resources on cultural competence when serving clients of differing cultures, genders, and sexual identities.

co-existing psychiatric conditions (Taylor et al., 2009).

- Maintain communication with the substance abuse treatment or other provider to monitor progress (Taylor et al., 2009).

- If immediate substance abuse treatment or other support is not available, the counselor or designated staff might meet with the woman weekly or bi-weekly to express concern and to acknowledge the seriousness of the situation (Taylor et al., 2009).

Working with Women Who May Have an FASD

When working with women of childbearing age, counselors may encounter clients who exhibit symptoms or characteristics suggesting that they themselves have an FASD. Research has identified intergenerational FASD as a pattern (Kvigne et al., 2003; May et al., 2005). Verifying the presence of an FASD is a process of observation, interviewing, and additional screening that takes time. The guidelines provided in the next chapter, *Addressing FASD in Treatment*, can prove helpful for counselors who want to pursue verification of a possible FASD in the client, and/or wish to modify their approach to delivering prevention or treatment/referral accordingly.

For more information on AEP prevention...

Vignettes 1–4 in Part 1, Chapter 3 illustrate scenarios where a counselor practices AEP prevention approaches. In addition, Part 3, the online literature review, also contains further discussion of screening and prevention interventions.

2 Addressing FASD in Treatment

Introduction

Value of Addressing FASD

Although the evidence base for effective substance abuse/mental health interventions with individuals who have or may have an FASD is limited (Premji, Benzies, Serrett, & Hayden, 2006; Paley & O'Connor, 2009), research has demonstrated that this population can and does succeed in treatment when approaches are properly modified, and that these modifications can lead to improved caregiving attitudes and reduced stress on family/care-givers as well as providers (Bertrand, 2009).

For the counselor, building competence with FASD has the obvious value of enhancing professional skills, as the counselor can provide FASD-informed care. For the client, addressing FASD has the potential to enhance the treatment experience for both the individual with an FASD and those around him or her, increase retention, lead to improved outcomes, reduce the probability of relapse (thus helping to break the cycle of repeated treatment, incarceration, displacement), and increase engagement rates in aftercare services. Access to FASD-informed interventions and accommodations, like those discussed in this chapter, has the potential to create protective factors for the client that can reduce secondary disabilities (Streissguth et al., 2004) and has been shown to lead to better outcomes (Bertrand, 2009).

For the client, addressing FASD provides an additional route to possible treatment success. Individuals with an FASD are a largely hidden population, yet these individuals frequently need services for substance abuse, and, especially, mental health (Streissguth et al., 1996). For every client that did not return for appointments, seemed noncompliant or resistant with no clear explanation of why, or just didn't seem to 'get it,' a knowledge of FASD could be an extra clue that helps solve that puzzle and enable success for both the client and the program.

Be Willing...

To effectively serve individuals who have or may have an FASD, what is needed most is a counselor who is willing. For many individuals with an FASD, it is not that they *can't* do the things necessary to succeed in treatment. Rather, it's that no one is willing to develop the understanding needed to help them succeed. While individuals with an FASD do present unique challenges, a willing counselor can make the difference between treatment success and treatment 'failure.'

- *Be willing* to understand the brain-based disabilities that are characteristic of these disorders: With any diffuse brain damage, including the damage that can result from prenatal alcohol exposure, some of the effects are permanent, and one cannot assume or teach the usual decision-making and self-care capabilities.
- *Be willing* to observe physical and behavioral factors and consider possibilities beyond defiance, noncompliance, or other more commonly diagnosed symptoms.
- *Be willing* to meet the client where they are and enable their growth.
- *Be willing* to set aside the false view that, because an FASD is permanent, "nothing can be done." Individuals with an FASD can and do respond positively to treatment that is modified to meet their unique needs.
- *Be willing* to develop treatment plans for this population with the identification and addressing of secondary disabilities as a built-in expectation, as research has shown that individuals with an FASD exhibit a unique prevalence of co-occurring disorders (O'Connor et al., 2002; Astley, 2010; Pei, Denys, Hughes, & Rasmussen, 2011; Kodituwakku & Kodituwakku, 2011).
- *Be willing* to redefine success and consider multiple treatment options and make modifications (frequency, duration, cultural issues, client strengths, etc.) to maximize the client's opportunities for recovery.
- *Be willing* to stretch the schedule. Success with a client who has an FASD can take longer, but it is achievable. Interventions should aim to "…support the life path of an individual with disabilities in a positive direction over time" (Olson, Oti, Gelo, & Beck, 2009).

It is important to note that this TIP is not encouraging counselors to forego the primary treatment issue that brought the client to their setting in the first place, in favor of treating FASD. This chapter is only providing a process for identifying FASD as a possible barrier to successfully addressing the primary treatment issue, and making appropriate modifications to your treatment approach to maximize the potential for positive outcomes. Even if the cognitive or behavioral barriers that you identify through this process do not ultimately result in a diagnosis or positive assessment for an FASD, these are still functional impairments presenting barriers to treatment, and thus the process remains valuable.

Identifying the Need for FASD Assessment, Diagnosis, and Services: Suggested Steps

The step chart on the next page illustrates a six-stage process that counselors can implement with clients for whom there are indications of an FASD. These steps will form the outline for the remainder of this chapter.

1. The Starting Point: Observing Indicators

Identifying Barriers and Causes

If there are indications of an FASD in the form of maladaptive behaviors, Step 1 represents a critical intermediate process: Be willing to consider the *root cause* of the behavior rather than just responding to the behavior. The

1. The Starting Point: Observing Indicators

2. Functional Observation and History/Interviewing

3. Assessment (External or Through an In-House Assessment Team)

4. Tailoring Treatment for Individuals with an FASD

5. Working with the Family

6. Transition and Connection to Community Supports

easiest way to think of Steps 1 and 2 is that Step 1 is the observation of a treatment barrier or group of barriers, Step 2 is the examination of a possible root cause (or causes).

So, in Step 1, you have a client who is not doing well in treatment, and you have exhausted your normal protocol of approaches for improving the efficacy of the treatment relationship. Since individuals with an FASD are at an increased risk of having substance use or mental health issues in the first place (Streissguth et al., 1996; Astley, 2010), what this step asks you to do is take a step back and consider whether the maladaptive behaviors that you are observing (e.g., frequently missed appointments) match the profile of an individual who may have an FASD (i.e., poor time management skills, memory problems).

When working with an individual who has an FASD, a counselor would be likely to observe problem indicators in the following functional domains:

- Planning/Temporal Skills
- Behavioral Regulation/Sensory Motor Integration
- Abstract Thinking/Judgment
- Memory/Learning/Information Processing
- Spatial Skills and Spatial Memory
- Social Skills and Adaptive Behavior
- Motor/Oral Motor Control

Problems in these domains will likely show up as deficits that interfere with treatment success, including:

- Inability to remember program rules or follow multiple instructions.
- Inability to remember and keep appointments, or to get lost on the way there.
- Inability to make appropriate decisions by themselves about treatment needs and goals.
- Inability to appropriately interpret social cues from treatment professionals or other clients.
- Inability to observe appropriate boundaries, either with staff or other clients.
- Inability to attend to (and not disrupt) group activities.

- Inability to process information readily or accurately.
- Inability to 'act one's age.'

When indicators occur in any these domains (and particularly when they occur across multiple domains), it is worthwhile to apply the FASD 4-Digit Code Caregiver Interview Checklist (Astley, 2004b) in Step 2 to determine if there is sufficient cause to 1) pursue evaluation for an FASD with this client, and 2) modify treatment to account for the client's functioning in these areas.

2. Functional Observation and History/Interviewing

An Appropriate Approach to Observation and Interviewing

If you have decided to move on to a fuller examination of the possible presence of an FASD based on indicators observed in Step 1, it is important to approach the topic with care and sensitivity. For the client, discussion of a possible FASD can cause feelings of shame, or possibly even anger or disbelief, about being identified with a "brain disorder." For the family of the individual, particularly for a birth mother, suggesting the possible presence of an FASD can lead to feelings of guilt or a feeling of being 'blamed,' and a perception that service systems are unhelpful or even a negative experience. It is critical for a counselor to take a no-fault, no-shame approach to the topic of FASD, continually reassuring the individual and the family that you are examining the possibility of an FASD only as a way to achieve the best possible treatment outcome.

The FASD 4-Digit Code Caregiver Interview Checklist

The FASD 4-Digit Code Caregiver Interview Checklist provided below is from the FASD 4-Digit Diagnostic Code (Astley, 2004b). The checklist is also reproduced in Appendix D, and can be considered for reproduction and inclusion in your treatment file for clients where you believe a form of FASD may be present.

However, please note: **This checklist is not presented as a validated FASD screening instrument**. It is simply provided as a tool that can be used over time to note typical problem areas for someone who might have an FASD (i.e., building a profile of FASD), and provides information that you can combine with your clinical judgment to make a better-informed decision about whether to direct a client toward a more extensive FASD assessment or diagnosis.

It should also be noted that the behaviors identified on this checklist can indicate other disorders, as well. Individuals with an FASD are frequently misdiagnosed (Greenbaum et al., 2009). Given their symptoms, they may be described as meeting criteria for Attention Deficit/Hyperactivity Disorder (ADHD), Attention Deficit Disorder (ADD), Oppositional Defiant Disorder (ODD), adolescent depression, or bipolar disorder. It is possible for FASD to co-occur with any of these diagnoses, but it is also possible that a condition on the fetal alcohol spectrum may better describe the pattern of target symptoms than these other diagnostic terms. A differential and comprehensive diagnosis is essential, whether in-house or through referral, and the information gathered through this checklist can help to inform a diagnostic process.

In a profile of the first 1,400 patients to receive diagnostic evaluations for an FASD at the Washington State FAS Diagnostic & Prevention Network (FAS DPN), caregivers completing an interview with a professional based in part on this checklist demonstrated an impressive ability to differentiate the behavior profiles of children with FAS/pFAS, children with severe ARND (SE/AE), and

The FASD 4-Digit Code Caregiver Interview Checklist

Severity Score: Severity of Delay/Impairment (Displayed along left margin)

Circle: **0** = Unknown, Not Assessed, Too Young **1** = Within Normal Limits **2** = Mild to Moderate **3** = Significant

Severity	Caregiver Observations
	Planning/Temporal Skills
0 1 2 3	Needs considerable help organizing daily tasks _____
0 1 2 3	Cannot organize time _____
0 1 2 3	Does not understand concept of time _____
0 1 2 3	Difficulty in carrying out multi-step tasks _____
0 1 2 3	Other _____
	Behavioral Regulation/Sensory Motor Integration
0 1 2 3	Poor management of anger/tantrums _____
0 1 2 3	Mood swings _____
0 1 2 3	Impulsive _____
0 1 2 3	Compulsive _____
0 1 2 3	Perseverative _____
0 1 2 3	Inattentive _____
0 1 2 3	Inappropriately [high or low] activity level _____
0 1 2 3	Lying/stealing _____
0 1 2 3	Unusual [high or low] reactivity to [sound touch light] _____
0 1 2 3	Other _____
	Abstract Thinking/Judgment
0 1 2 3	Poor judgment _____
0 1 2 3	Cannot be left alone _____
0 1 2 3	Concrete, unable to think abstractly _____
0 1 2 3	Other _____
	Memory/Learning/Information Processing
0 1 2 3	Poor memory, inconsistent retrieval of learned information _____
0 1 2 3	Slow to learn new skills _____
0 1 2 3	Does not seem to learn from past experiences _____
0 1 2 3	Problems recognizing consequences of actions _____
0 1 2 3	Problems with information processing speed and accuracy _____
0 1 2 3	Other _____
	Spatial Skills and Spatial Memory
0 1 2 3	Gets lost easily, has difficulty navigating from point A to point B _____
0 1 2 3	Other _____

Severity	Caregiver Observations
	Social Skills and Adaptive Behavior
0 1 2 3	Behaves at a level notably younger than chronological age _____
0 1 2 3	Poor social/adaptive skills _____
0 1 2 3	Other _____
	Motor/Oral Motor Control
0 1 2 3	Poor/delayed motor skills _____
0 1 2 3	Poor balance _____
0 1 2 3	Other _____

Source: Astley, S. J. (2004). *Diagnostic guide for Fetal Alcohol Spectrum Disorders: The 4-Digit Diagnostic Code*, Third Edition. Seattle, WA: University of Washington. Accessed June 1, 2012 at **http://depts.washington.edu/fasdpn/pdfs/FASD-2004-Diag-Form-08-06-04.pdf**. Used with permission from the author.

children with moderate ARND (ND/AE) (Astley, 2010).

In addition, the box "Risk Assessment Questions" contains a group of questions developed at the FAS Community Resource Center in Tucson, Arizona. These questions can further assist providers seeking to determine whether an evaluation for an FASD is warranted.

3. Assessment (External or Through an In-House Assessment Team)

Assessment for the presence of an FASD is an interdisciplinary process best accomplished through a team approach. The sad reality is that the existing network of qualified assessment teams and facilities in the United States is insufficient to meet demand, and behavioral health experts have repeatedly observed the urgent need for an increase in FASD

Risk Assessment Questions

Yes/No	Additional Areas of Consideration
	Client History
Y N	Are there alcohol problems in family of origin?
Y N	Was the client raised by someone other than the birth mother?
Y N	Has the client ever been in special education classes?
Y N	Has the client had different home placements?
Y N	Has the client ever been suspended from school?
Y N	Has the client ever been diagnosed as ADHD?
	How many jobs has the client had in past 2 years? _____
Y N	Can the client manage money effectively?
	Are the client's friends older or younger (for an individual with an FASD, friends will tend to be younger due to lag between physical age and functional age)? _____

Adapted from: Kellerman, T. (2005). Recommended assessment tools for children and adults with confirmed or suspected FASD. Tucson, AZ: FAS Community Resource Center. Accessed June 5, 2012 at **http://come-over.to/FAS/AssessmentsFASD.htm**.

assessment, diagnosis, and treatment capacity (Institute of Health Economics, 2009; Interagency Coordinating Committee on FASD, 2011).

However, many substance abuse and mental health treatment settings may have an interdisciplinary staff team and/or sufficient referral relationships to attempt FASD assessment internally, creating an opportunity to help fill a gap in the behavioral health field. If this is the case with your agency, this section discusses some of the essential elements of FASD assessment, as well as available resources that can help your agency develop this staff capability. (The first interdisciplinary FASD diagnostic clinic [the Washington State FAS Diagnostic and Prevention Network (FAS DPN)] was established in Washington State in 1993 as part of a CDC-sponsored FASD prevention study [Clarren & Astley, 1997]. A comprehensive description of the interdisciplinary model used by the Washington State FAS DPN is presented by Clarren, Carmichael-Olson, Clarren, and Astley [2000]; see Appendix A: *Bibliography*). In addition, for sites that cannot provide FASD capacity internally, referral options do exist, and this section will provide information on accessing those resources.

In-House FASD Assessment: The Essential Elements

Effective in-house assessment for FASD is built on three core components: 1) building the right team, 2) accessing the right resources, and 3) gathering the right information.

Building the Right Team

FASD assessment, as will be explained below, involves gathering information and making evaluations in a variety of functional areas, and is an involved process that can overwhelm the client and his or her family. This necessitates a wide range of professional skill sets, not only to perform the various clinical and observational tasks, but also to help the client and family navigate the process smoothly. The box "In-House FASD Assessment: An Ideal Core Team" describes an ideal in-house FASD assessment team and its functions.

Part 2, Chapter 2 of this TIP outlines appropriate processes if these professionals need to be added and/or accessed through referral relationships.

Accessing the Right Resources

Appendix C, *Public and Professional Resources on FASD*, provides information and links for accessing FASD information and training from a variety of national and regional sources.

In-House FASD Assessment: An Ideal Core Team

Case Coordinator	• Reviews history and current stability
	• Assesses needs of individual and caregiver
	• Post-diagnosis, connects individual/family to positive supports
	• Is often a social worker, but in this case could be the role of the counselor
Psychologist[1] and Speech Language Pathologist	• Assess basic and higher levels of brain function
Physical Therapist, Occupational Therapist, or Vocational Rehabilitation Counselor	• Assesses motor and sensory issues (including sensory-motor integration, and balance and gait issues)

Physician	• Assesses dysmorphology, neurological findings, and basic health determinants • Also contributes to behavioral health profile
Family Navigator	• Helps the family through the process • Ideally is an actual caregiver of someone with an FASD • Ideally is available to help the family connect with parent support and other needed resources

Based on TIP consensus panel recommendations and *Canadian Guidelines for Diagnosis* (Chudley, Conry, Cook, Loock, Rosales, & LeBlanc, 2005).

[1] The psychologist should be trained to do neuropsychological testing.

Among these are two excellent resources for agencies seeking to develop FASD capabilities; the Washington State FAS DPN and the CDC's FASD Regional Training Centers (RTCs).

- One of the primary sites for FASD assessment and diagnosis in the United States is the Washington State FAS DPN, based at the University of Washington in Seattle. Established in 1993 through Washington State Senate Bill 5688 and support from the CDC, March of Dimes, Chavez Memorial Fund, and the Washington State Department of Social and Health Services, the Washington State FAS DPN provides FASD diagnostic services as well as training in FASD. Training resources include the FASD 4-Digit Diagnostic Code Online Course and a 2-day FASD Diagnostic Team training for interdisciplinary clinical teams (or individual clinical team members) seeking to establish FASD services in their community. Visit the FAS DPN's homepage (**http://depts.washington.edu/fasdpn/**) to find out more about their services.

- The CDC's RTCs develop, implement, and evaluate educational curricula regarding FASD prevention, identification, and care, and incorporate the curricula into training programs at each grantee's university or college, into other schools throughout their regions, and into the credentialing requirements of professional boards. Visit the CDC's RTC homepage (**http://www.cdc.gov/ncbddd/fasd/ documents/flyerfasd_rtcs.pdf**) to find out about currently funded RTC sites and available services.

Gathering the Right Information

A useful tool that your team can use to gather and organize the necessary information to support a formal FASD diagnosis is the *New Patient Information Form*. This form was developed by the Washington State FAS DPN and is part of the *Diagnostic Guide for Fetal Alcohol Spectrum Disorders: The 4-Digit Diagnostic Code* (Astley, 2004b, Third Edition, pp. 103-114). If your agency decides to refer a client for an FASD diagnosis, this information will provide a necessary foundation for the diagnostic process. The *New Patient Information Form* can be downloaded for free from (**http://depts.washington.edu/fasdpn/ htmls/diagnostic-forms.htm**).

In addition to basic information about the client and your agency, the *New Patient Information Form* provides a template for gathering information in the critical areas of Growth; Physical Appearance and Health; Neurological Issues; Attention Deficit and

Hyperactivity; Mental Health Issues; School Issues; Alcohol Exposure; Information About the Patient's Biological Parents; Medical History of the Biological Family; Pregnancies of Birth Mother; Pregnancy, Labor, and Delivery of this Patient; List of Professionals Currently Involved in Patient's Care; Placements (foster, adoptive, etc.); and What to Bring to the [diagnostic] Clinic.

To further ensure collection of appropriate information and build staff knowledge and capabilities related to FASD, it will be valuable for your team to become familiar with the basic guidelines of the most widely used diagnostic approaches to the various disorders in the spectrum. A comprehensive comparison of the current FASD diagnostic systems is presented in a chapter entitled "Diagnosing FASD" (Astley, 2011), and is reprinted in Appendix E, *Comparison of Current FASD Diagnostic Systems* with the author's permission.

External: Assessment and Diagnosis

The reality for many programs will be that, for reasons of cost and/or lack of community resources, building an in-house FASD assessment team or diagnostic capability will be unrealistic. If this describes your agency, the FASD diagnosis and training sites discussed

under *Accessing the Right Resources*, above, should be accessed so that you can refer your client to an appropriate provider. Agencies can also use the **Resource Directory** (**http://www. nofas.org/resource-directory/**) provided by the National Organization on FAS (NOFAS) to help locate FASD-related services.

At the same time, referral for assessment and diagnosis should be paired with treatment modifications and accommodations that are discussed in the next section. This can be done with or without a formal diagnosis of a form of FASD. If you and your clinical team have identified symptoms indicating an FASD through Steps 1 and 2 of this chapter, the methods discussed in the next section can still help the treatment process.

Many providers will not have an existing relationship with the FASD assessment or diagnosis provider to whom they refer a client. In such cases, it is vital to actively assist the client through the transition and provide regular follow-up to ensure client satisfaction and full and open communication between agencies and with the client. (Also the client's family, if they are involved in treatment.) The box "Overview of the Diagnostic Process (As Performed by the FAS DPN)" summarizes the phases of the diagnostic process as performed

---

Overview of the Diagnostic Process (As Performed by the FAS DPN)

A comprehensive description of the FAS DPN interdisciplinary FASD diagnostic process is presented by Clarren et al. (2000).

Phase	Description
Phase 1	• Clinical intake: Caregivers complete a comprehensive "New Patient Information Form" prior to the clinic visit to report current concerns and developmental, social and alcohol exposure history. Past medical, educational, psychological, social, and legal records are also obtained. • Record review: Psychologist reviews all available medical, developmental, clinical, educational, and other records, and presents a case summary to the FASD diagnostic team on the day of the diagnostic evaluation. Clients 18 and older are referred elsewhere for their neuropsychological evaluation.

Phase	Description
Phase 2	• <u>Psychometric screening/evaluation</u>: Diagnostic team members (occupational therapist, psychologist, speech–language pathologist) screen/assess the patient's current neurobehavioral performance (e.g., language and communication, executive function, cognition, sensory–motor skills). • <u>Physical examination</u>: Physician examines diagnostic parameters of growth and facial dysmorphology (and general health, sleep problems, medications used, etc.). • <u>Caregiver(s) interview</u>: Physician and psychologist conduct a caregiver interview (up to 2 hours) using the 4-Digit Code Caregiver Interview checklist.
Phase 3	• <u>Diagnosis and intervention recommendations</u>: Diagnostic team reviews and synthesizes data, derives the 4-Digit Code, and generates intervention recommendations. • <u>Diagnostic summary</u>: Diagnostic team shares the diagnosis and intervention recommendations with caregiver(s) in a brief case conference. Adolescent and adult clients are included in the case conference. • <u>Diagnostic summary report</u>: Diagnosis, assessment results, and intervention recommendations are integrated into a comprehensive 6- to 8-page diagnostic summary report (**http://depts.washington.edu/fasdpn/pdfs/4-digit-medsum-web-2006.pdf**) and submitted to the patient's medical record. • <u>Follow-Up Debriefing</u>: A private follow-up debriefing is conducted with the caregiver (and client, if old enough) to discuss the impact of the diagnosis and review specific recommendations.

Table originally appeared in Jirikowic, Gelo, & Astley (2010) with minor modifications.

by the Washington State FAS DPN. The phases of this process are likely to be similar in other interdisciplinary FASD diagnostic clinics.

When the Client Already Has a Diagnosis of an FASD

If a client has already been diagnosed with an FASD at the time of presentation to your setting, the guidelines in the next section should automatically be considered. In addition, as indicated in the table *Overview of the Diagnostic Process* in the previous section, the diagnosis report may also be a source of intervention and modification guidelines and should be thoroughly reviewed by the counselor with the client (and the family, if involved in the treatment process). A comprehensive summary of the types of intervention recommendations provided in relation to 120 youths following their FASD diagnostic evaluations

at the Washington State FAS DPN is provided by Jirikowic et al. (2010).

At the same time, further assessment by medical, mental, and allied health professionals may still be needed to determine the client's current level of function in important areas, particularly if the diagnosis occurred years earlier. "Refreshing" the functional information will help the counselor tailor the treatment plan and counseling strategies to the client's strengths, needs, and preferences. Forms of re-testing and assessment can include the following:

- Being familiar with any medications the client is taking and observing any behaviors or physical symptoms that might indicate the need to reevaluate medication use or dosage;
- Hearing and speech tests to identify any progress in communication or barriers

that may affect the client's treatment and ongoing recovery;

- Occupational therapy and physical therapy evaluations to assess the client's daily living skills and motor function, vocational skills, and preferences and possibilities;

- Determining current achievement levels in reading, spelling, and math; and

- Use of an appropriate, standardized interview or questionnaire to determine how the client compares to peers in receptive, expressive, and written communication; personal, domestic, and community daily living skills; and interpersonal relationships, play and leisure time, and coping skills.

4. Tailoring Treatment for Individuals with an FASD

Introduction
This section will discuss appropriate approaches to modifying treatment and/or making necessary accommodations for clients who exhibit indicators suggesting an FASD, or who show cognitive and behavioral barriers to treatment success, as identified in Steps 1 and 2 of this chapter.

This discussion is divided into two sections; 1) general principles for working with individuals who have or may have an FASD (regardless of age), and 2) specific considerations for adolescents who have or may have an FASD. The chapter then moves on to Step 5, *Working With the Family*, and Step 6, *Transition and Connection to Community Supports*.

As noted above, if the individual already has a diagnosis of an FASD, the diagnostic report may also include recommendations for appropriate interventions and modifications to treatment. The counselor should review this report thoroughly, if it is available.

General Principles for Working with Individuals Who Have or May Have an FASD

Safety Considerations
Safety is a primary health issue for individuals of all ages with an FASD (Jirikowic et al., 2010). Starting a treatment process without first addressing safety issues is futile and potentially dangerous: The clinician must first evaluate physical safety for the adolescent or adult with an FASD. This includes issues of violence, harm to self (such as self-mutilation) or others, victimization, adequate housing, and food. In typical adolescents and adults, psychiatric severity can be significantly reduced when co-occurring issues are treated together and mental health and substance abuse treatment are provided as an integrated program (Hser, Grella, Evans, & Huang, 2006).

For older individuals who have or may have an FASD, there are special safety considerations. This population has a number of risk factors for accidents and injury; poor decision-making, impulsivity, impaired motor coordination, working memory, attention, emotional and sensory regulation, and susceptibility to peer pressure. Even seemingly routine tasks like crossing the street safely may be impossible for those who are more severely affected. Other examples of possible safety and health concerns in adolescents and adults with an FASD are remembering medication schedules, decisions about legal and illegal substances, driving, and risk-taking situations in which poor social problem-solving (McGee, Fryer, Bjorquist, Mattson, & Riley, 2008), impulsivity, and peer pressure combine to compromise safety.

Vignette #9 in Part 1, Chapter 3 of this TIP elaborates the process of working with a caregiver to develop a personalized Safety Plan on behalf of an individual with an FASD. In addition, Appendix F, *Sample Crisis/Safety Plan*, contains a sample plan that has been adapted from the work of the *Families Moving Forward Program* (**http://depts.washington.edu/fmffasd/**), and can be printed and used with a client and/or their family member(s)/caregiver(s).

Risk for Abuse

Children with physical, psychological, and sensory disabilities—including FASD—are known to be more vulnerable to violence and maltreatment, or to be at a greater risk of these forms of abuse (Olivan, 2005). This vulnerability is brought about by a variety of factors, including dependence on others for intimate and routine personal care, increased exposure to a larger number of caregivers and settings, inappropriate social skills, poor judgment, inability to seek help or report abuse, and lack of strategies to defend themselves against abuse. Murphy and Elias (2006) report figures from the National Center on Child Abuse and Neglect indicating that children with disabilities are sexually abused at a rate 2.2 higher than that for children without disabilities. The United States Department of Justice reports that 68 to 83 percent of women with developmental disabilities will be sexually assaulted in their lifetimes, and less than half of them will seek assistance from legal or treatment services (Pease & Frantz, 1994). In a study of 336 males and females in treatment for alcohol abuse or dependence, more than 56 percent had also experienced childhood sexual or physical abuse (Zlotnick et al., 2006).

In one long-term study, 80 percent of young adults who had experienced abuse as a child met diagnostic criteria for at least one psychiatric disorder at age 21. These individuals exhibited many problems, including depression, anxiety, eating disorders, and suicide attempts (Silverman, Reinherz, & Giaconia, 1996). Other psychological and emotional conditions associated with abuse and neglect include panic disorder, dissociative disorders, attention-deficit/hyperactivity disorder,

depression, anger, posttraumatic stress disorder, and reactive attachment disorder (Teicher, 2000; De Bellis & Thomas, 2003; Springer, Sheridan, Kuo, & Carnes, 2007).

Astley (2010) has documented a high prevalence of abuse, neglect, and multiple home placements among 1,400 patients identified with an FASD—70 percent were in foster/adoptive care and had experienced, on average, three home placements. In fact, in a separate study, Astley and colleagues (2002) identified a prevalence rate of FAS in foster care that was 10-times higher—1/100—than in the general population—1/1000. Children in foster care face a risk of maltreatment, which can affect their physical health and lead to attachment disorders, compromised brain functioning, inadequate social skills, and mental health difficulties (Harden, 2004). Another study among young women with FASD found that they had poor quality of life scores and high levels of mental disorders and behavioral problems relative to standardization samples and other at-risk populations (Grant et al., 2005).

Risk for Suicide

In addition, individuals with an FASD are at significant risk of suicide at all ages studied (Huggins et al., 2008). A person with an FASD may not appear to plan or execute a suicide attempt effectively; this is not indicative of the seriousness of the intent.

High Risk of Repeated Involvement with the Legal System

People with an FASD can have specific types of brain damage that may increase engagement in criminal activity (Kodituwakku et al., 1995; Page, 2001; Mattson, Schoenfeld, & Riley, 2001; Page, 2002; Moore & Green, 2004; Clark et al., 2004; Schonfeld, Mattson, & Riley, 2005; Schonfeld, Paley, Frankel, O'Connor, 2006; Brown, Gudjonsson, & Connor, 2011). These can include:

Suicide Intervention/Prevention for Individuals with an FASD

- Standard suicide assessment protocols need to be modified to accommodate neuropsychological deficits and communication impairments:
  - Instead of "How does the future look to you?" ask "What are you going to do tomorrow? Next week?" (Difficulties with abstract thought.)
  - The seriousness of the suicidal behavior does not necessarily equal the level of intent to die (lack of understanding of consequences).
- Obtain family/collateral input.
- Be careful about words used regarding other suicides or deaths.
- Intervene to reduce risk:
  - Address basic needs and increase stability.
  - Treat depression.
  - Teach distraction techniques.
  - Remove lethal means.
  - Increase social support.
- Do not use suicide contracts (impulsivity issues).
- Monitor risk closely.
- Reinforce and build reasons for living.
  - Be literal.
- Strengthen advocate-client relationship.

Source: Huggins, J. E., Grant, T., O'Malley, K., & Streissguth, A. (2008). Suicide attempts among adults with Fetal Alcohol Spectrum Disorders: Clinical considerations. *Mental Health Aspects of Developmental Disabilities, 11*(2), 33-42.

- Lack of impulse control and trouble understanding the future consequences of current behavior;
- Trouble understanding what constitutes criminal behavior (for example, a youth with an FASD may not see any problem with driving a car he knows was stolen if he wasn't the one who stole it);
- Difficulty planning, connecting cause and effect, empathizing (particularly if the experience is not explained in a very concrete way), taking responsibility, delaying gratification, and making good judgments;
- Tendency toward explosive episodes, often triggered by sensory overload, slower rates of processing the information around them, and/or feeling "stupid;"
- Vulnerability to peer pressure and influence (e.g., may commit a crime to please friends), and high levels of suggestibility; and
- Lower level of moral maturity (due in part to social information processing deficits).

The number of people in the criminal justice system with an FASD has not specifically been determined. Data are limited, and populations vary by state. In addition, few systems conduct any screening or can provide diagnosis. Streissguth and colleagues (2004) conducted an evaluation of 415 clinical patients with FASD at the University of Washington. Trouble with the law (including arrest, conviction, or otherwise) was reported in 14 percent of children and 60 percent of adolescents and adults with an FASD. In addition, Fast, Conry,

& Loock (1999) evaluated all youth referred to a forensic psychiatric assessment for FASD in Burnaby, British Columbia, Canada. Of 287 youths assessed, 67 (or 23 percent) were found to have an alcohol exposure-related diagnosis. Although this result should not be generalized to the entire prison population, it does reveal a possible disproportionate representation of individuals with an FASD in the juvenile justice system.

It is important for counseling professionals to consider a client's criminal history and any factors that place the client at risk for further criminal involvement. Because persons with an FASD have problems learning from experience, they may repeat crimes and cycle through the legal system multiple times.

Clinicians may encounter individuals with an FASD who are participating in court-ordered treatment. Such individuals need help navigating the legal system. The clinician can consult with the client's attorney and assist in educating him or her about FASD. In addition, the clinician can assist in finding resources to help the client understand any legal proceedings and requirements. The National Legal Aid & Defender Association (**http://www. nlada100years.org/**) or the American Bar Association (**www.americanbar.org**) may be able to identify resources at the local level.

Vulnerability of Individuals with an FASD
Individuals with an FASD are vulnerable not only to criminal activity but also to victimization (Freunscht & Feldman, 2011). Their poor judgment may lead them to associate with people who victimize them physically, emotionally, and financially. Their impulsivity may lead them into dangerous situations. Women with an FASD may get involved with negative associations for food, shelter, attention, or drugs (Page, 2003). In addition, their impaired sense of boundaries can lead to sexual victimization. Because of their unpredictable

behavior, they may need 24-hour supervision (Streissguth, 1997).

Even with compensatory strategies, the person with an FASD may be less able to use judgment, consider consequences, or understand abstract situations (Kodituwakku, 2007; Astley, 2010; Freunscht & Feldman, 2011). Impulsivity is an ongoing issue. Social isolation and loneliness may drive the person to seek out any type of friendship and lead to victimization. A discussion or pursuit of safeguards for the person may be necessary:

- Recognize that victimization may occur, and keep vigilant for situations that may arise in the person's life.

- Role-play personal safety and specific scenarios that people face (e.g., who is a stranger vs. who is a friend) to allow the individual to practice taught skills and perhaps allow them to pursue safe activities (De Vos, 2003). Consider videotaping the client doing it right in the role-play, so he or she can watch it over and over, reinforcing the lesson. Watching the video also helps move the information from short-term memory to long-term memory. (In many cases, though certainly not all, long-term memory has been observed to function better than short-term memory for individuals with an FASD).

- Establish written routines and structured time charts, and have these where they are easily seen throughout the day.

- Provide a buddy system and supervision to help decrease opportunities for victimization.

- Consider a guardianship of funds to protect the individual. A trustee can ensure that the necessities of life are covered, including rent, food, clothing, and finding an advocate. The clinician may want to include such provisions in the aftercare plan.

- Help the client find a healthy, structured environment in aftercare to help them avoid criminal activity.

Family Safety and Support
For all families caring for an individual with an FASD, or when parents themselves have an FASD, establishing family safety and support is vital. A crisis/safety plan should always be put in place (see Appendix F for an example *Crisis/Safety Plan* form). To stay safe and well-supported, it is important to help the client (and caregivers) identify available services, determine which ones are effective for them or their children, and understand how to work productively with service providers (Streissguth, 1997). (See Appendix G for a *Services and Supports Checklist* that can be reviewed with clients as a worksheet.)

For birth families in recovery, the counselor can help families cope with FASD during the recovery process. This is best done by building a protective environment for clients and their children. This may include helping them obtain safe, stable housing, assisting with daily living skills (such as bill paying and food shopping), and overseeing home situations. It is also important to establish a network of community service providers who will be available for aftercare to promote ongoing recovery and avoid relapse (Millon, Millon, & Davis, 1993).

For more information about this topic, see Step 6, *Transition and Connection to Community Supports*).

Modifying a Treatment Plan

Factors to Consider
When modifying a treatment plan for an individual who has or may have an FASD, the following should be considered:

- **Help the client adjust to a structured program or environment and develop trust in the staff.** Individuals with an FASD tend to be trusting (Freunscht & Feldman, 2011) and need a great deal of structure, but may have trouble adapting to changes in routine and to new people.

- **Share the rules early and often.** Put instructions in writing and remind the client often. Keep the rules simple and avoid punitive measures that most individuals with an FASD will not process. If a rule is broken, remind the client of the situation and help to strategize ways they can better follow the rule in the future.

- **Take a holistic approach,** focusing on all aspects of the client's life, not just the substance abuse or mental health issues. Include basic living and social skills, such as how to dress, groom, practice good hygiene, present a positive attitude, and practice good manners. Help the client develop appropriate goals within the context of his or her interests and abilities.

- **Provide opportunities to role-play or otherwise practice appropriate social behaviors,** such as helping others. Areas of focus may include impulse control skills, dealing with difficult situations such as being teased, and problem-solving.

- In an inpatient setting, **allow time** for the client to be stabilized and acquire the basic skills to cooperate with others before discussing his or her substance abuse or mental health issues. In an outpatient setting, it may help to develop a rapport with the client and establish trust and communication before addressing the primary treatment issue.

- **Assume the presence of co-occurring issues.** It is likely that a high percentage of people with an FASD have at least one co-occurring mental disorder (O'Connor et al., 2002; Streissguth et al., 2004; Clark et al., 2004; Astley, 2010). In a study of 1,400 patients with FASD, Astley (2010) documented that 75 percent had one or more co-occurring disorders, with the most prevalent being ADHD (54 percent). In a study of 80 birth mothers of children with FAS, 96 percent had from one to nine mental disorders in addition to alcoholism (Astley et al., 2000b); the most common was phobia (76 percent). Forty-four percent of the women had mental disorders diagnosed by the age of 8 years.

- When possible, **include the family or caregivers in activities**, such as parent education about FASD and substance abuse and/or mental health, strategies for providing care for an individual with an FASD and a substance abuse or mental health problem (e.g., avoiding power

struggles), and building the client's self-esteem. Help family and caregivers practice positive communication skills such as active listening, use of literal language, and avoiding "don't" (i.e., focusing on what *needs* to be done rather than what *should not* be done).

- **Include the client in treatment planning/modification**, and build family/caregiver meetings into the plan as well, with a clear purpose and agenda. Recognize that some family members may also have an FASD, and work with them accordingly.

- **Incorporate multiple approaches to learning**, such as auditory, visual, and tactile approaches. Avoid written exercises and instead focus on hands-on practice, role-playing, and using audio- or video-recording for playback/reinforcement of learning. Use multisensory strategies,

The Navigator

A person who has impaired vision is given a seeing eye dog. A person with impaired hearing is given an interpreter or a hearing aid. These external devices are necessary for the person with physical impairments to be able to function to maximum potential in life.

The person with an FASD has a physical impairment in the area of the brain, particularly the forebrain or frontal lobes, which regulate the executive functions. A navigator refers to the presence of another responsible person (parent, teacher, job coach, sibling) who can mentor, assist, guide, supervise, and/or support the affected person to maximize success (which may need to be redefined as the avoidance of addiction, arrest, unwanted pregnancy, homelessness, or accidental death).

Because some individuals with an FASD may appear to be bright and normal, the disability that is brain damage may only be apparent in test results, or in actions that place the person at serious risk. It is the risk of danger to the person and to others that makes a navigator such a useful and important concept. A navigator can seem like a form of enabling or an encouragement of co-dependency. More accurately, however, a navigator is an appropriate form of advocacy to ensure that the individual receives whatever assistive devices are needed for him or her to participate in life in as normal a capacity as reasonably possible.

For many individuals with an FASD, the navigator can be someone with whom they "check in" on a regular basis, or vice versa. For others, the navigator will play a more constant advocacy role, and may share the role with others. (See Vignette #9 for an example of a father playing the role of a navigator, and sharing the role with a coach and one of his son's relatives.)

Adapted from: Kellerman, T. (2003). External brain. Accessed June 5, 2012 at **http://come-over.to/FAS/externalbrain.htm**.

such as drawing, painting, or music, to assist the client in expressing feelings. These strategies take advantage of skills that many individuals with an FASD have. They can also help the client share difficult feelings that may be hard to talk about, such as fear and anger.

- **Consider sensory issues** around lighting, equipment sounds, and unfamiliar sensations and smells. Individuals with an FASD can be very sensitive to these environmental factors.

- **Arrange aftercare**, and encourage family/caregivers to participate in a support group to continue to learn parenting skills and to be encouraged in the recovery process (see Step 6, *Transition and Connection to Community Supports*).

Counseling Strategies

Due to the cognitive, social, and emotional deficits seen in FASD, counseling clients with these conditions requires adaptability and flexibility. Research data, clinical observation, and caregiver reports all suggest that it is crucial to tailor treatment approaches. Traditional approaches may not prove optimally effective, and more effort may be needed to convey basic concepts and promote a positive therapeutic relationship and environment. The following are recommendations designed to help providers:

- Set appropriate boundaries;

- Be aware of the client's strengths;

- Understand the impact of any abuse the client has experienced;

- Help the client cope with loss;

- Address any negative self-perception associated with an FASD;

- Focus on self-esteem and personal issues;

- Address resistance, denial, and acceptance;

- Weigh individual vs. group counseling;

- Consider a mentor approach; and

- Assess comprehension on an ongoing basis.

Boundaries

Establishing a trusting and honest relationship while maintaining boundaries is important with any client. Because persons with an FASD often lack social skills and have social communication problems (Kodituwakku, 2007; Greenbaum et al., 2009; Greenspan, 2009; Olson & Montague, 2011), they may breach boundaries by making inappropriate comments, asking inappropriate questions, or touching the counselor inappropriately. To set boundaries, it may help to have the client walk through the rules and expectations and demonstrate expected behavior. Frequent role-playing can help the client learn to apply concepts and figure out how to respond to various situations.

Persons with an FASD frequently experience difficulty with memory (Rasmussen, 2005; Riggins et al., 2012). Added to this, they may be able to repeat rules but not truly understand them or be able to operationalize them. Thus, it is important to review rules regularly. It is much more effective to limit the number of rules, review them repeatedly, and role-play different situations in which the person will need to recall the rules. Repetition is key.

Strengths

Many people focus on the deficits in persons with an FASD, but they also have many strengths. Some of these can be used in the treatment setting as part of counseling. Family may be a strength area: Parents report their children with FASD were engaged with their families and willing to receive—and even seek—help (Olson et al., 2009), as well as demonstrating a willingness to provide assistance with ordinary tasks (Jirikowic et al, 2008). Based on extensive clinical experience, Malbin (1993) identifies a number of other strength areas. For example, some people with an FASD are quite creative. They can express themselves through art and music, which may prove more effective than traditional talk therapy. Other approaches may involve storytelling and writing. These techniques can also be used for practical matters, such as developing a poster with treatment goals. In addition, visual aids can assist by drawing on areas of relative strength, so drawn or pictured goals may aid recall better than a written or spoken list of instructions.

History of Abuse

Given the risk of abuse among persons with an FASD and among individuals with substance abuse and/or mental health issues, it is likely that a client with a combination of these will have some personal abuse history (Astley et al., 2000b). The counselor working with persons with an FASD needs to be sensitive to the possibility of childhood abuse and other forms of victimization, and their impact on the counselor–client relationship. A common theme that counselors need to be attentive to is *powerlessness*, a theme often reflected in the following types of client communications and behaviors:

- Clients undervaluing their own competencies.
- Clients viewing others' needs and goals as more important than their own.
- Clients' inability to obtain nurturance and support for themselves.
- Clients' feelings of depression, anger, and frustration about their lives.
- Clients' low expectations for their own success.

Loss and Grieving

All individuals with an FASD have experienced losses in their lives. The fact that they are not like their peers is a loss of the ability to be like everyone else. Some have lost the hopes and dreams of what they wanted to be. Others lose their family or a secure future.

Some lose the opportunity for meaningful peer relationships and friendships. These losses can affect people in many ways and need to be addressed. The counselor can help to address these areas of loss through a number of strategies:

- Use active listening strategies, such as repeating what the person has said;
- Be honest;
- Raise awareness of experiences of separation and loss;
- Acknowledge and validate losses experienced;
- Acknowledge the client's feelings about loss;
- Avoid "good parent/bad parent" issues;
- Encourage communication; and
- Refer for further treatment (e.g., mental health) when necessary.

Self-Perception

Self-perception is a major issue with FASD. Despite the advent of the disease model, many people still view alcohol problems as a sign of moral weakness or a character flaw. This negative stereotype can be particularly severe in relation to pregnant women who drink, making the topic difficult to discuss (Salmon, 2008). Added to this, the negative judgment toward the mother may also be visited on the child. A counselor needs to be aware of this, and approach the issue carefully and sensitively if he or she suspects a client has an FASD.

Given their cognitive, social, and emotional deficits, persons with an FASD may think they are powerless to change. It is important to work through this issue with the client. They need to understand that they are not responsible for their disability and that they deserve respect. They also need to know that change is possible.

Self-Esteem and Personal Issues

The combination of abuse, loss, grief, and negative stereotypes can lead to self-esteem issues in any individual. Self-esteem is regularly an issue for individuals with an FASD (Olson, O'Connor, & Fitzgerald, 2001). Those who also have substance abuse or mental health problems face a double-edged sword: Their self-esteem can be damaged by their experience with an FASD and by their substance abuse or mental health issue. The clinician can use several strategies to help address self-esteem and personal issues:

- **Use person-first language**. An FASD may be part of who a person is, but it is not the person's entire identity. Someone can have an FASD, but nobody is an FASD.

- **Do not isolate the person**. Sending persons with an FASD out of the room to think about what they have done or responding to issues in a group session by simply ejecting them will often increase their sense of isolation and does not help them learn appropriate behaviors.

- **Do not blame people for what they cannot do**. Demanding that people repeatedly try to do things they cannot do is a lesson in frustration. It is important to have patience and understand individual limitations. People with an FASD may need something repeated several times because they have trouble remembering, not because they refuse to pay attention.

- **Set the person up to succeed**. Measures of success need to be different for different people. It is important to identify what would be a measure of success for the individual with an FASD and reinforce successes in concrete terms (e.g., "You did a great job of being on time for our session today. Thank you.") Training in social skills, anger management skills, and relaxation skills can help. In order for skills-building programs to be most successful for the person with an FASD, they need to be repeated periodically.

Resistance, Denial, and Acceptance

Individuals who have or may have an FASD may deny that they have a disability. Although some are relieved to know the cause of their difficulties, others may struggle to confront or accept their situation. The counselor needs to take time to help the person cope with the lack of understanding that often surrounds FASD. Women with an FASD, for instance, may fear becoming like their mothers and having a child with an FASD. An individual with an FASD may have difficulty with forgiveness of the birth mother, or may feel that it is inevitable that they will pass on FASD to their children. Counselors should reassure clients that they are not responsible for their disability, help them resolve their feelings about the birth mother, and educate them about the science of their condition (i.e., that it is not inevitable that they would pass on the condition). This process may take awhile, and the person may drift back and forth from accepting the disability to denying it. Exploring the reasons for the denial and understanding the client's fears can help.

Individual Counseling vs. Group Sessions

Individuals with an FASD may struggle to function in a group setting. Studies have shown increased levels of sensory sensitivities in this group, at least for children (Jirikowic et al., 2008). Clinical observations suggest individuals with an FASD can become overwhelmed by sensory input from large groups, noise, small spaces that cause crowding and touching of others, and visual distractions. Given the executive function deficits that are common in this clinical population, individuals with an FASD may not be able to process everything in the discussion and become lost. They may also 'talk too much,' and/or not be able to effectively convey their feelings and ideas in group discussions.

Individual counseling may be needed to avoid some of the issues that arise in clients with an FASD who lack social skills and find group settings confusing or overwhelming. Talk therapy can be modified to incorporate role-playing, practice dialogues, play therapy, art therapy, and other methods that can draw on the strengths seen in individuals with an FASD. Printed material may be helpful, but should be written in simple language with a clear, non-distracting page layout.

If group work is necessary, the counselor can assist the client who has or may have an FASD by making some accommodations:

- Explain group expectations concretely and repeat these ideas often.
- If a person monopolizes conversation or interrupts, use a talking stick as a concrete visual reminder of who should be speaking. Hand the stick to the person whose turn it is to speak and pass the stick to others as appropriate.
- Give the person time to work through material concretely within the group time so he or she can ask questions or you can check understanding of material. The client may need extra time to process information. Listen for key themes to emerge slowly through the person's talk and behaviors.
- Allow the client to get up and walk around if he or she gets restless.
- Use concrete representations, such as marking the floor, to show the concept of boundaries.
- Make adaptations for the whole group to avoid singling out the client.

Use of a Mentor

Programs that work with individuals with an FASD have found that mentoring can be effective, as it provides a consistent, stable, one-to-one relationship and allows for the development of a personal bond with a trained individual who has knowledge and experience working with those who have an FASD (Malbin, 1993; Schmucker, 1997; Grant et al., 2004; Denys, Rasmussen, & Henneveld, 2011). A mentor can:

- Assist with the development of concrete and consistent rules and goals that will guide behaviors in specific situations;
- Improve comprehension in discussions with others (e.g., providers or other clients); and
- Assist with the development of personal scenarios for the adult to work out responses and practice through role-play.

Ongoing Assessment for Comprehension of Information

Extensive clinical observations reveal that individuals with an FASD may appear to understand when they do not. Parents often say their family member with an FASD "just doesn't get it." This means that individuals with an FASD may repeat information without actually understanding the content, and so will be unlikely to follow through. Because of this, it is important to provide consistency and re-check the retention of information often:

- Ask the client to summarize what you have said.
- Review written material, such as rules, at each session.
- Do not assume that the client is familiar with a concept or can apply it simply because you have reviewed it multiple times; have discussions that explore their understanding beyond simply being able to repeat the concept.

Clinical wisdom holds that the only consistent thing about FASD is that those who are affected behave inconsistently. This means, for example, that a client may demonstrate that they know something on Monday, but have trouble recalling that same information on Tuesday. The clinician can benefit by following the rule to: REPEAT, REPEAT, REPEAT.

Sexual Abstinence, Contraception, and Pregnancy

Adolescents and adults with an FASD should be well informed and consulted about decisions regarding abstinence, contraception, and pregnancy. There are many ways to support pregnancy, delivery, and parenting by an individual with an FASD. The client may have questions about whether or not the FASD can be passed on to any offspring; caregivers must clarify that only prenatal exposure to alcohol can cause an FASD. If the client has children, the parenting skills taught to the client should account for the possible presence of an FASD in both parent and child; the skills learned must be appropriate to each of them and work for each of them.

Clinical experience reveals that women with an FASD can be vulnerable to exploitation and unintended pregnancy (Grant et al., 2004; Merrick, Merrick, Morad, & Kandel, 2006). It can be difficult for them to use contraception effectively due to memory lapses, problems following instructions, or difficulty negotiating contraceptive use with a partner. Counselors can help clients evaluate their family planning needs and assist in obtaining reliable, long-term birth control methods.

Although it may be unusual in a treatment setting, very practical and basic assistance may be important for a woman with an FASD. The counselor may need to accompany the client to a doctor's appointment to help her understand her options and choose the best one. One study found improved use of contraception among young women with an FASD by implementing a community intervention model of targeted education and collaboration

with key service providers, and by using paraprofessional advocate case managers as facilitators (Grant et al., 2004).

Clinical consensus based on evaluation of common behavioral characteristics of FASD suggests that the causal relationship between HIV/STDs/viral hepatitis and substance use disorders may be heightened among those who also have an FASD. Care plans for individuals with an FASD entering substance abuse treatment should include communicable disease assessment.

Medication Assessment

In some cases, medication options may be appropriate to treat some of the functional or mental health components of FASD (Coe, Sidders, Riley, Waltermire, & Hagerman, 2001). The counselor may want to refer the client for an assessment to determine whether he or she can follow a regimen of taking a pill every day or getting a shot every few months. It is also important to consider the possible physical impact, since persons with an FASD may have health problems and be prone to side effects. Medications for individuals with an FASD may not work at rates similar to other populations and/or may require different dosages to work (O'Malley & Hagerman, 1999). Including a mentor or supportive family member in the discussion may help the individual with an FASD to be more comfortable asking questions and better understand what is being said.

Job Coaching

In a study of 90 adults with a diagnosed form of FASD, most had some work experience but the average duration was only 9 months (Streissguth et al., 1996). Some of the general barriers to successful work for people with disabilities are external; discrimination by employers, co-workers, and family, transportation issues, completing applications and job testing, social skills, and the lack of support at interviews. Other barriers are internal, and need to be addressed early on in the vocational process; self-esteem and self-worth, fear of success, self-sabotage, and having a realistic view of strengths and career goals. All of these internal factors affect career choice, self-presentation at the interview and the job, and ultimate vocational success (Fabian, Ethridge, & Beveridge, 2009; Leon & Matthews, 2010). These issues should be addressed through counseling and skills-building prior to standard vocational tasks.

A job coach or vocational rehabilitation counselor may need to remain involved with an individual with an FASD beyond the time when he or she seems to "know" the job, and be understanding if the individual has days or situations in which he or she can't remember what to do or gets overwhelmed. Individuals with an FASD may do well enough on a job that a coach or counselor decides they "get it" and stops providing support, when in fact it was the support that enabled success.

Vocational Rehabilitation

Vocational Rehabilitation should be viewed as an interdisciplinary team process. It may be up to a parent or caregiver to coordinate information. The team may include a physician for medical and health issues, an occupational/physical therapist, a psychologist for counseling to address some of the above issues, teachers, case managers, and job placement agencies (Gobelet, Luthi, Al-Khodairy, & Chamberlain, 2007). Some adults and families will choose sheltered workshops because of concerns about safety, transportation, long-term placement, work hours, maintaining disability benefits, social environment, and work skills issues (Migliore, Grossi, Mank, & Rogan, 2008). At the same time, the majority of adults with an intellectual disability prefer integrated employment over sheltered workshops, regardless of disability severity (Migliore, Grossi, Mank, & Rogan, 2007).

Special Considerations for Adolescents Who Have or May Have an FASD

It is important to remember that adolescents are quite different from adults, and adolescents with an FASD differ from teens that develop in typical fashion. Adolescents with an FASD may function at social and emotional levels well below their chronological age, with an uneven cognitive and physical profile (some skills less impaired than others). The treatment process must incorporate the nuances of the adolescent's experience. In modifying treatment plans for adolescents with an FASD, it is important to consider cognitive, emotional, and social limitations, as well as risk factors that led to their substance abuse or mental health issue. Many youth with an FASD have grown up in less-than-ideal environments, facing parental substance abuse, economic deprivation, abuse, and multiple foster care placements. These situations can increase their risks for substance abuse and mental disorders.

A summary of clinical and empirical evidence shows that adolescents will commonly exhibit learning and behavior challenges, especially in adaptive function (getting along from day to day), and in remaining organized and regulated (Streissguth et al., 2004; Spohr, Willms, & Steinhausen, 2007). They often learn information slowly (especially what is said to them), tend to forget things they have recently learned, and make the same mistakes over and over. They can often have trouble shifting attention from one task to another. Like those with ADHD, they may be impulsive and find it hard to inhibit responses, and may be restless or even obviously hyperactive. In general, they may have trouble regulating their behavior. Even though adolescents with FASD may be talkative, they have social communication problems (such as leaving out important details or explaining things in a vague way). Adolescents with FASD tend to show poor judgment, are suggestible (and therefore easily

Treatment Tips From the Field

In addition to the guidance provided in this chapter, providers in British Columbia provided the following anecdotal suggestions for effective programming for individuals who have or may have an FASD.

Treatment Planning	• If medication is used, simplify medication schedules and provide support.
	• Avoid using students as therapists.
	    • May reinforce loss issues related to childhood/youth.
	    • May not be skilled with FASD.
	• Reassess concepts of dependency and enabling.
	• Use reminders.
	    • Use texting to provide reminders and stay connected.
	• Find something that the person likes to do and does well (that is safe and legal) and arrange to have the person do that regardless of behavior.
	• Create "chill-out" spaces in each setting.
	• Be creative about finding ways for the individual to succeed.
	    • Establish achievable, short-term goals.
	    • Reconsider zero-tolerance policies.
	• Be consistent in appointment days and times.
	    • Consider shorter, more frequent meetings or sessions.
	    • Arrange for someone to get the person to appointments for at least 6 months.
	    • Have the meetings on the same days each week.
	    • Discuss each meeting with the person.
	    • Use open meeting times, if necessary.

Assisting Navigation and Success	• Have pictures of the counselors on their office doors. • Identify possible buddies (e.g., family, friends, church or other organizations) to ensure the client gets to appointments, etc. • Identify persons who are appropriate supports for the client, as well as persons who are not helpful. • Program important numbers and reminders into their cell phone for them.

Language	• Do not use metaphors or similes.
	• Do not use idiomatic expressions and proverbs.
	    • "A day late and a dollar short."
	    • "People in glass houses shouldn't throw stones."
	• Don't use sarcasm, and be careful about joking with the person.

Source: Rutman, D. (2011). *Substance using women with FASD and FASD prevention: Service providers' perspectives on promising approaches in substance use treatment and care for women with FASD.* Victoria, British Columbia: University of Victoria.

influenced by others), and show immature social skills. Because of this, they may be too friendly with people they do not know well, too trusting, and have difficulty recognizing dangerous situations.

Treatment Plan Modification

It is generally believed that traditional forms of therapy, such as "talk therapy," are not the most effective choice when working with adolescents with an FASD. Their cognitive

Adolescent Development Issues in FASD

The following table outlines some of the more common developmental delays and deficits experienced by individuals with an FASD through the adolescent years (ages 12–21), and useful treatment approaches. This table is based on an expert clinical consensus.

Normal Development		FASD	Intervention
Age Range: 12-21	Ability to evaluate own behavior in relationship to the future	Lack of connection between thoughts, feelings, and actions	Repeated skills training with role-playing and videotaping; videotaping of person's behavior
	Understanding consequences of behavior		
	Importance of peer group	Difficulty resisting negative peer influences	Connect person with pro-social peers, mentors, and coaches
	Development of intimate relationships	Difficulty with accurately interpreting social cues (e.g., words, actions, nonverbal cues)	Social skills training; repeated discussions of sexuality and intimacy as appropriate

deficits prevent them from developing insight or applying lessons to their real lives. However, with creativity and flexibility, a treatment plan can be developed that includes techniques counselors are familiar with and comfortable with, adapted to fit the needs of the client (Baxter, 2000).

Addressing Peer Influences

Clinical observations indicate that adolescents with FASD are socially immature, and research documents that adults with FASD are more suggestible (Brown et al., 2011). Developmental literature makes clear that peer influences are important in the adolescent stage, and that deviant peer influences can lead to antisocial behavior. The counselor should address issues such as peer pressure in treatment to set the stage for less risky behavior outside treatment. Linking an adolescent with an FASD with a mentor is a sound treatment strategy.

Ongoing Assessment for Comprehension of Information

As with adults, it is important to check often to make sure the adolescent client understands what has been said. Ask the client to summarize what you have said. Review written material, such as rules, at each session. *Repeat, repeat, repeat*, even if the client says, "You've told me this a hundred times."

For adolescents, applying concepts can be difficult. Cognitive deficits, the frustration of having an FASD, and typical teen rebellion can make communication especially hard. Role-playing different situations, providing opportunities to share and process feelings, and giving the client time to process information is important. It also may help to use alternative methods of expression, such as drawing, to assist the client in sharing his or her understanding.

Educational Support (IDEA and FAPE)

The Individuals With Disabilities Education Act (IDEA) entitles every young person to a *f*ree and *a*ppropriate *p*ublic *e*ducation (FAPE) in the least restrictive environment. If the client is eligible, this can continue until age 21. If you have a client who has or may have an FASD and is in school, it is important to consult with the school regarding any provisions in that client's individualized education plan (IEP), either those identified by the school that should be carried over to treatment or vice versa. In a study of 120 children undergoing FASD diagnosis at a Washington State FAS DPN clinic, Jirikowic and colleagues (2010) found that over 90 percent did require intervention recommendations associated with their educational plan.

In the outpatient setting and during aftercare, it is a good idea for the psychologist to consult with the school counselor or case manager (if the client has one) regarding educational needs. Areas such as social skills may be addressed in the IEP, and are important to address during treatment and as part of aftercare. It also helps to be aware of any academic issues that may affect the client's treatment, such as stress about academic performance or difficulties with classmates.

Parents may not be aware of the laws regarding education of children with disabilities and may feel overwhelmed. They may be having problems dealing with their child's school and wonder what to do. The counselor can help by informing the client and family about IDEA and FAPE requirements and helping outline possible interventions to suggest to the school.

The U.S. Department of Education provides an online overview (**http://www2.ed.gov/about/offices/list/ocr/docs/edlite-FAPE504.html**) of the stipulations of FAPE and who qualifies for educational support under its terms.

In addition, vignette #10 in Part 1, Chapter 3 of this TIP discusses some of the key aspects of developing an IEP for an individual who has an FASD.

Psychosexual Development

Early and ongoing social experiences play a key role in psychosexual development. Adolescent tasks include having and maintaining intimate relationships, managing complex emotions and social situations, and developing independent thinking. The adolescent with an FASD may not achieve these milestones all at the same time, at the usual age range, or at all. Many adolescents with disabilities are delayed or prevented from achieving these goals by social isolation or a variety of functional limitations. Social skills may be broken down into manageable tasks, just as in every other area of instruction. This includes the basics first, such as mastering appropriate greetings, eye contact, body language, personal space, self-advocacy skills, and telephone and computer skills. A foundation in some or all of these basic skills will allow for the development of more complex skills. Mentors and peers may be very effective in this regard.

Vocational Coaching

Young adults with a disability need advocacy and support with a variety of new agencies and support services throughout the transition and adult years. A life skills curriculum should include how to use the internet to search for employment and employment enhancement services, awareness of issues associated with safe work environments, interviewing strategies, appropriate use of medication, managing finances, dealing with workplace routines and expectations, being cautious about at-risk situations, and knowing when to ask for help (Winn & Hay, 2009). Role-playing each of these skills with the client will be beneficial.

Counselor Self-Assessment

Working with clients with an FASD can raise issues for you, the counselor. You might feel resentment about being "stuck" with such challenging clients, or harbor negative attitudes toward women who drink while pregnant. The client with an FASD can trigger feelings of guilt and shame in a counselor who drank while pregnant or has a child with an FASD.

Understanding how to cope with clients with an FASD can help the counseling professional serve such clients more effectively. Olson and colleagues (2009) have underlined the importance of the need to **Reframe**, **Accommodate**, and **Have Hope** for caregivers raising those with FASD. These same strategies can help counselors, and are combined with the recommendations of Malbin (1993) and Schmucker (1997) to create the following recommendations for counselors providing FASD-related services.

REFRAME

Reframe your perception of the person's behavior. He or she is not trying to make you mad or cause trouble. He or she has brain damage and may have a history of abuse or other family dysfunction. You need to explore behaviors, stay patient, and tolerate ambiguity.

- Understand that FASD involves permanent brain changes.
- The client is not refusing to do things. He or she can't do them or does not understand what you are asking him or her to do.
- Clients often are not lying purposely. They are trying to fill in gaps in memory with their own information.
- Perseverating behaviors are an attempt to control or make sense of their own world.
- Transition and change are very difficult for the person with an FASD. Acting out when things change may be a reaction to fear of transitions or difficulty processing change.

ACCOMMODATE

- **Expect to repeat things many times in many ways**. Clients with an FASD may ask the same question every time you see them. Remember that these clients have cognitive deficits. They are not asking just to test your patience. Be patient and avoid looking bored going over the same information multiple times.
- **Use a written journal or goal sheets** to remind people how far they've come and where they are headed. Due to their memory difficulties, clients with an FASD will not always remember what supports or programs have been developed with them or their goals. Keep a positive attitude and focus on what the person has accomplished, rather than on goals yet to be met.
- **Realize that there is no set approach**; what works one time may not work the next. As part of the dysfunction of FASD, the client may experience things differently day to day or even hour to hour, and variability is the norm. Keep an open mind and be flexible. Avoid statements such as "But it worked last time."

HAVE HOPE

- **Be good to yourself**. Even with a realistic plan and an established routine, nothing is perfect. Things change and setbacks occur. By expecting bumps in the road of a person's journey through life, we can learn to not take these dips personally. By offering the person with an FASD nonjudgmental and informed support, we offer hope.
- **Know yourself**, and **take the time to reflect on your comfort level in dealing with issues surrounding FASD**. Gain knowledge if needed. Gain comfort in tackling the subject by role-playing with colleagues. Know your limits and get outside help or referrals as required. Plan to connect to appropriate community resources.

Thinking Ahead and Planning for the Future
It is important to think ahead and plan for the future with adolescents and young adults with FASD. If they are able to build an independent life, counselors can help the client learn how to self-advocate and self-monitor, and should communicate these skills to the client's caregivers, as well. It is important to think ahead about education on topics such as (1) safe sex; (2) communicating clearly with partners about consensual activity; (3) use of cigarettes and alcohol; (4) use of illicit substances, such as marijuana and drugs; (5) the consequences of criminal activity; and (6) ideas of what to safely do when the individuals goes through times of feeling irritable and negative (calming strategies).

5. Working with the Family

Introduction
Multiple studies have spoken to the value of involving the family in the treatment of an individual who has or may have an FASD, if possible (Schmucker, 1997; Grant, Ernst, Streissguth, & Porter, 1997; Olson et al., 2009; Olson, Rudo-Stern, & Gendler, 2011). Involving the family in planning, choosing, and shaping services for the client has become a key intervention concept in the field of developmental disabilities, as greater family involvement has been linked to better outcomes (Neely-Barnes, Graff, Marcenko, & Weber, 2008). Family-centered care is also strongly advocated for individuals with co-occurring mental health issues and a developmental disability like an FASD (McGinty, Worthington, & Dennison, 2008).

As with many clients in substance abuse and mental health settings, it is advisable to take a broad view of family. Many individuals with an FASD will have resided with foster parents and/or in kinship care (foster and adoptive scenarios being the most common), and care scenarios may extend well beyond the more typical ages of independence, like 18 or 21. Ultimately, who the client chooses to see as family or as the important caregiver in their life should be incorporated into the process, if possible.

As the table on the next page makes clear, involving the family can be as much about meeting their needs as the client's. The most frequently unmet family needs can be met with emotional support and, later in the counseling relationship, offering opportunities to "look forward" to the future and discuss both hopes and worries. Other frequently unmet needs can be met by helping caregivers find methods for self-care and respite. FASD education and appropriate intervention will meet other common needs, but may be less important (at the start) than support and direct assistance to help understand and meet caregivers' own needs.

Approaching the Family
It is imperative to obtain permission to approach family on the topic of an FASD. If the birth mother is still involved in the individual's care and is not aware of the possibility of an FASD, it is vitally important not to make her feel shamed or judged. The counselor should be prepared to address feelings of guilt. The family may also experience many of the feelings of anger, grief, and loss that the client experiences. All members of the family should be made to feel as comfortable as possible expressing these feelings.

If the family agrees to be involved, there are a number of ways that the counselor can support both them and the client. It is vital to use "reframing" to help the family better understand the client's behaviors as being at least partly caused by brain-based disabilities (Olson et al., 2009). A positive view of the affected individual, of the relationship between the caregiver and the individual, and of the caregiver process has been associated with

Top Unmet Needs for Caregivers
Raising Children who have FASD and Behavior Problems

Percentage Indicating Need is Unmet	Type of Family Need
69.2%	Discuss feelings about my child with someone who has gone through the same experience.
61.7%	Have help in preparing for the worst.
60.8%	Have enough resources for myself or the family.
58.8%	Have help in remaining hopeful about my child's future.
58.0%	Get a break from my problems and responsibilities.
55.8%	Be reassured that it is usual to have negative feelings about changes in my child's behavior.
52.9%	Have complete information on my child's thinking problems.
51.0%	Be shown what to do when my child is upset or acting strange.
48.1%	Be told why my child acts in ways that are different, difficult or strange.
47.1%	Have different professionals agree on the best way to help my child.
47.1%	Pay attention to my own needs.

'Important' is defined as parent report that a need was 'important' or 'very important' (where there were two other levels indicating less importance). 'Unmet' was defined as parent report that a need was met 'not at all' or 'a little' (where there were two other levels indicating that a need was met more completely). Items shown here were the most frequently endorsed items; the remaining items (of 20) received far less frequent endorsements.

Source: Olson, H. C., Oti, R., Gelo, J., & Beck, S. (2009). "Family Matters:" Fetal Alcohol Spectrum Disorders and the family. *Developmental Disabilities Research Reviews, 15*, 235-249.

more positive outcomes for the individual and family (Blacher & Baker, 2007). The counselor can then help the family reach out to extended family and friends to help them reframe the situation. Reframing can help everyone more positively understand the client's behavior, and appropriately adjust the home and school environments. Treatment approaches that stress problem-focused management and stress reduction may be a useful addition to parent training (Olson et al., 2009). Other suggestions include:

- As with the client, review the diagnostic report thoroughly with the family (if it is available). Chapter 3 of Part 1, *Clinical Vignettes*, contains a vignette illustrating this process.

- Help the family arrange for respite care or a community support worker: Caregivers may feel stressed or burned out by the responsibilities of caring for someone with an FASD.

- Assist family in coming up with ways to educate extended family and friends about FASD to help them understand the client's behaviors and adjust the home environment accordingly.

- Connect family and friends with support groups or other community resources (see Step 6).

- Help find long-term mentors for clients. Family members or friends who have become exhausted or burned out dealing with an FASD may be willing to help after a mentor has stepped in for awhile and the client has made progress.

- Encourage parents and caregivers to maximize independence, even if they are used to "helping" or completing tasks for the client.

- Help the family access needed services and supports (see Appendix G, *Services and Supports Checklist*, for a list that can be used as a worksheet).

The *Families Moving Forward Program* intervention is a scientifically-validated behavioral consultation program tailored for families raising preschool and school-aged individuals with FASD or confirmed prenatal alcohol exposure. The intervention includes methods and materials that appropriately trained counselors can use when working with families of a client who has an FASD, even if the client is older (**http://depts.washington.edu/fmffasd**). See Appendix F, *Sample Crisis/Safety Plan*, and Appendix G, *Services and Supports Checklist*, for materials that have been adapted from the *Families Moving Forward Program* for this TIP.

If the client had an existing diagnosis of an FASD before presenting in your setting, involving the family is still valuable. Caregivers are probably already well-versed in FASD and the difficulties of obtaining effective services, and can be as much of a resource of information for the counselor as the counselor is for the family.

6. Transition and Connection to Community Supports

Transitional Services

Part of the counselor's role is to prepare for discharge of the client. This involves working to establish a network of community resources and providers of service who will continue to provide support and advocacy when your role

is complete. Providing these supports with education about FASD and the client's unique patterns of behavior is an important part of successful transitioning. See Appendix G, *Services and Supports Checklist*, for a worksheet that can be used to quickly identify linkages the counselor and client may want to explore.

Network of Providers

Counselors need to be familiar with available resources in the community, such as psychiatrists, social workers, developmental disability providers, and physicians. Counselors can include referrals to these resources in the transition plan and work with case managers at their facility as appropriate. For clients who are still in school, it is also important to consider the transition to school, and to work with school administrators and/or the school counselor to determine how best to address the client's ongoing needs within the school setting.

It may also be necessary to consult an advocate or legal representative if the client has had any legal problems. Adolescents with an FASD can get pulled into illegal activity or manipulated into relapses.

Mentorship

Locating a long-term mentor within the person's sphere of relationships can be another way to support the transition process. Providing tips and strategies for things that have worked well with the client during treatment can enable the mentor to provide support in the future (Schmucker, 1997). There are also organized programs that can help to identify mentors, though these resources are scarce and differ by community.

If the family is involved in treatment and the client had an existing diagnosis of an FASD before treatment, it is likely that they will have developed relationships with a variety of providers and can thus potentially be a useful resource for information on services available in the community. There are a number of things that should happen during transition planning that a parent or caregiver could help to facilitate, such as introduction to the relevant service providers and transfer of information to those agencies.

Assessment of Living Skills/Planning for Safety

Even if taught as part of treatment, basic functional living and social skills will need to be re-assessed before transition to help the client function more effectively and safely in the community. The provider should work with the client to:

- Assess ability to handle money, pay bills and rent, buy groceries, etc. The clinician can consider a representative payee, if necessary.

- Anticipate housing needs: Will the client live alone? With caregivers? With others in structured housing or a group setting? An individual with an FASD is likely to need dedicated, long-term caregiver support in any setting, but this is particularly vital if they will be living alone. Assistance is likely to be needed with negotiating public transportation, handling interpersonal relationships, grocery shopping, and structuring leisure time (Streissguth et al., 1996).

- Identify job desires and possibilities, as well as what is needed for job success.

- Review appropriate social interaction.

- Review processes for checking whenever the client is unsure of a situation or response, or is in trouble.

- Ensure that learned skills are practiced in the new environment.

- Continue supports at least until the client adjusts to the new environment.

If a mentor, family member, or other caregiver is identified for the client, Vignette #9 in Part 1, Chapter 3 of this TIP walks through the process of working with that person or persons to develop a personalized Safety Plan on behalf of an individual with an FASD.

Connection to Community Supports

Both the client and the client's family and caregivers (if involved) can benefit from connection to support systems in their community. As with referral for assessment or diagnosis, it is vital that the counselor actively assist the client through transition to other providers and follow up regularly to ensure client satisfaction and full and open communication between agencies and with the client (and the client's family, if they are involved in the treatment process).

Appendix C, *Public and Professional Resources on FASD*, provides links to a number of support organizations for individuals with an FASD, including NOFAS (**www.nofas.org**), the Birth Mothers Network (also known as the Circle of Hope; visit the NOFAS Web site and the FAS Community Resource Center (**http://www.come-over.to/FASCRC/**).

NOFAS can be a particularly valuable resource, as it houses not only the Birth Mothers Network but also an extensive affiliate network whose members provide a broad range of FASD-related services to individuals and their families. In addition, NOFAS's "Living With FASD" page (**http://www.nofas.org/living/**) contains links to financial assistance programs such as Supplemental Security Income (SSI), Social Security Disability Insurance (SSDI), and Medicaid, as well as family and mother support programs such as Women, Infants and Children (WIC).

An emerging community resource for individuals with an FASD is the Self-Advocates with FASD in Action (SAFA) Network. Members include individuals with an FASD and their support persons. The SAFA Network provides speakers and training on living with an FASD, and also peer support for other individuals and families coping with these disorders. The SAFA Network can be contacted through SAMHSA's FASD Center for Excellence (**www.fasdcenter.samhsa.gov**, or toll-free at 1-866-STOP-FAS).

Job Support
Your local One-Stop Center (**www. careeronestop.org**) may provide links to your state Department of Labor and Workforce Development, the local division for vocational rehabilitation services, and/or specific state initiatives for development of customized employment for people with disabilities. For individuals with an FASD, customized employment should include a protocol that addresses their special needs.

Self-Help Participation
The person with an FASD will need support to participate successfully in a 12-Step program. Many areas of the country have "Double Trouble" meetings; these are 12-Step self-help groups designed to meet the special needs of people with addiction and mental health issues (Vogel, Knight, Lauded, & Maura, 1998). Double Trouble meetings may be more flexible about impulsive behaviors than routine meetings. The counselor should be cautious about referring a client who has or may have an FASD into a self-help group, due to issues of victimization as well as the possibility that the individual's special needs will not be met.

Another significant resource for people with an FASD and co-occurring issues is the recovery movement in the mental health field. Recovery centers (also known as "drop-in" centers) offer a variety of supports, groups, and meetings in some areas.

> **For more information on treatment approaches with individuals who have or may have an FASD...**
>
> Vignettes 5–10 in Part 1, Chapter 3 of this TIP illustrate scenarios where a counselor works with a client who has or may have an FASD, or provides assistance to family members/caregivers. In addition, Part 3, the online Literature Review, also contains further discussion of interventions, protective factors, and co-occurring issues.

3 Clinical Vignettes

Introduction

This chapter presents vignettes of counseling/intervention sessions between various service professionals and either 1) women of childbearing age where FASD prevention is warranted, and/or 2) individuals who have or may have an FASD or their family members. The vignettes are intended to provide real-world examples and overviews of approaches best suited (and not suited to) FASD prevention and intervention.

The Culturally Competent Counselor

This TIP, like all others in the TIP series, recognizes the importance of delivering culturally competent care. Cultural competency, as defined by HHS, is…

"A set of values, behaviors, attitudes, and practices within a system, organization, program, or among individuals that enables people to work effectively across cultures. It refers to the ability to honor and respect the beliefs, language, interpersonal styles, and behaviors of individuals and families receiving services, as well as staff who are providing such services. Cultural competence is a dynamic, ongoing, developmental process that requires a long-term commitment and is achieved over time" (U.S. Department of Health and Human Services, 2003, p. 12).

A critical element of this definition is the connection between attitude and behavior, as shown in the table on the next page.

Areas of Clinical Focus

In this chapter, you are invited to consider different methods and approaches to practicing prevention of an AEP and/or interventions and modifications for individuals who have or may have an FASD. The ten scenarios are common situations for behavioral health professionals and focus on:

Attitude	Behavior
Respect	• Acknowledging and validating the client's opinions and worldview • Approaching the client as a partner in treatment • Communicating with clients in their primary language, either directly or through an interpreter • Respecting the client's self-determination
Acceptance	• Maintaining a nonjudgmental attitude toward the client • Considering what is important to the client
Sensitivity	• Understanding the client's experiences of racism, stereotyping, racial profiling, and discrimination • Understanding the life circumstances, daily realities, and financial constraints of the client
Commitment to Equity	• Intervening on behalf of clients when a problem stems from racism or bias • Actively involving oneself with minority individuals outside the counseling setting to foster a perspective that is more than academic or work-related
Openness	• Recognizing the value of indigenous helping practices and intrinsic help giving networks in minority communities • Building ongoing collaborative alliances with indigenous caregivers • Seeking consultation with traditional healers and religious and spiritual leaders and practitioners in treatment of culturally different clients, when appropriate
Humility	• Acknowledging the limits of one's competencies and expertise and a willingness to refer clients to a more appropriate counselor when necessary • Seeking consultation and pursuing further training or education, or a combination of these • Constantly seeking to understand oneself as being influenced by ethnicity and culture and actively seeking a nonracist identity • Being sensitive to the power differentials between the client and the counselor
Flexibility	• Using a variety of verbal and nonverbal responses, approaches, or styles to suit the cultural context of the client • Using cultural, socioeconomic, and political contextual factors in conducting evaluations and providing interventions

This table originally appeared in TIP 48, *Managing Depressive Symptoms in Substance Abuse Clients During Early Recovery* ((SMA) 08-4353). The authors of this TIP gratefully acknowledge the authors of TIP 48.

1. Intervention with a woman of childbearing age who has depression, is consuming alcohol, and may become pregnant (AEP Prevention)

2. Examining alcohol history with a woman of childbearing age in substance abuse treatment for a drug other than alcohol (AEP Prevention)

3. Intervention with a woman who is pregnant (AEP Prevention)

4. Intervention with a woman who is pregnant and consuming alcohol, and who is exhibiting certain triggers for alcohol consumption, including her partner (AEP Prevention)

5. Interviewing a client for the possible presence of an FASD (FASD Intervention)

6. Interviewing a birth mother about a son who may have an FASD and is having trouble in school (FASD Intervention)

7. Reviewing an FASD diagnostic report with the family (FASD Intervention)

8. Making modifications to treatment for an individual with an FASD (FASD Intervention)

9. Working with an adoptive parent to create a safety plan for an adult male with an FASD who is seeking living independence (FASD Intervention)

10. Working with a birth mother to develop strategies for communicating with a school about an Individualized Education Plan for her daughter, who has an FASD (FASD Intervention)

Organization of the Vignettes

To better organize the learning experience, each vignette contains an **Overview** of the general learning intent of the vignette, **Background** on the client and the setting, **Learning Objectives**, and **Master Clinician Notes** from an "experienced counselor or supervisor" about the strategies used, possible alternative techniques, timing of interventions, and areas for improvement. The Master Clinician is meant to represent the combined experience and expertise of the TIP's consensus panel members, providing insights into each case and suggesting possible approaches. It should be kept in mind, however, that some techniques suggested in these vignettes may not be appropriate for use by all clinicians, depending on that professional's level of training, certification, and licensure. It is the responsibility of the counselor to determine what services he or she can legally/ethically provide.

1. INTERVENTION WITH A WOMAN OF CHILDBEARING

AGE WHO HAS DEPRESSION, IS CONSUMING ALCOHOL, AND MAY BECOME PREGANT (AEP PREVENTION)

Overview: This vignette illustrates how and why a counselor would address prevention of an AEP with a young woman who is being seen for depression.

Background: This vignette takes place in a college counseling center where Serena, 20, is receiving outpatient services for the depression that she's been feeling for about 4 months. In her intake interview, Serena has indicated that she consumes alcohol, is not pregnant, and is sexually active. She has had two prior sessions with the counselor, during which they have discussed Serena's general background, family interactions, social supports, and her outlook on school.

In today's session, they have been discussing her boyfriend, Rob. A therapeutic relationship has begun to form between Serena and the counselor, and the counselor would now like to explore Serena's alcohol use and whether it is a possible contributing factor in her depression. While doing this, the counselor will identify an opportunity to deliver an informal selective intervention to prevent a possible AEP.

Learning Objectives:
1. To illustrate that clients often have multiple issues that need to be addressed besides their primary reason for seeking counseling.

2. To demonstrate a selective intervention ("FLO") for preventing an alcohol-exposed unplanned pregnancy.

3. To recognize that prevention of an AEP can be accomplished by eliminating alcohol use during pregnancy or preventing a pregnancy during alcohol use; often the most effective route is to prevent the pregnancy.

Vignette Start

The session is already in progress. Serena has been discussing how she and her boyfriend Rob tend to fight a lot, but she continues to spend time with him because they have fun at parties.

COUNSELOR:	So, how long have you and Rob been together?
SERENA:	About 7 months.
COUNSELOR:	And you've said that the two of you are sexually active.
SERENA:	Yeah, I usually sleep over on the weekend, after the parties.
COUNSELOR:	Do these fights occur at any particular time?
SERENA:	Not really. When we're stressed, mostly, over school or work or whatever. Then I feel more depressed cuz we're fighting, and he gets upset because I'm depressed. It's like a circle. That's why we go to the parties, to unwind and forget about stuff.
COUNSELOR:	And then you tend to end up spending the night with him.
SERENA:	Usually.
COUNSELOR:	Are you using any protection, or birth control?
SERENA:	No.
COUNSELOR:	And during these parties, are you drinking?
SERENA:	Sure.
COUNSELOR:	About how many drinks do you have?
SERENA:	I don't really know. My cup's never empty, it just gets refilled at the keg.
COUNSELOR:	Are there other times when you drink alcohol?
SERENA:	No, it's really just at the parties.

Master Clinician Note: Serena is presenting high-risk behavior by combining alcohol use and unprotected sex. The counselor seeks to identify the link between alcohol, unprotected sex, and pregnancy.

COUNSELOR:	I know you're not expecting this, but if you were to find out right now that you were pregnant, how would that change things for you?
SERENA:	Oh lord, that would *totally* turn my life upside down. And Rob's. God, he'd freak.
COUNSELOR:	So, you do *not* want to get pregnant.
SERENA:	No, I definitely do not wanna get pregnant.

Master Clinician Note: Serena has made it clear that she does not want to become pregnant, so the counselor shifts to addressing the gap between Serena's behaviors (being sexually active but not practicing safe sex) and her stated desire (to not get pregnant).

COUNSELOR: I understand, and I'm concerned about your health and what you want for your future. So, if you plan to keep attending these parties and being sexually active, then maybe we can talk about contraception. Did you know that half of all pregnancies in the U.S. are unplanned?

SERENA: Wow. No, I didn't know that.

COUNSELOR: It's true. It's possible that you could get pregnant, and the drinking could impact the health of that baby. Let's talk about how we can avoid those things.

SERENA: Okay.

The counselor gives Serena a pamphlet that describes effective contraception.

COUNSELOR: Would you be willing to read this? It's short, but it has good information. Perhaps we can go over it when we meet next week.

SERENA: Okay. I thought I was here to talk about depression, though.

COUNSELOR: Yes, absolutely, our first goal is to help you stop feeling depressed. And as you've said, you definitely don't want to have a baby, so I think it's important for us to discuss ways to avoid getting pregnant, so that that's not something that adds to your worries.

SERENA: Oh, okay. I see what you mean.

COUNSELOR: So next week I can answer any questions you have about that material, and then we can talk about some positive goals you want to lay out, like feeling less depressed, or fighting with Rob less, or not getting pregnant. Does that sound okay?

SERENA: Yeah, thanks.

Master Clinician Note: This vignette does not "solve" the issue of Serena's depression. However, as part of examining the possible causes, Serena has talked about a pattern of regular at-risk drinking, combined with unprotected sex. Because of this, the counselor—who by now has established a good rapport with Serena—has taken the opportunity to carefully include a selective intervention for preventing an AEP.

In an informal way, the counselor has used the steps of the "FLO" intervention discussed in Part 1, Chapter 1 of this TIP. During intake and again at this visit, Serena has indicated that she consumes alcohol and is sexually active. The counselor provides **F**eedback on these responses (by discussing the possibility of an AEP), then **L**istens as Serena indicates that she does not want to become pregnant. The counselor thus shifts the focus of medical advice to the **O**ption of contraception and provides Serena with educational material.

At the same time, the counselor has not lost sight of depression as Serena's primary treatment issue. In this session, the counselor has laid the groundwork for continuing to discuss Serena's at-risk drinking and her problematic relationship with Rob as possible components of the depression, but in the context of positive goals that Serena can aim for (i.e., finding ways to feel less depressed, fight with Rob less, and avoid an unwanted pregnancy).

2. EXAMINING THE ALCOHOL HISTORY WITH A WOMAN OF CHILDBEARING AGE IN SUBSTANCE ABUSE TREATMENT FOR A DRUG OTHER THAN ALCOHOL (AEP PREVENTION)

Overview: This vignette illustrates the value of asking about alcohol use in a female substance abuse treatment client of childbearing age, even though her primary drug is not alcohol.

Background: Chloe is being seen at an outpatient treatment center for methamphetamine abuse. The counselor has the health history that was provided during intake. It indicates that Chloe reports as non-pregnant, but is 28 (of childbearing age) and is sexually active.

The counselor wants to explore whether Chloe is using other substances, as well as screening for a possible mental health problem. Given that the client is sexually active, there is a risk of an unplanned pregnancy, therefore the counselor begins with alcohol.

Learning Objectives:
1. To emphasize the importance of probing for alcohol use even if it is not the primary drug.

2. To recognize that quantity of use is subjective. The use of a visual helps the client understand what a one-drink equivalent is.

3. To recognize that if a mental health issue presents itself, it will need to be addressed concurrently.

Vignette Start

COUNSELOR:	Hi, Chloe.
CHLOE:	Hey.
COUNSELOR:	Please have a seat. I have some questions that I would like to ask you, Chloe. You're in treatment for methamphetamines, correct?
CHLOE:	Yes.
COUNSELOR:	If it is okay with you, I would like to ask you first about your use of some other drugs. I would like to start with alcohol. Do you know how much alcohol you drink?
CHLOE:	You mean, altogether? I don't know.
COUNSELOR:	Okay, in an average week, how much alcohol would you say you drink?
CHLOE:	Well, usually I just drink enough to wash down my pills.
COUNSELOR:	What pills are those?
CHLOE:	The, whatayacallit, desoxyn.
COUNSELOR:	And what do you wash these pills down with? What kind of alcohol?
CHLOE:	Usually vodka. With some orange juice in it.
COUNSELOR:	And do you do this every time you take the pills?
CHLOE:	Not every time, but most times.

COUNSELOR: Okay. And how much vodka do you drink to wash down the pills?

CHLOE: One drink.

COUNSELOR: Here, let me show you something real quick. This is a picture of different glasses that people tend to use for drinking alcohol. Which one do you use?

Master Clinician Note: The counselor uses the visual below to help Chloe more concretely understand her level of consumption. However, this visual does not reflect every available drinking size or container, so any discussion of a standard drink should incorporate the client's personal experience (i.e., "If you don't see your glass on here, what do you use?").

12 oz. of beer or cooler	8–9 oz. of malt liquor 8.5 oz. shown in a 12-oz. glass that, if full, would hold about 1.5 standard drinks of malt liquor	5 oz. of table wine	3–4 oz. of fortified wine (such as sherry or port) 3.5 oz. shown	2–3 oz. of cordial, liqueur, or aperitif 2.5 oz. shown	1.5 oz. of brandy (a single jigger)	1.5 oz. of spirits (a single jigger of 80-proof gin, vodka, whiskey, etc.) Shown straight and in a highball glass with ice to show the level before adding a mixer*
~5% alcohol	~7% alcohol	~12% alcohol	~17% alcohol	~24% alcohol	~40% alcohol	~40% alcohol
12 oz.	8.5 oz.	5 oz.	3.5 oz.	2.5 oz.	1.5 oz.	1.5 oz.

CHLOE: None of them. Well (*Chloe indicates the 8.5 ounce drinking glass*), that looks like what I use, but it's not all vodka.

COUNSELOR: How much do you fill with vodka, and how much orange juice?

CHLOE: About half and half.

COUNSELOR: All the way to the top?

CHLOE: Yeah, but with ice in it.

COUNSELOR: Okay, so that's going to be about three to four ounces of vodka, and an ounce and a half of hard liquor is equal to one drink. So, it looks like you're having the equivalent of two to three drinks every time you wash down the pills.

CHLOE: Hmm. I didn't know that.

COUNSELOR: Is there any other time when you use alcohol?

CHLOE: I may have some when I'm feeling bad. It takes the edge off.

COUNSELOR: Can you tell me more about how you feel when you "need to take the edge off?"

CHLOE: I just feel very upset, worried. Sometimes sad.

COUNSELOR: That must be hard for you. About how often do you feel worried and/or sad?

Master Clinician Note: The counselor expresses empathy for the client and how sad/worried she is feeling. This expression of empathy assists in establishing more of a caring relationship, so that further questions around alcohol use can be explored in a helpful manner. The counselor also explores more with the client about how she is feeling when she talks about "taking the edge off" to see what might be the result of her drug use and to see if she needs a mental health evaluation. A mental health evaluation might explore whether medication is indicated that could assist Chloe in reducing her alcohol use.

CHLOE (*laughs*):   A lot.

COUNSELOR: It must be difficult to feel so sad and worried a lot. Can I ask you a few more questions about this?

CHLOE: Okay.

COUNSELOR: Did you feel very sad or worried this week?

CHLOE: Yeah.

COUNSELOR: So, when you felt this way this week, did you need to use alcohol to feel better? Or, as you said, to take the edge off?

CHLOE: (*shrugs*) Yeah, I had three or four drinks.

Master Clinician Note: The counselor does not assume that the client is deliberately under-estimating, but keeps in mind that clients may minimize when self-reporting alcohol use (Taylor et al., 2009).

COUNSELOR: Did you also feel like this *last* week?

CHLOE: Probably.

COUNSELOR: How about last month? Did you need to use alcohol to try to feel better then also? That would have been August.

CHLOE: I'm sure I did.

COUNSELOR: So Chloe, you would say that you're feeling sad and worried, and using alcohol to help you feel better, has been going on for quite a while, is that right?

CHLOE: Yeah, most of this year.

Master Clinician Note: Given the frequency of poly-drug use among clients in substance abuse treatment, this counselor did not assume that methamphetamine was the only substance that Chloe was using. Through some simple probing, the counselor has identified that not only has Chloe been drinking, she has been doing so at a high-risk rate. At a future time when dealing more specifically with the amount Chloe is drinking, the counselor might show her a chart with drinking frequencies to help Chloe see what level of drinking is defined as heavy and/or problematic for women.

Chloe has also talked about a pattern of self-medication. The reason or trigger for this may be depression; Chloe has said only that she drinks when she is "feeling like s&@*." This will require further exploration. For now, the counselor knows that a potential co-occurring mental health issue, a co-occurring substance abuse issue, and prevention of a possible AEP should all be factored into the treatment plan.

3. INTERVENTION WITH A WOMAN WHO IS PREGNANT (AEP PREVENTION)

Overview: This vignette illustrates that screening for alcohol use should be done at every visit with women who are—or are at an indicated likelihood for becoming—pregnant. Alcohol-exposed pregnancies occur in all demographics, regardless of socio-economic status, age, ethnicity, or marital status.

Background: April, 27, works full-time. She recently found out she is pregnant with her first child. She and her husband have relocated to a new city, and she is being seen at a private OBGYN office for the first time.

Learning Objectives:

1. To recognize that asking about alcohol use during the first visit only is not enough; screening should occur at every visit.

2. To identify that a woman could begin drinking during the pregnancy if she is experiencing a relapse.

3. To highlight there is no known safe amount of alcohol use during pregnancy.

Vignette Start

1st Office Visit

PRACTITIONER: Hello, I'm Dr. Johnson. I see on the chart that you are pregnant. Congratulations!

APRIL: Thank you.

PRACTITIONER: I have a number of questions that I need to ask you before the exam.

Practitioner inquires about health history and eating habits, recommending an increase in fruit consumption.

PRACTITIONER: A few other quick questions. How much do you smoke per day?

APRIL: I don't smoke.

PRACTITIONER: That's good! How much coffee and water do you drink?

APRIL: I have a cup of coffee in the morning, that's about it. I try to drink water all the time. I don't know how much I have per day. Probably a few glasses worth.

PRACTITIONER: Okay, how often do you drink alcohol?

> **Master Clinician Note:** The practitioner has included alcohol as part of a general health exploration rather than asking the question by itself, which can make some clients nervous. Still, April looks a little concerned.

APRIL: I don't drink any alcohol.

PRACTITIONER: Okay, that's good to hear. Not to worry, that's just a general question that I will be asking during all of our visits. There's no safe time, amount, or kind of alcohol to drink during pregnancy, so we recommend women not drink during their pregnancy.

2nd Office Visit: *We pick up the conversation after the practitioner has again gone over the general health questions about smoking and level of intake of water and coffee.*

APRIL: I'm actually trying to drink more water now, and less coffee. I carry a water bottle around with me all the time.

PRACTITIONER: Okay, that's good. How much alcohol have you had?

APRIL: None, really.

PRACTITIONER: Have you had *any* alcohol?

APRIL: One glass. We were having dinner with some friends.

> **Master Clinician Note:** This interaction demonstrates the value of re-screening in relation to alcohol. April stated in the first visit that she does not drink. However, during this second visit, she has revealed that she does drink on occasion. It will be important for the practitioner to repeat the benefits of abstinence during pregnancy and probe for level of alcohol use, while remaining supportive and nonjudgmental.

PRACTITIONER: I see. Well, as we discussed at your last visit, no alcohol use during the pregnancy is the best policy. We just want to take the best possible care of your baby. About what size was that glass, would you say?

> **Master Clinician Note:** The practitioner can use a visual aid, as in the previous vignette, to help April understand how much really equals one drink. The practitioner has also repeated the importance of abstinence during the pregnancy, and tied the guideline specifically to the health of April's baby.

3rd Office Visit: *At this visit, April again indicates alcohol consumption, this time "a couple of drinks" at a dinner party. The practitioner explores further.*

PRACTITIONER: How many drinks did you have?

APRIL: Well, my friend handed me a glass of cabernet when I arrived, because she said I would love it. I reminded her that I was pregnant, but she said a couple wouldn't hurt and that she had a few when she was pregnant and her kids were fine.

PRACTITIONER: So, you drank the cabernet. Did you have any others?

APRIL: Well, then I had some with dinner, too. I felt like I had been really good during the pregnancy, so I just decided to have a few drinks this one night.

PRACTITIONER: So, you ended up having a few drinks that night.

APRIL: Yes, but just that one time. And it was only wine.

PRACTITIONER: I know that the temptation to have some drinks at a party or a celebration can be great, but there are a couple things to keep in mind. One is that science has shown that alcohol can harm the baby. We don't know yet how much alcohol consumption is too much, so it's very important to avoid all alcohol during the pregnancy.

The practitioner pauses for the client to process what has been said.

APRIL:	Okay.
PRACTITIONER:	Also, it's important to understand that *any type* of alcohol you drink can hurt the baby, not just certain kinds. Wine, hard liquor, beer…any beverage with alcohol in it. So it's important to avoid all of them during the pregnancy.
APRIL:	Gotcha.

> **Master Clinician Note:** Given that April has continued to drink even after her first couple of visits, the practitioner takes the educational process a step further this time, clearly noting that science has established a risk and that there is no "acceptable" form or amount of alcohol. A counselor or practitioner may also want to discuss the possibility of equipping April with some tools to help her abstain during the pregnancy (e.g., relaxation techniques, recreation, avoiding trigger situations such as parties). The need to continue to monitor April's alcohol consumption should be clearly noted in the medical record.

4. INTERVENTION WITH A WOMAN WHO IS PREGNANT AND CONSUMING ALCOHOL, AND WHO IS EXHIBITING CERTAIN TRIGGERS FOR ALCOHOL CONSUMPTION, INCLUDING HER PARTNER (AEP PREVENTION)

Overview: This vignette illustrates a method for obtaining the alcohol history of a pregnant woman.

Background: Isabel, 30, has been referred to an outpatient mental health treatment center for feelings of depression. She is Hispanic, married, and pregnant (in her third trimester), and has one other child. The counselor and client have completed the intake process and Isabel has participated in the development of her comprehensive treatment plan. This is their third meeting. The counselor and Isabel agreed at the end of their last session that this would be about potential health risks with the pregnancy.

Learning Objectives:

1. To learn how to use a practical visual tool (a calendar) to more accurately and effectively identify client drinking patterns and possible triggers for alcohol consumption.

2. To identify verbal cues that can indicate that a topic is becoming uncomfortable for a client, and apply effective techniques when a client becomes upset.

Vignette Start	
COUNSELOR:	Hi, Isabel. How are you?
ISABEL:	Fine, how you doing?
COUNSELOR:	I'm fine, thanks. When we met last, we finished working on your treatment plan. You have had a little bit of time to think about the plan now. Do you have any thoughts or concerns about what we developed?
ISABEL:	No, not really.
COUNSELOR:	How are you doing with the pregnancy?

ISABEL:	Pretty good. Things are going pretty well.
COUNSELOR:	Great. Now, at the end of your last visit here, we said we would spend part of today's session talking about alcohol use during pregnancy. You indicated during your intake that you drink socially, so let's talk about that a little more. Knowing about when and how much you drink will help us to see if there is any need to be concerned about any health issues for you or the baby. Is that okay with you?
ISABEL:	*[Sounding a little concerned.]* What do you mean "concerned about health issues?" I am not an alcoholic.

Master Clinician Note: The counselor wants to reassure Isabel that she has not formed a negative opinion of her. The counselor now also needs to be aware that Isabel may try to minimize the frequency and amount of alcohol consumed so that she is not viewed as an alcoholic.

COUNSELOR:	*[Calmly and reassuringly.]* I am sorry, Isabel. I wasn't trying to say that you have an alcohol problem. Nothing you have told me during our previous sessions would lead me to believe that you are an alcoholic or have a drinking problem. You said you only drink socially, correct?
ISABEL:	Yes. I don't drink every day or even every weekend.
COUNSELOR:	Good. That's just what I thought. I know, just from the short time we have been seeing each other, that you would never do anything to hurt your child. But, would you agree that drinking socially for one person might be different than drinking socially for another?
ISABEL	Of course.
COUNSELOR:	Alcohol can have an influence on individuals who are anxious, depressed, and even on women who are pregnant, and possibly their unborn child. That influence can depend on the frequency and amount of alcohol consumed. So knowing the social situations and how much you drink at those occasions will help us determine if you need to make any changes between now and when the baby is born. If it is okay with you, let's see if we can identify those situations.
ISABEL:	Okay, I'll give it a try.
COUNSELOR:	Thanks. That's great. So first let me ask you this: Normally, when you aren't pregnant, how often would you say you drink alcohol?
ISABEL:	Well, most of the time I'm not normally a drinker.
COUNSELOR:	Okay, that's good. When you *do* drink, about how much do you have?
ISABEL:	I can't really say. It depends.

Master Clinician Note: The counselor wants to get an accurate picture of Isabel's drinking during pregnancy, so she brings out a calendar. The visual is helpful as it allows both client and counselor to put their eye contact elsewhere, which can contribute to the ease of discussion. The counselor explains that it also helps to trigger memory by looking at dates.

COUNSELOR:	Okay, so let's start by figuring out when you first found out that you were pregnant.
ISABEL:	I went to Dr. Murphy's office and they did a pregnancy test. I had not had my period. I can look at the calendar, but I am pretty sure it was sometime in May.
COUNSELOR:	Do you think it was the beginning of May or the middle?
ISABEL:	It was the middle, and then I went home and told Marco.
COUNSELOR:	Ok, so you found out you were pregnant in the middle of May. *[Counselor marks the calendar.]* When did Dr. Murphy tell you your due date would be?
ISABEL:	Around December 22.
COUNSELOR:	Great, so we know you're in your third trimester now. *[The counselor circles the third trimester with a colored pencil, then circles the other trimesters with different colors.]* It looks like you probably got pregnant somewhere around the beginning of April. *[The counselor also marks this on calendar.]* Did your alcohol drinking change after you found out you were pregnant in mid-May?
ISABEL:	Yes, I pretty much quit drinking after that. But right before, around the beginning of May *[points to calendar]*, Marco had just gotten a job and we went out with some friends. We went to party that one time, and I drank a little, but I don't think that would harm the baby. It wasn't a lot.
COUNSELOR:	You're doing great. Do you remember what you were drinking?
ISABEL:	I had one rum and Coke. Mostly Coke, with a little rum.
COUNSELOR:	Was that all?
ISABEL:	I had one wine cooler which I sipped for the rest of night. That wasn't too much, was it?

Master Clinician Note: The counselor senses that Isabel is getting a little anxious about this line of questioning and tries to be reassuring and non-judgmental.

COUNSELOR:	Two drinks in one night don't sound like a lot to me. I'm only asking because I want to help you do the best for the baby between now and the time you deliver. So let's see: It seems like you are saying that you mostly drink on special occasions. Is that right?
ISABEL:	Yes, those are the times I usually drink, and sometimes when Marco has friends over to watch a game I might have a beer or two.
COUNSELOR:	Okay. Can you remember any other occasions when you might have been drinking during your pregnancy?
ISABEL:	I drank a little on my birthday in July.
COUNSELOR:	Did you go out for your birthday?
ISABEL:	No. Marco surprised me when I got home. He made me dinner with flowers and wine and everything.

COUNSELOR:	He sounds very thoughtful.
ISABEL:	*[Smiling, shrugs a little.]* He can be.
COUNSELOR:	So, do you remember how much wine you had that night?
ISABEL:	I had maybe two or three glasses. I have read that drinking a little wine would not hurt the baby. I try to be aware not to do anything that would hurt my baby. I drank a little with my first child and he is healthy.
COUNSELOR:	I know that, Isabel. No mother would do anything on purpose to hurt her baby. I know how hard you're working to take care of yourself during the pregnancy, and that's really important. Did Marco drink with you on your birthday?
ISABEL:	Marco drinks all the time. He drinks beer every day. I'm sure that I'm okay, because you know I'm not like Marco. I don't come home and a have a six pack.
COUNSELOR:	Okay. So, you drank these two times before you got pregnant. And right about here is when you would have found out you were pregnant. *[The counselor points to circled first trimester on calendar.]* Are there any other days in these months that you can think of, or any events?
ISABEL:	*[Pauses, squirms a little in her chair.]* Well, there was one time Marco and I had an argument about the amount of time he spends with his friends. He goes out on Friday nights and drinks with his friends, doesn't come home sometimes until the next morning. He went out and I had some of my girlfriends over and I wound up getting drunk. I was so bad I was throwing up. I was embarrassed. I had to go to the bedroom and they had a bucket and they were saying "Isabel, are you okay?" But that's the only time I can think of.
COUNSELOR:	And what were you drinking then?
ISABEL:	We were drinking rum and Coke.
COUNSELOR:	Okay, do you know how many drinks you had?
ISABEL:	We were drinking and playing cards. I must have had three or four, at least.
COUNSELOR:	How many drinks does it take to make you feel high?
ISABEL:	It depends. A couple glasses of wine, or one rum and Coke, if it is strong.

Master Clinician Note: The counselor is gradually asking more detailed questions about Isabel's alcohol use. Although Isabel claims not to be a drinker, a pattern of usage is emerging through the use of the calendar. Isabel is bringing up Marco often, so the counselor takes this cue and probes further about her husband.

COUNSELOR:	It sounds like whenever you drink it has something to do with Marco. Are there times that you drink by yourself?
ISABEL:	No.
COUNSELOR:	Okay, so tell me about drinking with Marco.

ISABEL:	*[Sighs.]* It's just mostly because we're with friends and I like to do what everyone else is doing. I want to be social. I don't drink every day with him. He'll come home with a six pack and drink beer while he is watching TV or sports. He loves baseball and basketball.
COUNSELOR:	So he drinks when he comes home from work. Does he want you to drink with him?
ISABEL:	He'll offer me a beer now and then, ya know, but that's his thing. That's what men do. I have too many other things going on. I really drink just a little. I really don't think that I am doing anything that is going to hurt the baby. I don't want to fight with Marco about his drinking or his friends. I have to come here to deal with my other problems.
COUNSELOR:	Is Marco excited about the baby?
ISABEL:	*[Relaxing a little at the change in subject.]* Oh yeah. Very. I'm excited, too. We're looking forward to this.
COUNSELOR:	How do you think it's going to be with his drinking after the baby is born?
ISABEL:	I don't know. I doubt he will change.
COUNSELOR:	Are you worried about that?
ISABEL:	No, he's a good guy. *[She sniffles and wipes her nose.]* He really is. I know you probably think he's an alcoholic or something. That's not how it is. We're not like that. *[She starts crying.]* I love this baby. So does he. We're trying to take care of it. *[Her crying continues, and she gets an anxious expression on her face.]*

Master Clinician Note: Isabel is becoming anxious, and is shifting the topic away from alcohol. This is a signal, or cue, to the counselor that the client is uncomfortable. The counselor needs to acknowledge what Isabel is feeling and be careful about how much further she probes on this issue during this visit.

COUNSELOR:	I know you have a lot on your plate and I think you are handling it quite well. You did quite a bit in today's session, and you did very well. I would like to end this session and talk a little about our next session. Would that be alright with you?
ISABEL:	Sure.
COUNSELOR:	I heard you say you had read something that drinking small amounts of alcohol was okay for a pregnant woman. Is that correct?
ISABEL:	Yes, I read it on poster, I don't remember where.
COUNSELOR:	I would like to give you something to read. It's short. It's about what can happen when babies are exposed to alcohol before being born. I would like you to read it so we can discuss it in our next session. Is that okay with you?
ISABEL:	Sure. The more I know, the more I can protect the baby, right?
COUNSELOR:	Absolutely.

Master Clinician Note: The mental health counselor is in a difficult position. Her use of the calendar helped to reveal a pattern of alcohol use by Isabel and her husband that exceeds what Isabel first admitted and is unsafe for the baby. It also helped to establish some of Isabel's triggers for drinking alcohol, which include her husband and being angry.

At the same time, discussing alcohol use and how it can hurt a baby can be an emotional topic for the mother. She is working hard to take care of her baby, and the topic of alcohol may have gone further than she is comfortable with. At the same time, it has been useful, as Isabel seems to be reaching a point where she has begun to question her use of alcohol during pregnancy.

This is a learning moment for the counselor. She can see the value of exploring alcohol use with her pregnant patients, but she also knows that, in the future, she can pay closer attention to verbal cues that indicate a client's discomfort; in Isabel's case, the changing of the topic and the repeated assertions that she doesn't think she has hurt her baby. The counselor should continue the session long enough to bring closure to the topic of alcohol use, while supporting the positive things that Isabel has done to take care of her baby. The door should be left open to come back to the topic of alcohol in future sessions.

If Isabel continues to show a pattern of alcohol use during the pregnancy, the counselor can help her identify other ways to deal with her anger besides drinking (stress management), and help her identify or find support systems in her life other than her husband if he is not being supportive of her abstinence during pregnancy (e.g., a pregnancy peer support group). If a mental health counselor does not feel comfortable addressing these issues, referral to a qualified substance abuse treatment counselor is advisable.

5. INTERVIEWING A CLIENT FOR THE POSSIBLE PRESENCE OF AN FASD (FASD INTERVENTION)

Overview: This vignette illustrates the clues the health care worker is receiving that suggest an impairment and possible FASD. A client with an FASD, with brain damage, will not receive the information from the worker the same way someone without FASD will receive it. The client may not have a diagnosis and may not immediately present as someone with a disability. There are a number of questions the worker could ask to determine whether they need to operate in a different kind of therapeutic environment with the client. The main goal of this vignette is for the health care worker to consider the *possibility* of an FASD, not to diagnose an FASD, which can only be done by qualified professionals. A woman who has an FASD is at high risk for having a child with an FASD.

Background: Marta is a single woman, 19, who recently had a baby, and is being seen at a Healthy Start center by a health care worker. This is the first time they are meeting. The health care worker's colleague asked her to meet with Marta as she knew that the health care worker was knowledgeable about FASD and was known as the office "FASD champion." The colleague has begun to suspect that Marta may need an evaluation for FASD, as she has repeatedly missed appointments or been late, gotten lost on the way to the center, failed to follow instructions, spoken at inappropriate times, and has repeated foster placement and criminal justice involvement in her case history. The only information in the history about Marta's biological mother is that she is dead. The colleague wants the health care worker to conduct an informal interview to assess the possibility of an FASD.

Learning Objectives:

1. To learn how to identify behavioral and verbal cues in conversation with a client that may indicate that the client has an FASD.

2. To learn how to apply knowledge of FASD and its related behavioral problems, in order to reassess clients with troublesome behaviors or concerns for factors other than knowing noncompliance.

Vignette Start

HEALTH CARE WORKER:	Hi Marta, how are you?
MARTA:	Good.
HEALTH CARE WORKER:	Your regular counselor has asked me to meet with you today for a few minutes to ask you a few questions, if that's okay. *[Marta nods in agreement.]* Okay, so tell me how you got here today.
MARTA:	*[Shrugs.]* I took the #10 bus, then I got off and walked.
HEALTH CARE WORKER:	Where did you get off the bus?
MARTA:	Madison Avenue.
HEALTH CARE WORKER:	Did you know you could have taken the bus to Washington Street instead of Madison Avenue? Then you would have been six blocks closer.
MARTA:	*[Shaking her head.]* I didn't know that.
HEALTH CARE WORKER:	Do you want me to write that down for you?
MARTA:	Okay.
HEALTH CARE WORKER:	*[Writes down the information.]* Here, you can keep this in your purse. *[Hands Marta the piece of paper.]*

Master Clinician Note: Individuals with an FASD sometimes exhibit poor working memory. The health care worker is not assuming that Marta has an FASD at this point. However, if she does, it is unlikely that she will remember the information about the bus route, so the health care worker writes it down.

HEALTH CARE WORKER:	Did you pay for your bus ride with cash or a bus card?
MARTA:	Today I paid with cash, but I don't always have it.
HEALTH CARE WORKER:	When are the times when you don't have money?
MARTA:	Sometimes friends borrow it, or other people.
HEALTH CARE WORKER:	What other people?
MARTA:	Well, like last time, a man on the corner asked me for money, so I gave it to him. Then I didn't have any for the bus.

Master Clinician Note: Marta has exhibited a double "red flag" for an individual with an FASD; poor money management skills, and a lack of understanding of consequence (i.e., giving away the money without understanding that she then wouldn't be able to pay for the bus).

HEALTH CARE WORKER:	Marta, I'd like to ask you a little more about some of the questions that you were asked when you first came here.
MARTA:	Okay, go ahead.
HEALTH CARE WORKER:	You told us that your mother is not alive. How old was she when she died?
MARTA:	Twenty-five, I think.
HEALTH CARE WORKER:	How old were *you* when she died?
MARTA:	Four.
HEALTH CARE WORKER:	I'm very sorry to hear that you've lost your mother.
MARTA:	*[Very matter-of-factly.]* I didn't lose her. She died.

Master Clinician Note: Marta is exhibiting very literal interpretation of language, which is common among individuals with an FASD.

HEALTH CARE WORKER:	You're right, that's what I should have said. That was probably a hard time for you. *[Marta nods.]* Did you know much about her?
MARTA:	*[Shakes her head and shrugs.]* Not really.
HEALTH CARE WORKER:	Do you know if she ever had any kind of problem with alcohol?
MARTA:	Like, being an alcoholic?
HEALTH CARE WORKER:	Yes.
MARTA:	*[Shrugs.]* I heard she drank, yeah.
HEALTH CARE WORKER:	Do you know if she drank alcohol while she was pregnant with you?
MARTA:	I don't know. *[Pauses for a moment.]* That's a weird question. Why are you asking that?
HEALTH CARE WORKER:	Did the question make you uncomfortable? Sometimes when women drink during pregnancy their kids end up having extra challenges. Do you know what I mean when I say challenges?
MARTA:	Sure.
HEALTH CARE WORKER:	Can you give me an example?
MARTA:	*[Shrugs]*. I don't know.

Master Clinician Note: Marta has stated that she understands when really she doesn't. Any young person might do this, but it is especially common for individuals with an FASD. Checking for cognition is important with clients that have or may have an FASD.

HEALTH CARE WORKER:	Needing extra help in school is an example of a challenge.
MARTA:	Right, okay.
HEALTH CARE WORKER:	Is it okay to ask a few more questions?
MARTA:	Yeah.
HEALTH CARE WORKER:	Thanks. This will only take a couple more minutes, I promise. How about you? Do you drink alcohol at all?

Master Clinician Note: Because this is an interview to see if there is reason to believe that Marta has an FASD, the counselor is probing to see if perhaps Marta's baby was also exposed to alcohol before birth.

MARTA:	No, I don't like the taste of it.
HEALTH CARE WORKER:	Me neither. So, you didn't have any alcohol while you were pregnant?
MARTA:	No, my foster mom and dad told me not to drink or smoke while I was pregnant.
HEALTH CARE WORKER:	That was very good advice. Tell me, where did you live when you were growing up?
MARTA:	First with my aunt, then lots of places. I was in foster care.

Master Clinician Note: It is not unusual for individuals with an FASD to no longer be in the care of their parents, and to have been placed multiple times in foster care.

HEALTH CARE WORKER:	Did you like school when you were growing up?
MARTA:	*[Looking down.]* Umm… I guess it was okay.
HEALTH CARE WORKER:	What classes did you like?
MARTA:	I liked art. And I liked Ms. Norton.
HEALTH CARE WORKER:	Who was Ms. Norton?
MARTA:	Ms. Norton was in the resource room.

Master Clinician Note: Time spent in the "resource room," while not a clear-cut clue, is certainly a strong indicator that the child was identified in school as having special needs. This is often the case with children who have an FASD. The counselor could further explore by asking a follow-up question like "Did you ever have extra help with your school work?" or "Did you ever have special classes or tutoring in school?"

HEALTH CARE WORKER:	How many students were in the class with you?
MARTA:	Five, including Eddie.
HEALTH CARE WORKER:	Who's Eddie?

MARTA:	*[Laughing a little to herself as she remembers.]* Eddie is the kid that I used to get in trouble with all the time. He was always coming up with ideas.
HEALTH CARE WORKER:	What do you mean when you say Eddie "came up with ideas?" Can you give me an example?
MARTA:	Well, like, one time we were walking home from school, and he saw a bike in someone's yard that he really wanted. So he told me to go get it for him. I did, but the man who lived there caught me and called the cops.
HEALTH CARE WORKER:	Did you realize that taking the bike could get you into trouble?
MARTA:	I had a feeling. I wasn't sure, but I wanted Eddie to keep liking me.

Master Clinician Note: Involvement in "trouble" or crime as an unintentional secondary participant is an FASD "red flag," particularly when the motivation is social (i.e., to make friends).

Master Clinician Note: Marta's case/vignette is oversimplified. In a matter of minutes, she has exhibited a handful of behavioral clues that suggest that she may have a disability. Not all individuals who may have an FASD will be this easy to 'spot.' This conversation is provided simply as a way to learn how such "red flags" might come up in conversation with a client. By identifying these red flags, which are particularly common in individuals with an FASD, the health care worker will be able to manage the case in a way that better suits the needs of the client, and can make a better-informed decision regarding the need for a more complete FASD diagnostic evaluation. Additional probing questions that could be asked include the following:

- How much alcohol did your mom drink when she was pregnant?
- Think about when you were a child. How did you do in school?
- Do you ever have trouble keeping appointments? How do you do with telling time?

Refer to Part 1, Chapter 2 for guidance on referring a client for a formal FASD diagnostic evaluation, and for strategies and treatment modifications that will improve treatment success with an individual who may have an FASD.

6. INTERVIEWING A BIRTH MOTHER ABOUT A SON WHO MAY HAVE AN FASD AND IS HAVING TROUBLE IN SCHOOL (FASD INTERVENTION)

Overview: Counseling professionals in mental health or substance abuse treatment may avoid talking to a female client or family member about their alcohol use during pregnancy, either to avoid communicating any shame or judgment to that individual, or out of a lack of knowledge about FASD. This case illustrates a scenario where such a discussion may prove fruitful, and the sensitivity required when starting the discussion.

Background: The vignette begins with a community mental health professional talking to Dixie Wagner, 35, about the behavior of Dixie's 7-year-old biological son, Jarrod. (Jarrod is not present at this session.) Jarrod is in trouble again for hitting another child, and this is causing distress for the mother that the mental health professional wants to address, which leads into a discussion of FASD.

Learning Objectives:

1. Cite methods to help the caregiver clarify the child's issues and discover why the child is having problems.

2. Specify skills needed to follow the caregiver's lead in asking probing questions.

3. Explore the negative perceptions surrounding prenatal alcohol exposure, and examine how lack of knowledge or fear of shaming may interfere with asking the right questions.

Vignette Start

MENTAL HEALTH PROFESSIONAL: Dixie, we talked briefly on the phone about Jarrod's school issues. It sounds to me like you are concerned for him. Today I'd like to hear more about your concerns, and then we can work from there. How does that sound?

DIXIE: Yes, that's fine. You're right, I'm very concerned about him.

MENTAL HEALTH PROFESSIONAL: Is it okay that we talk about the kinds of behaviors that led to Jarrod hitting a fellow student? Was the student a friend of Jarrod's?

DIXIE: That is exactly what's so disturbing about this situation; it was someone I thought was a good friend, a kid named Garrett. Jarrod looks up to Garrett and talks about him all the time. I was excited that he wanted to be friends with Garrett. I was very surprised to get a call from the principal.

MENTAL HEALTH PROFESSIONAL: You're right. Friends are so important for all children this age. Has Jarrod been having problems with his peers?

DIXIE: *[Sighs].* He's always had a hard time getting along with kids his own age. He starts off happy and friendly. He wants everyone to like him. Sometimes I think his enthusiasm might be too much for some kids. Sometimes he says such crazy things. I don't know if he thinks the kids will laugh at what he says or if he is really being serious. Slowly I can see the kids moving away from him. It breaks my heart. He ends up playing by himself. He really wants everyone to like him. He'll talk to anyone! We always say Jarrod has never met a stranger he didn't like. I worry a little that he'll listen to the wrong person when he gets older. Most of the time he's just so sweet and loveable.

MENTAL HEALTH PROFESSIONAL: Okay, so what I'm hearing is that Jarrod has been having problems making and keeping friends his own age, although he really wants to have a friend. Is that right? *[Dixie nods.]* How about in the school setting? How do you think he is doing in class and with his school work?

DIXIE: Well, he's been labeled a "talker" in class, and we've gotten plenty of notes from the teacher because Jarrod likes to chat with his neighbors and that annoys them sometimes, and the teacher. He has a lot of energy, and sometimes loses focus on his work. He can get frustrated, and may have a hissy fit

---

at school when he doesn't want to do his work. He likes to do a good job. Sometimes he just won't finish his work. So the teacher will send it home for us to do with him. Every night we sit down and spend a lot of time on homework, but that usually ends up in Jarrod fighting and yelling at us.

MENTAL HEALTH PROFESSIONAL: So, Jarrod generally has a hard time focusing and sitting still. These hissy fits, as you call them, how many of these will he have in a typical school day? Can you tell me a little more about that? Are you noticing any consistent struggles?

DIXIE: I guess he's had several since starting school this year. The hissy fits are like toddler temper tantrums. I can't believe he is still having tantrums. We never really know why he has them, especially at school. I know he leaves every day happy to be going to school, but when he gets home he's tired and cranky, and very angry. He doesn't know where his homework is in his backpack. This leads to raised voices, either me or my husband. The teacher always tells us Jarrod was given the homework, so he must be deliberately misplacing it. If we do find the homework assignment, Jarrod will sit and work really hard for awhile, but then he starts to whine and cry that he is tired and doesn't remember what the teacher told him that day. My husband and I review his spelling words with him every day. He sits and really tries hard to remember them. But he never passes the test on Friday. We spend lots of time with him on his homework. It's like we have to re-teach him everything he learned from the day. Many times it ends in a hissy fit. It's not like we don't help him. We've done this with him since he was in first grade.

MENTAL HEALTH PROFESSIONAL: Jarrod sounds like he is facing some challenges with his school work. Are there other times or activities when he struggles?

DIXIE: Well, when he gets off the bus in the afternoon, he is out of control. He runs around, bumping into furniture and screaming. Sometimes he will knock down the dog. I am sure he doesn't mean to hurt the dog, though, because he really loves it. The teacher says he has trouble standing in line for lunch, and pushes the other students next to him. She also says he has a hard time on the playground for recess. He prefers to stay inside with her. And about 2pm every day, Jarrod gets very sleepy.

MENTAL HEALTH PROFESSIONAL: I see. Is he getting enough sleep?

DIXIE: We start the bedtime routine about 7:30, right after dinner. The kids will take showers, brush their teeth, and then we'll read a book together. We struggle to get Jarrod to brush his teeth. He hates taking a shower, but once the water is in the tub, he loves taking a bath. Everyone gets a chance to pick a book when it's their turn. Jarrod always picks a picture book about Kermit the frog. But when it is time to go to bed, Jarrod is wide awake, talking or playing his video games. We've had to put him in his own room so my other children can go to sleep. Jarrod is up before my husband, usually before 5am, because he's never needed much sleep.

MENTAL HEALTH PROFESSIONAL: So what I am hearing is that you and your husband have set up a nighttime routine for all the children, but Jarrod has a hard time with the routine. It sounds like Jarrod is only getting a few hours of sleep at night. This may be a reason why Jarrod is having problems in school, since he is tired, but I would like to hear more from you. What else is worrying you?

DIXIE: This isn't school-related, but that boy can't keep his room clean! I run a tight ship, and an unmade bed is not welcome. He can never find anything. I raise my voice, and still no results. My other kids listen to me. I have no idea why Jarrod disobeys me all the time.

MENTAL HEALTH PROFESSIONAL: Can you describe a typical room-cleaning episode?

DIXIE: I'll say "Did you clean your room?" and he says "Yes" and then I'll go and check and nothing is put away. There are clothes on the floor. Dirty and clean clothes will be in his dresser drawers. The bed is unmade. He'll leave wet bath towels on the floor. And there he sits playing a video game. Nothing is done and he still says "Yup, it's clean!" He just doesn't listen. Sometimes I punish him. That doesn't work, either.

MENTAL HEALTH PROFESSIONAL: That can't be easy, and I can see where that could be frustrating for you and your husband. Do you think it's a case of Jarrod not having the organizational skills needed to keep his room clean, or that he doesn't understand what you're asking him to do?

DIXIE: I think he understands, he's just resisting. I know he can do it, but usually not until I stand over him and make him do it, one thing at a time. It's exhausting.

MENTAL HEALTH PROFESSIONAL: Well, That sounds like a lot of kids Jarrod's age. But what I'm getting at is when you break down the specific tasks for Jarrod—one thing at a time, like you say—he does what he's told and does it correctly. Is that right?

DIXIE: Yes, we have found that there isn't a better kid when you work with him one-on-one.

MENTAL HEALTH PROFESSIONAL: You're providing me with a lot of needed detail. Thank you. Knowing his behaviors out of school really does help me understand how we might be able to help him *in* school. I'd also like to follow up on something you mentioned earlier, about Jarrod's friends. How is he with kids his own age, besides Garrett?

DIXIE: Besides the kindergarten twins who live next door, Jarrod has no one to play with. We tried to get him into soccer, but he ran after the soccer ball no matter what side had it and the kids made fun of him. We tried cub scouts with my husband helping out as den leader, but Jarrod would be very bouncy and talkative, grabbing the other kids' project, sometimes breaking them. The kids would be polite, but eventually started to shun him. Eventually he would go off by himself and play with a toy.

MENTAL HEALTH PROFESSIONAL: This must be hard for you and your husband.

DIXIE: We were told last year that Jarrod was immature for his age, but the teacher said boys tend to mature later than girls. The teacher wanted to wait and see if Jarrod matured over the year before we did any official school testing.

MENTAL HEALTH PROFESSIONAL: So, let's recap what we have talked about. Jarrod tries to be social and verbal, is trusting, and wants to be a good friend. He also has trouble cleaning his room, staying on task, and doing his school work, but when he does sit down for homework, he can be very diligent in getting his work done. Then there may be some sensory issues, like brushing his teeth or taking a shower, and the bus tends to be a problem. Of course, we cannot forget the fight with Garrett. Out of all these things, I don't see a child with an aggressive nature. What I am concerned about, though, is that Jarrod might be facing some difficulties that will lead him to get into another fight.

DIXIE: This isn't making sense to me.

MENTAL HEALTH PROFESSIONAL: Well, I don't have a real clear picture yet. However, one of things that could be at work is that Jarrod could have some cognitive issues that are creating differences in the way he processes information. These deficits can occur for a whole range of reasons. Sometimes children are born with them, and as they grow, their brains are different from most kids.

DIXIE: You mean like ADHD? We've had people suggest ADHD before.

MENTAL HEALTH PROFESSIONAL: ADHD may be one issue, but other things could be at work, too. Is it okay that we talk about before Jarrod was born? This is something that I've asked some of my clients before, and it may be helpful here, as well. I'd like to ask about Jarrod's birth, and when you were pregnant with him. It will help us understand Jarrod's environmental background. Were there any complications during your pregnancy with Jarrod?

DIXIE:	No, everything was fine. In fact it was a pretty easy pregnancy. I didn't have much morning sickness.
MENTAL HEALTH PROFESSIONAL:	Would you say that you planned your pregnancy with Jarrod?
DIXIE:	No, not really. He's our third, and we weren't really planning on a third.
MENTAL HEALTH PROFESSIONAL:	Now, many pregnancies are unplanned. About half in this country, in fact. Were you pregnant for awhile before you knew?
DIXIE:	Yeah, I found out kind of late. *[Starts to become defensive.]* But I had a good doctor, and good prenatal care.
MENTAL HEALTH PROFESSIONAL:	What did your doctor tell you about the use of alcohol during your pregnancy?
DIXIE:	My husband and I are social drinkers, but we always have been. I don't smoke. I drank during my other pregnancies. My doctor even told me to do it sometimes, because I get really stressed out and it's how I used to relax. I really think you're way off here.
MENTAL HEALTH PROFESSIONAL:	Your doctor told you that the occasional drink was okay? That it would relax you?
DIXIE:	Yes, he did, and why would he say that if it wasn't true? He's a pediatrician, for god's sake. Where is this going? Are you saying I did something wrong to hurt Jarrod?
MENTAL HEALTH PROFESSIONAL:	No I do not think you would do anything to hurt Jarrod. Some doctors still give that advice, even though the evidence now suggests that alcohol can harm a fetus. It won't necessarily harm *every* fetus, but it can hurt some. I recognize that this is hard to talk about. I only want to explore the possibility. We both have the same goal, to help Jarrod. He has exhibited a pattern of behavior that makes an FASD something worth examining, even if it's just to rule it out. Do you know about FASD?
DIXIE:	*[Sits forward in her chair, holding up her hands in a defensive manner.]* So, wait. What you're saying is that I drank alcohol and hurt Jarrod while I was pregnant. Is that it?
MENTAL HEALTH PROFESSIONAL:	Only experts can determine whether a person has an FASD. Changes in the brain due to alcohol can only be identified by certain professionals, but what I do suggest is that we start to look at why Jarrod might be experiencing some of the problems that you and his teacher have identified. I am seeing a pattern of behavior that may suggest an FASD. We all want the best for Jarrod, and knowing what is happening in his head may help all of us meet his needs.

DIXIE:	[Leans back, crossing her arms, more relaxed but still wary.] What is this stuff, FASD?
MENTAL HEALTH PROFESSIONAL:	It stands for Fetal Alcohol Spectrum Disorders. See, alcohol is an environmental factor that can affect a developing fetus. I mentioned alcohol because some women are unaware of the effects that alcohol can have on an unborn baby. Scientists refer to the effects of alcohol on the fetus as FASD.
DIXIE:	I've never heard of it. Are you saying you think Jarrod has that? [Sits forward in her chair; tears well up in her eyes.] What you're saying is that I drank alcohol and changed Jarrod's brain while I was pregnant. Is that it? This is my fault?
MENTAL HEALTH PROFESSIONAL:	I'm not leaping to that conclusion. If Jarrod does have an FASD, there is no blame here. I just think it's worthwhile to discuss the possibility, because it may help your son, which is what we both want.
DIXIE:	[Sits back in her chair and slumps a little.] Yeah, I wanna help him. I want nothing more. My husband and I have done everything we can. [She sniffles some more and shakes her head, considering; the counselor offers a box of tissues.] This has been so hard. It's been going on so long. We've seen so many doctors, and heard so many diagnoses, and no one's ever right. Nothing works. But no one's said anything like this before. And when you sit there and tell me that this might all be because I had some drinks while I was pregnant... [She sniffles some more.]

> **Master Clinician Note:** It's important at this point for the mental health professional to respond to the fact that the client is feeling blamed and becoming agitated.

MENTAL HEALTH PROFESSIONAL:	Then I have to apologize to you. If that's what you're feeling, then I'm to blame, not you. I haven't done my job properly. It's incredibly important to me that you understand that my only goal is to work with you to identify a potential root cause for the problems that Jarrod having, because it's clear that his situation is causing *you* distress. That's all I want to do. There are many cases of FASD. Jarrod would not be the first or the only one. No mother on earth does anything to intentionally hurt her baby. I know you certainly didn't. I have a child of my own. I know the feeling of being a mother, and it's very, very clear to me how much you love your son.
DIXIE:	I just... I don't even know what to say. I feel like you're pointing a finger at me. [She is angry, beginning to cry.] You're in *mental* health. No offense, but what do you know about *medicine*? Or about my son? About how much I love him? Or about what we've been through? I can't even understand that you're sitting there saying I did this to him.

I mean, I hear your "no blame" crap, but I'm feelin' real blamed right about now!

MENTAL HEALTH PROFESSIONAL: Well, like I said, I do apologize if that is how you feel. Maybe we just need to rule out FASD. If it happened, you were going on the advice of your doctor. Would it be alright if we focused on what you want to do next for Jarrod?

DIXIE: *[Waving her hand to stop the counselor.]* What's it called again?

MENTAL HEALTH PROFESSIONAL: Fetal Alcohol Spectrum Disorders. FASD. I can give you a pamphlet that talks about the basics of it.

Master Clinician Note: It is advisable to provide FASD information that does not include pictures, particularly of children with prominent facial dysmorphology (e.g., thin upper lip, smooth philtrum). These facial characteristics are present in only a small percentage of children who have an FASD, and if the client's child does not resemble the children in the pictures, this may enable the client's desire to believe that their child can't possibly have an FASD.

DIXIE: *[Taking the pamphlet.]* So I should read this?

MENTAL HEALTH PROFESSIONAL: Yes, it would be good if you and your husband both read it and discussed whether you think it describes Jarrod's situation.

DIXIE: I still say you're wrong. But, what if it does? What happens then?

MENTAL HEALTH PROFESSIONAL: To start, I think you could begin the process for the school to start testing Jarrod for a learning disability. There are several tests that could help them understand the best way to teach Jarrod so that he doesn't get so frustrated. There are a few pieces of the testing that you will have to complete, like his developmental history, when he walked and talked, things like that. I think you should also look at doing another test for ADHD. In the meantime, we can set up another appointment to talk about FASD, possibly with your husband, as well. And if the two of you are okay with it, I can help you access a more complete evaluation.

DIXIE: Where does that happen?

MENTAL HEALTH PROFESSIONAL: It may be best to complete the assessment with a developmental pediatrician at the local hospital. I am sure that doctor will want to see the test results from school. If you like, there is a support group for families called the Circle of Hope. I could give you the phone number or e-mail address for them if you need someone else to talk to who has been through this. How would that be?

Master Clinician Note: Although the mental health professional makes repeated attempts to assure Dixie that she does not need to feel blame about the possibility that Jarrod has an FASD, Dixie has still become upset. This is a very natural response, and counselors should be prepared for birth mothers to feel as though they are being 'blamed' for their child's condition when FASD is discussed. However, many pregnancies are unplanned, some doctors do still recommend a glass of wine as a way for a pregnant woman to relax, and many women do not realize until well into their first trimester that they are pregnant. The mental health professional utilizes these realities as a way to reassure Dixie and disconnect her from a sense of guilt and consistently reiterates their shared goal, to find the best way to help Jarrod. She also effectively coordinates care by putting Dixie in touch with additional testing and offering a support group number.

7. REVIEWING AN FASD DIAGNOSTIC REPORT WITH THE FAMILY (FASD INTERVENTION)

Overview: The purpose of this vignette is to provide counselors with guidance on how to review a diagnostic report (or Medical Summary Report) with family members of a child who has been just diagnosed with FAS.

Background: The client, Jenine, is the caregiver of her grandson, Brice. Jenine is meeting with a counselor from the Indian Health Service to review Brice's Medical Summary Report for the first time. In a prior session, Jenine confided that she felt overwhelmed.

Knowing how detailed a Medical Summary Report can be, the counselor suggested that Jenine bring trusted family members and elders to this session. Together they arranged for Jenine's sister, aunt, and an elder to attend.

Learning Objectives:

1. To recognize that clients will need support after an FASD-related diagnosis.

2. To identify how to help the client prioritize the child's and the caregiver's needs.

3. To recognize that the client will need to be educated to understand that the child's behavior problems are due to damage to brain caused by prenatal alcohol exposure.

Vignette Start

COUNSELOR: Welcome, everyone. It is so good for Brice that you could be here. I am very happy to try to answer all of your questions today. We'll go through the basics, so that we can work on what is best for Brice. Does that sound good?

JENINE: Yes.

AUNT: Yes.

ELDER: Yes.

Master Clinician Note: The counselor is listening to everyone in order to validate the feelings and concerns of all individuals attending the session.

COUNSELOR: As I mentioned when you arrived, I am so glad that each of you are here today to support Jenine through this diagnostic process. Together, we can come up with a plan and move forward from there. The plan will build on Brice's strengths, as well as the diagnosis. We'll get started today, but it will take more meetings and community support to understand this diagnosis. A lot of detailed information can be overwhelming, but again, together, we will work through this process.

JENINE: Okay.

COUNSELOR: Before we review the report, let's talk about FAS. What kinds of things have you learned about FAS?

JENINE: I have been reading a lot on the internet.

> **Master Clinician Note:** It is advisable for the counselor to caution the client and all attending the session that the quality and reliability of online information about all forms of FASD varies. She should provide the client with a reading list of up-to-date sources, but advise them to put it down when they need a break to avoid feeling overwhelmed.

COUNSELOR: Okay, I like the internet as a source of information because there can be some helpful sites. At the same time, not all internet information is up-to-date. Here is a list of three Web sites that I recommend. They are updated all the time. They're really the best place to start. The first site publishes some basic facts and I'd like to review that with you all for a few minutes.

> **Master Clinician Note:** The counselor can now review the report with Jenine and her support persons. The counselor can use the review to assess the knowledge level of the client and her sister and elder, in order to determine how much education and support will be needed throughout the process. It is also advisable to inquire about other family members (grandparents, brothers, sisters, aunts and uncles, extended family) to assess how they will feel about the child's disability and to gain insight into cultural differences.
>
> A sample Medical Summary Report can be viewed at the Web site of the Washington State FAS Diagnostic & Prevention Network (FAS DPN): **http://depts.washington.edu/fasdpn/pdfs/4-digit-medsum-web-2006.pdf**.
>
> After completing the review, the counselor should focus on Brice's priority problem area, as well as the most significant need(s) of the caregiver.

COUNSELOR: Okay, now that we've worked our way through the report, we need to focus on the number one area where Brice is having problems. Is that in school or at home?

JENINE: Both, but I can handle home. School is getting out of control. I hope that this diagnosis gets him the help he needs.

COUNSELOR: Well, I know that a diagnosis is not always the pathway to services that we expect. But what I did see in the report was a clear description of Brice's speech and language difficulties, so I think that we can get him the speech therapy services that will help in school.

JENINE: That would be wonderful. Brice stutters, and really has a hard time coming up with the right word on the spot.

COUNSELOR: Okay, then let's make the top priority for Brice to get services and therapy for speech. Does that sound like the best place to start?

JENINE: Yes, let's do that.

AUNT: I will help.

ELDER: We will help, too.

COUNSELOR:	Now let's discuss a top priority for you, Jenine. I want to check in with your stress level. If you are stressed, then it will be hard to be truly supportive for Brice. And it is my experience that parents and caregivers of children who have special needs do deal with burn-out.
JENINE:	Yeah, that sounds like me.
COUNSELOR:	Then since that's the case, let's use a couple of sessions to make a plan. If we have any medical questions, I can consult with a pediatrician to try to get those answered for you. Next, we'll get the speech therapy going for Brice.
JENINE:	Okay. How am I going to pay for all of this? All of these services?
COUNSELOR:	I know some of that is being paid through your insurance company. I'm more or less the case manager for Brice, so anything not covered, we'll work together to address how those things will get paid for.
JENINE:	Okay. Now, what's going to happen in school now, with this diagnosis?

Master Clinician Note: Even though answers to these questions cannot all be provided immediately, the counselor assures the client that they will work together to establish plans to address them.

COUNSELOR:	I think that it will be a process, and that will be the focus of our time next week. We'll want to think about how you can best approach the school to get Brice's special needs met. We'll also discuss how to talk to your family and friends as well as his teachers about FAS.
JENINE:	Okay.
COUNSELOR:	One thing we can definitely do today is make a list of Brice's strengths. It's very important that our plan for helping him focuses not just on his diagnosis but also on his positive abilities. Can you all help me with that?
JENINE:	Sure. He has a lot of wonderful qualities, he really does.
COUNSELOR:	I know he does. We're going to build on those. So, let's recap. Our first priority is to get the process started on Brice's speech therapy. We also need a plan to help you, Jenine, when you're feeling burned out. We want to talk about payment for services. And we want to address what this diagnosis means in terms of special needs at school. Does that sound right?
JENINE:	Yes.
AUNT:	Yes.
ELDER:	Yes, it does.
COUNSELOR:	Good. I'm writing all this down, and I'll give everyone a copy. And we'll set up a time for our next meeting. Let's pick a time that works for everyone.

Master Clinician Note: A diagnosis of any form of FASD can be overwhelming for a family. Although this vignette lacks specifics, the overarching theme of importance is that the counselor is positive, is willing to work with the family to make a plan to address any areas of concern, and is available to help them through the process. For families and caregivers of an individual with an FASD, having this navigational assistance can be tremendously helpful and relieve much of the stress that can go along with caring for such an individual. In addition to addressing the areas identified by the family as priorities, it will be important in future sessions for the counselor to:

- Consistently point out the child's positive attributes;
- Recommend a specific support group for the family, if available;
- Emphasize the need for respite care; and
- Ask the client about ways to involve the child in an area of interest, like music or sports or art. This can provide a 'break' for both the child and the caregiver.

8. MAKING MODIFICATIONS TO TREATMENT FOR AN INDIVIDUAL WITH AN FASD (FASD INTERVENTION)

Overview: The purpose of this vignette is to demonstrate how to modify treatment plans for a client with an FASD.

Background: The client, Yvonne, is an adolescent female with a history of truancy and fighting. She has been mandated to counseling for anger management, and has missed her last two appointments. When the counselor phoned her about the missed appointment, Yvonne's mother suggested that Yvonne may not be taking her medication, and hinted that Yvonne may be depressed.

Learning Objectives:

1. To adjust expectations regarding age-appropriate behavior, since individuals with an FASD may be adult-aged by calendar years, but are much younger developmentally and cognitively.

2. To demonstrate the value of collateral information and how to ask an individual for consent.

3. To demonstrate the importance of seeking involvement from parents and caregivers.

4. To identify how concrete thinking plays a role in comprehension for clients with an FASD.

5. To cite the value of time spent developing rapport and establishing trust.

Vignette Start

COUNSELOR:	Hi, Yvonne. We've missed a couple sessions, so I haven't talked to you in awhile. How has everything been going? *[Yvonne does not respond.]* Are you taking your medicine?
YVONNE:	Yep.
COUNSELOR:	I understand that you are not coming home at night. I'm concerned that on those nights you're not able to take your medicine.
YVONNE:	I take my medicine! Can I go?

COUNSELOR: Well, we have more time today, so let's keep talking. You know, I need a break. Do you?

YVONNE: Yes, I want to leave.

COUNSELOR: Well, I don't want you to leave yet, but we can go for a walk. Would you like to walk around the courtyard, or go to the cafeteria?

YVONNE: Outside. I want to walk in the courtyard.

COUNSELOR: Yeah, let's do that. It'll get us out of this stuffy office.

They exit to the courtyard.

Master Clinician Note: Yvonne is clearly confrontational. The counselor is navigating around the resistance by not repeating questions and insisting on answers, and changing the physical environment to one that Yvonne chooses. The counselor then begins a rapport-building process by holding off on treatment talk in favor of getting to know Yvonne personally.

COUNSELOR: So, tell me a little bit about things that you like to do. We've only seen each other one time, and that was a few weeks ago. I'd like to know more about the kinds of hobbies and things you like to do.

YVONNE: I love being outside. I love being with animals. My pets are the best.

COUNSELOR: Mine, too. I have three dogs, all Dalmatians. What kinds of pets do you have?

YVONNE: We have a dog named Scooter, he's a chocolate lab, and we have a cat, Cory. I don't know what kind of cat he is. My brother also has a little lizard, but I think it's pretty gross.

This continues for several minutes. At an appropriate time, the counselor begins to shift the conversation back to treatment issues.

COUNSELOR: Let's talk a little about your treatment plan, what is working and not working for you.

YVONNE: Okay.

COUNSELOR: Sometimes clients do not like to take medication, or they don't remember to take their pills. Do you ever forget to take your medication?

YVONNE: Sometimes.

COUNSELOR: Okay. Well, that's not surprising. Taking medication is hard to remember for a lot of people. Sometimes there are bad side effects, or sometimes it's just a bother.

YVONNE: Yeah, it's annoying.

COUNSELOR: What annoys you about your medication?

YVONNE: I don't know.

Master Clinician Note: The counselor should not leave it at "I don't know," but probe further. With a client who has an FASD, the probes should be very specific.

COUNSELOR:	Does the medication make you feel bad?
YVONNE:	No, not really.
COUNSELOR:	Is it hard to remember to take it?
YVONNE:	Yeah. I have a lot of stuff to do, ya know.
COUNSELOR:	Yeah, I know what you mean. Ya know, I take a vitamin each day with my lunch. That way, whenever I eat lunch, I know to take the vitamin. They go together. Since I go home for lunch, I keep my vitamins at home on the counter, next to the 'frig. I also put a reminder in my phone so that at noon, my phone says "Take vitamin." I think we could work out a system like that for you, something easy that reminds you to take your medication that won't be annoying.
YVONNE:	Okay.
COUNSELOR:	Let's start by writing this down.

The counselor works with Yvonne to develop a few simple, concrete steps to help her remember to take her medication. Once back in the office, the steps are written down and then reviewed with Yvonne to make sure she comprehends them.

COUNSELOR:	Does that look okay?
YVONNE:	Yeah.
COUNSELOR:	When did we say you should start using that plan?
YVONNE:	Right away.
COUNSELOR:	That's right.

> **Master Clinician Note:** The counselor does not merely ask "Does that look okay?" but also asks a follow-up question to make sure Yvonne understands. Since this is a client that has been noncompliant with medication, the counselor also schedules another session at an early date to reinforce the new plan, rather than waiting a week or longer.

COUNSELOR:	Okay, let's try this treatment plan for the next few days. I'd like to see you in three days so that we can see how it worked.
YVONNE:	Okay.
COUNSELOR:	I'll write all this down for you. Also, I'd like to ask that your mom help you with taking the medication. Would it be okay if I talked to your mom after today's session? The three of us could spend a few minutes discussing how she can help you remember to take your medication.
YVONNE:	Yeah, that'd be okay.
COUNSELOR:	I know she's picking you up today, so let's also ask if she can drop you off for your next appointment.
YVONNE:	Okay.
COUNSELOR:	*[Reinforcement of rapport-building].* Will you bring me a picture of Scooter and Cory? I'd like to see what they look like.

| YVONNE: | Sure. I'd like to see your Dalmatians. |
| COUNSELOR: | I'll bring a picture, too. Let's program a reminder into our phones for our next appointment, with a special note to bring pictures. |

Master Clinician Note: The counselor has employed a number of steps to build rapport, avoid confrontation, and simplify processes for a client that has an FASD:

- Although clinicians are trained to ask open-ended questions, this counselor made the questions quite specific. For example, when the question "How has everything been going?" got no response (it's a fairly abstract question to someone with an FASD), the counselor avoided confrontation and switched to something specific: "Have you been taking your medication?"

- The counselor never used the word "why." A person with an FASD will most likely struggle with understanding or communicating their motivations.

- The counselor limited choices to avoid overload; for example, instead of "What would you like to do?" the counselor offered a specific choice: "Would you like to walk around the courtyard, or go to the cafeteria?" This simplified the choice for Yvonne, and also changed the environment to one she likes, allowing her to share a little more easily.

- The counselor broke down the medication plan into small chunks, wrote them down, and reviewed the steps one at a time with Yvonne. If Yvonne had not seemed to be grasping the plan, the counselor could have considered reviewing it several more times, or even role-playing to solidify each step.

- The counselor scheduled a quick-turnaround follow-up visit so as not to lose valuable time if the plan isn't working, and is bringing the mother into the process as reinforcement.

- Lastly, the counselor built rapport and found a common ground around something that Yvonne really enjoys, her pets.

9. WORKING WITH AN ADOPTIVE PARENT TO CREATE A SAFETY PLAN FOR AN ADULT MALE WITH AN FASD WHO IS SEEKING LIVING INDEPENDENCE (FASD INTERVENTION)

Overview: The purpose of this vignette is to demonstrate how counselors can help develop a safety plan for clients with an FASD. This vignette focuses on creating a safety plan with a caregiver, as many individuals with FASD have someone in their life who provides advocacy and support. If there is no such person in the life of the client with FASD, an important treatment goal will be to identify persons who can fill that role.

Background: In this vignette, Mike's son, Desmond, is 21 years old, and has been diagnosed with an FASD. Mike adopted Desmond when he was five years old. Since Desmond turned 16, and Mike's wife left him (partly due to the difficulties of parenting Desmond), Mike has been Desmond's sole caregiver. Lately, Mike has become increasingly distressed about his son and life in general, and has sought counseling from a mental health provider.

We are picking up this session after Mike has mentioned that Desmond is excitedly preparing to live on his own, with the move-in date just a month away. Mike is sure his son can't handle all the responsibilities of independent living. He has tried to talk to Desmond about this, his son doesn't seem to listen or agree. Mike is realizing that there is a lot he has not talked about with his son.

The counselor took time to gather a good deal of background information. Mike is here on his own in this visit, but the counselor has met Desmond. Desmond has intellectual abilities in what is called the borderline range (just below average). Like many individuals with an FASD, he acts like someone who is younger. In the first session, when the counselor asked Mike to estimate Desmond's "acts-like" (i.e., functional) age, Mike said that Desmond still acts like someone who might be in 10th grade. As the counselor has gotten to know Desmond, this estimate seems accurate. The counselor has also carefully reviewed Desmond's Medical Summary Report (from age 11) and his latest school testing (age 20, when he graduated from high school). She now better understands his unique learning profile.

> **Master Clinician Note:** Clinical wisdom in the field of FASD, and now some scientifically validated treatments, hold that knowing the unique cognitive/learning and behavioral profile of the affected individual is crucial to understanding the reasons for their actions. This helps to reframe caregiver understanding in light of the individual's brain-based disability.

Mike also told the counselor that Desmond was diagnosed with ADHD at age 8, which helped with an accommodations plan at school and a medication regimen. When Mike tried to transfer responsibility for taking the medication to Desmond 3 years ago, he couldn't remember to take it on his own. When Mike and Desmond's doctor realized Desmond showed no decline in function off the medications, they decided to stop the regimen. Without a clear benefit, and because Desmond could be pressured to give away his stimulants to peers, stopping the medication seemed wise.

Learning Objectives:

1. To show how to identify and validate caregiver concerns, and how to integrate common issues for individuals with FASD in safety planning.

2. To show that safety for a client with an FASD requires a plan that decreases risk, increases protective factors, and focuses on comprehensive life skills planning.

3. To illustrate how to assist caregivers as they proactively develop strategies to ensure their child's safety.

4. To demonstrate that individuals with FASD need a plan that is practical, useful, developmentally appropriate, uses concrete language and visual aids, uses role-play, and takes into account their unique cognitive/learning and behavioral profile.

Vignette Start

[The dialogue starts with the counselor meeting with Mike in an individual counseling session. The counselor requested that Mike come in on his own for this session, but expects to meet with Mike and Desmond together in at least some future visits.]

COUNSELOR: What are your greatest concerns about Desmond living on his own?

MIKE: Well, I've always been there for him, and I'm really concerned that he could get into trouble out there in the real world. He has a lot of good points, and I know Desmond's tough. We got through it when his mom left a few years back. I know he turned 21 and he's *feeling* independent, but I know that he can't *be* totally independent. There's too much stuff I help him with, all the time. But I do need some time of my own. Some days...well...there are those days that

I'm zapped—done. The truth is: I'm at my wit's end. I work my butt off. Besides that, I don't take vacations from being a parent. I've sacrificed. Don't get me wrong, I love him, but there are days.... Well, you know. I'm sorry, my head's somewhere else today.

COUNSELOR: I know how much stress parents of a young person with an FASD can be under, and how much strength it takes to parent a child with a disability, especially alone. Take all the time you need to explain what's on your mind. Sounds like there are many sides to this situation.

> **Master Clinician Note:** Mike's thoughts are somewhat discursive due to stress, and perhaps due to grief about the challenges of his son's upcoming life transition. Creating safety protection for Desmond is an important way to help Mike, but the counselor should remain aware that Mike also has his own needs. Research shows that caregivers have many unmet family needs, often focusing on dealing with the emotional aspects of caregiving. The counselor is allowing Mike to express all sides of the situation. This includes negative feelings, but the counselor is also listening for signs of positive "expressed emotion," deemed to be a protective factor. The counselor is also thinking about how to promote caregiver self-care.

[Mike expresses his concerns for several more minutes. The counselor listens and normalizes, validates and reflects Mike's emotions and thoughts, and also makes clarifying summary comments. Providing Mike with time to express his emotions and thoughts and to have his perspective heard allows the counselor to move ahead with more skills-based techniques. These include problem-solving, identifying social supports, identifying and clarifying treatment goals, and cognitive restructuring.]

COUNSELOR: Okay, thank you. I think I have a sense of your concerns, both for Desmond and for your own situation.

MIKE: Yeah. I mean, this is one tough gig.

COUNSELOR: It is, and feeling "burned out" is natural. At the same time, if Desmond is going to be on his own to some degree, as he moves into his life as a young adult, that means a huge transition for both of you.

MIKE: That's an understatement.

COUNSELOR: The good news is that I can provide you with some strategies to help you cope, in the short-term and the long-term. The key here is that the definition of independence and safety is different for a person with an FASD or other developmental disabilities. I think it's important that we start by identifying one or more advocates or "champions" for Desmond. These can be professionals or family members; people who are willing to help him—and help you—manage various parts of his life. So, who can act as an advocate for Desmond? Who are his supports?

MIKE: I can be an advocate, first and foremost. And so can my aunt. Desmond gets along with her really well and sometimes she has him help at her law office doing filing, that kind of stuff. Also, she is one of the few people he'll talk to when he gets upset or angry, and she's good at calming him down. He also helps out with the middle school football team, so Coach Gray looks out for him, but they don't see each other much in the off-season. But...I think he would still be willing to help Des out. Yeah, I think they can help when I can't. And maybe Des can reconnect with his mom.

COUNSELOR: It sounds like Desmond has a number of advocates and supports, but that he mayneed help with both identifying *when* he needs help and, then, *how* to best communicate to get that help. I am so impressed and pleased that Desmond is involved with your aunt and Coach Gray. That gives Desmond's days and weeks more structure and meaning and more opportunities to connect socially. Everyone likes to feel useful! I bet there are more folks who can act as support persons or advocates. We'll try to figure out all those folks in our next session, and what each support person can do. To help move us along, here is the first page of a worksheet to do at home, to make a list of people you think of, their contact info, and what kinds of things they can help with.

[Shows Mike the first part of the Crisis/Safety Plan Worksheet.]

Think about family friends, any providers that work with Desmond, people who know him in his circles, like other people that help with the football team or friends from the community, kids from his high school youth group, church, anything like that. If possible, it is especially important to find someone in their 20's—more Desmond's age, who has good problem-solving skills, to be a kind of "mentor." Can you bring that back next time?

MIKE: *[Nods, takes the first part of the Crisis/Safety Plan Worksheet.]* I'll try to get it done. I don't know about that mentor idea; can't think of anyone right away. But it does help to write things down. If I don't have time for the worksheet… well, you know.

COUNSELOR: Sounds good. This may be a chance to ask your aunt and Coach Gray for ideas, too, as there may be someone that Desmond already knows that could be a good mentor. In terms of the worksheet, I will leave that to you.

Master Clinician Note: Clinical wisdom, and now some new interventions for caregivers of adolescents and young adults with FASD, such as the *Partners for Success Program* (information available through the CDC-funded FASD Regional Training Centers), hold that mentors can be very useful in intervention. Mentors can be community college students, aides who work in developmental disabilities services, younger relatives or family friends, or students studying to work in social services. A mentor is someone who can act as a very competent peer or a caregiver closer in age to the affected individual. They can build an ongoing and positive relationship, be available for check-ins to provide input and guidance on solving problems with peer relationships and lifestyle problems, and work toward helping the affected individual become more self-aware. They may also be able to connect the individual to pro-social and competent peers, and help find appropriate, positive recreational activities for leisure time.

COUNSELOR: Okay, let me ask you: Have you worked much with developmental disability services to help Desmond with life skills, how to live as independently?

MIKE: No, hardly at all. Desmond doesn't qualify for those kinds of services because of his FASD, and his ADHD diagnosis doesn't help, either. He doesn't have really low scores on his IQ test. And, you know, even though he struggles sometimes, he really tries to be friendly and sociable, and he talks a good game. Sometimes I think his good points actually keep him from getting all the help he needs.

COUNSELOR: It must be hard that others don't always see that he struggles with a lot of things. At that same time, it's good to know that he has so many strengths. Alright then, I think you and I will need to work together to identify the most important things to think about as Desmond becomes as independent as he can safely be.

MIKE: I think my biggest concern is that others will take advantage of Des. Especially if he has a place of his own and people want to stay with him. He tends to do things like steal to be someone's friend, or fall in with wrong crowds, then it's always him that gets caught. I'm not going to be there to prevent that if he's on his own. I mean, Des is willing to accept help, and that's good, but he may not always realize he needs to ask, especially when he gets worked up.

COUNSELOR: I hear you. That sounds like a really big worry for you, so let's talk about some way to provide safety and structure for Des as he moves into having this new freedom. This will be a safety plan, basically. We'll have to find what works and doesn't work for him, and this will be an ongoing process. We can come up with an initial plan, then when he gets into his own place, we can meet together with Des a few times to modify the plan. We'll kind of be testing it out. Adjusting a plan is always a good idea.

MIKE: I've done a lot on my own, talking with Des about what is an appropriate situation and what's not. Appropriate money use. Appropriate touching. This has been all from me. No doctor or therapist helped me out. I should write a book on it. At least I got through to him about drinking, because he just tells people he's allergic, and so far, so good. But now...well, that's another worry.

Master Clinician Note: For parents of individuals with developmental disabilities, it is very helpful to be proactive. At the same time, "looking forward" is an emotional process. The clinician will have to judge how far ahead the caregiver really wants (and needs) to plan. The clinician also needs to use reflective listening and summary statements to help the caregiver process their own emotional reactions as they do future planning. Beyond this, the clinician can help caregivers plan ahead in a practical way. Because Desmond is a young adult (though functionally an adolescent), and is starting to build an independent life, the clinician can coach Mike on how to help Desmond self-advocate and self-monitor.

One important direction is to coach Mike in creating concrete, behavioral "benchmarks" for his son, so Desmond can show daily or weekly progress and also show his father that he is ready for this life transition. This could include practicing things such as buying groceries as if he were already living on his own, and/or troubleshooting, such as thinking out loud about what to do in real-life situations—e.g., if he gets sick, the toilet starts overflowing, etc. If Desmond resists doing this (which would not be unlikely given his functional age), the counselor can work with father and son to integrate rewards for Desmond after he shows certain behaviors or masters specified tasks. An age-appropriate reward for someone functioning at an adolescent level could be more 'space,' i.e., increased time between check-ins from his father after Desmond demonstrates mastery.

Mike has educated his son carefully about drinking, which is good, but he should think about other areas he needs to talk about with Desmond, as well, including 1) safe sex; 2) communicating clearly with partners about consensual activity; 3) use of cigarettes; 4) use of illicit substances, such as marijuana and other drugs; 5) the consequences of criminal activity; and 6) ideas on what to safely do when Desmond has times of feeling irritable and negative (calming strategies).

COUNSELOR: I'm glad you already laid the groundwork! For now, let's write down some of the ideas you already figured out. We'll make cards. Two kinds, actually. First, when Des comes in we can make an identity card that says "I have an FASD" for Desmond to give to caregivers, police, co-workers, etc. Then we can make Safety Cards that he can use as reminders in his new routine. The Safety Cards can be one thing to talk to Desmond about when he comes with you to see me. We will also plan to talk about specific behavior benchmarks or things you want to see him doing before he moves out. We can talk to Des about how having him do this will let you be more comfortable giving him space and independence. *[The counselor and Mike work together to identify areas of safety concern for Desmond.]*

Master Clinician Note: Choice and level of language used on Safety Cards will differ depending on the intellectual level of the individual with an FASD. Areas of safety concern may include:

- Household reminders (buying groceries, paying bills, cleaning the apartment, taking out the trash, maintaining personal cleanliness, etc.)
- Useful phone numbers (advocates, police, hospital, primary providers, etc.)
- Transportation (routes, times, and costs)
- Work and school schedules
- Personal and household safety reminders (turning off appliances, locking doors and windows, etc.)
- High-risk behavior warnings (e.g., unsafe sex, alcohol or drug use, getting really irritable and upset)

There are programs for caregivers raising affected youth that have other useful ideas for ways to plan ahead (e.g., the *Families Moving Forward Program* and *Partners for Success Program*).

COUNSELOR: What else could help you with keeping Desmond safe?

MIKE: Well, I think, as long as he applies these things we're writing down for him and I check in on him regularly, things may go okay. For awhile, anyway. Then I just need to get organized with my aunt and Coach, so they're helping to keep an eye on him. Like I said, he's pretty good about accepting help and listening to us when we give him advice. That's one of the most important things I taught him—*accepting* help. But he really has trouble *asking* for help, or watching for signals that he's getting into trouble.

Master Clinician Note: Research on FASD and, more generally, on developmental disabilities has uncovered important protective factors. Many of these are well-known, such as positive family and peer relationships, appropriate social services and freedom from substance abuse by the individual, peers, or family members. Other protective factors may be less obvious but are no less important. For the caregiver, these include decreased stress and depression, a sense of parenting efficacy, positive expressed emotion and a viewpoint on the affected individual, and adequate caregiver support and self-care. For the affected individual, these include a willingness to ask for (and value) help from others, positive, time-filling extracurricular activities, adequate and refreshing sleep, connections to pro-social and competent peers, a positive self-perception, a sense of meaningfulness through activities such as a job, talents that others recognize and value, spirituality, and more.

COUNSELOR: Will Des be working?

MIKE: He's going to continue as an assistant with the football team as a volunteer. And he can keep helping my aunt. When he gets done with his training, we think he'll be able to do inventory and stocking at the grocery store.

COUNSELOR: Okay. Let's start figuring out how all this is going to work. So, I think it may make sense for you to manage Des's budget, at first anyway, by doing his shopping and grocery list-making until new routines are established.

MIKE: Yeah, I expected that. I'm gonna be checking in on him every day for as long as I need to, then less often if I'm sure he's doing okay. I made sure the apartment isn't far away, even though we have to pay a bit more. He isn't showing a real interest or understanding of all the little things required to live on your own; budgeting, or don't buy all your groceries at the gas station just because that's where you get gas, stuff like that. He can use my car if he asks permission, and tells me where he's going and when he'll be back. Mostly, he's going to be taking the bus. I can't imagine him knowing how to take care of his own car, even though he's a pretty good driver.

COUNSELOR: Clearly, you've already thought a lot of things through! Okay, so, why don't you bring Des next time? That will give me a chance to see if I think he needs the support of his own mental health counselor. With his ADHD, and times he gets irritated, that might be a good idea down the road. He has lots of supports, but we should think about this angle, too.

MIKE: That sounds like a plan. I appreciate your help, Doc. I feel like the load is a little lighter.

COUNSELOR: I'm glad. Remember—if you bring that worksheet back next time we can move forward more quickly with our plan.

Master Clinician Note: This session shows what it is like to work with the caregiver of someone with FASD. A possible future session could include Desmond's aunt and the coach, to create advocacy or "look-out" tasks they could all divide up to help Desmond stay organized while Desmond first starts living on his own. In sessions that include Desmond, the clinician will need to change pace and style. Specific ideas that would help Desmond, and can be used with most other affected individuals:

- Work with the affected individual to identify his or her goals, including how to generate an effective goal, "mini-steps" to achieve the goal, and needed supports.
- Discuss warning signs that they need help.
- Discuss and practice through role-play how to ask for help.
- Create a written Crisis/Safety Plan.

This vignette would play out differently depending on the culture and ethnicity of the caregiver and youth. Research shows there are different expectations for independence and type of family relationships in different cultures. This interacts with the impact of developmental disabilities. In some cultures, for instance, adult children are not expected to move out of the family home, though they will still increasingly assume more leadership and adult responsibilities within the family. In cultures where the extended family tends to be closer, affected individuals may have more resources and support from relatives, or a greater likelihood of available peer models to serve as caregivers or mentors. Research also shows that some protective factors may differ by culture: Attachment to and identification with the values of one's culture of origin is a protective factor for immigrant youth. Yet this can also be a risk: Data suggest that these youths may also be at higher risk for marginalization and discrimination. Recommending involvement in culturally relevant and pro-social leisure time activities can be a productive way for an individual with an FASD to learn about their own culture.

10. WORKING WITH A BIRTH MOTHER TO DEVELOP STRATEGIES FOR COMMUNICATING WITH A SCHOOL ABOUT AN INDIVIDUALIZED EDUCATION PLAN FOR HER DAUGHTER WHO HAS AN FASD (FASD INTERVENTION)

Overview: This vignette illustrates how a social worker can make useful suggestions for a parent or caregiver's first meeting with educators at the beginning a new school year.

Background: The start of the school year is 2 weeks away. Denise is a birth mother who is meeting with a social worker to get some advice on how to educate the school staff about working with her daughter, Elise, who is 11. Elise has recently been identified as having an FASD, although she has been tested as having a "normal" IQ and is in a mainstream learning setting. This social worker was part of the diagnostic team that assessed Elise for FASD, but this is her first time helping with Elise's school issues. Denise is hoping to develop learning strategies that she can discuss with the school staff in an Individualized Education Plan (IEP) meeting.

Learning Objectives:
1. To describe typical challenges that children with an FASD may face in the classroom.

2. To demonstrate how collaboration and creativity can lead to accommodations that result in improved outcomes for a child with an FASD.

Vignette Start

DENISE:	Now that we're gearing up for a new school year, with a new teacher who is also new to the school, I need some tips on talking to her. I want to avoid last year's fiasco with the parent aide who complained that Elise was disrespectful and "the worst."
SOCIAL WORKER:	This will be 6th grade for Elise this year, correct?
DENISE:	Correct.
SOCIAL WORKER:	And what happened last year?
DENISE:	The parent aide was a nightmare from the get-go. I had heard it all before: "Your kid won't listen" or "Your kid isn't motivated" or "Your kid *never* does her homework." I knew this aide was gonna be a problem, but I couldn't be in the classroom because I was working full-time. Poor Elise got in trouble day after day for the same stuff; homework not completed, late to class, missing class, getting in fights. Honestly, I think the parent aide did not get any insight into FASD from the teacher at all.
SOCIAL WORKER:	That's unfortunate, but not uncommon, as you know. Educators will sometimes relate differently to a birth mother than they do to adoptive or foster parents. We've talked about those issues before, and it is something that may come up again.

Master Clinician Note: Whether intentional or not, the birth mother of a child with an FASD can be perceived negatively by others, including educators, for having "caused" her child's disorder. The social worker is gently preparing Denise for this possibility and reinforcing the positive nature of how she advocates for her child.

DENISE: I know. I've been there.

SOCIAL WORKER: Well, it's important to remember that you're a fantastic mom, dealing with issues that not many people would have the courage to handle. You're open and willing to learn, to educate yourself about what will work best for Elise, and she is successful because of all the love and support you give her.

DENISE: Thank you, I appreciate that. When I set up the meeting, do you think you can attend with me?

Master Clinician Note: If the social worker cannot attend an IEP meeting with the client, they should still encourage them to have a support person with them, if at all possible; someone else who is familiar with the caregiving situation.

SOCIAL WORKER: I won't be able to attend with you, unfortunately, but I absolutely suggest that you bring someone with you to all meetings. I recall that your sister-in-law has helped out a lot. Is she available, or a good friend?

DENISE: My sister-in-law is the best, yeah. She'd be a great support. She knows the questions to ask.

SOCIAL WORKER: Great. We'll come up with the suggestions and strategies, and you and Elise and your sister-in-law can talk and jot down any additional key issues that you think of. Definitely include Elise. It's her education, after all. Will she be part of the meeting with the school?

DENISE: We weren't planning to include her in the actual meeting, no. She wasn't in it last year. We do talk to her about the issues, though.

SOCIAL WORKER: Well, she's at an age now where it might be worthwhile to consider including her. She's in middle school now, and at this age it might be beneficial to her to see how caring people are planning her supports. Plus, it teaches her to self-advocate, and she can offer specific information and suggestions about problems she's having, or environmental issue that are bothering her; lighting, noise, etc.

DENISE: Okay, we'll talk to her about joining us.

SOCIAL WORKER: Great. And you're meeting with her teacher only? Are there any volunteers in the class this year?

DENISE: I'm not sure.

SOCIAL WORKER: You might wanna ask. If there are volunteers, it would be great if they can attend, as well.

DENISE: Okay.

SOCIAL WORKER: And be sure to allow enough time in the meeting to discuss concrete solutions. Accommodations can take a lot of time to work out. It shouldn't be left to the end of the session.

DENISE: I'll try to address them right up front. What suggestions do you have?

SOCIAL WORKER: I have a couple suggestions for the meeting itself, and then some examples of free, simple accommodations that can improve Elise's school experience. These go beyond the stuff on a standard IEP form. You did a plan last year, correct?

DENISE: Yes, we did.

SOCIAL WORKER: And she'll be in the same school?

DENISE: Yes.

SOCIAL WORKER: Okay, good. So there's already a record with the school of an accommodation history.

DENISE: Right. And it really is just frustrating to have to do this every year. I'm always surprised that one teacher can be great and the next is like a blank slate.

SOCIAL WORKER: I find that, as well. Many families have to start over every year with the school, transferring information, as school personnel changes each September. At the same time, the child is growing and changing, too. Elise is growing older, and what worked for her last year might need to be revised this year. Also, the accommodations in last year's plan might not have been implemented, at least not fully. Elise can speak to that if she's in the meeting. So, let's go through a few simple things that I've found have worked for other clients and their children.

Master Clinician Note: Denise is clearly frustrated with the educational process, and this is understandable. At the same time, the social worker is tempering this frustration and laying the groundwork for a more successful IEP meeting by helping Denise remember the reasons why annual meetings are worthwhile even if difficult. For the meeting itself, the counselor makes the following suggestions:

- To spotlight the child's aptitudes and hobbies, bring pictures of the child enjoying these activities and/or examples of things they've done or created (e.g., artwork, crafts).
- Parent should be encouraged to "catch more flies with honey than with vinegar." The parent's frustration with the system as a whole should not be targeted at the individuals on the other side of the table.
- Parent should approach the meeting with a mindset of using statements such as "My child needs…" rather than "I want my child to…" The federal law is for educators to meet the child's needs, not the parent's wishes.

DENISE: I like those ideas, thanks. What accommodations were you thinking of?

Master Clinician Note:
- Example 1: Federal law limits schools in terms of sanctioning children who act out as a result of a disabling condition, such as an FASD. If the child is acting out, a Behavioral Modification Plan should be considered instead.

SOCIAL WORKER:	This first example is really important because I see so many kids with FASD who get into trouble when they're revved up. As a parent, you probably see this often with Elise, and you know her triggers, but educators won't. I worked with a middle-school-aged child, a boy, and his caregiver. The boy was acting out, hitting the bus driver. The school threatened to get the police involved, and the boy was kicked off the bus. I suggested that he be given time at end of each day to relax. It turned out that one of his favorite places was the library, because he could listen to music, so he ended up being able to use last period to go there and sit with headphones on, and we arranged with the librarian to keep an eye on him and monitor the time for him. We called it his "chill zone." After that, he was always cool for the bus ride home.
DENISE:	I like that. Elise gets antsy very easily, especially with headphones on, but she'll sit still to read and draw. The library might work.

Master Clinician Note:
- Example 2: Watch for cases when bad behavior is a result of modeling other children with behavioral issues.

SOCIAL WORKER:	Another student I worked with, a girl, was getting out of control during the day. She sat in the front row of her classroom, but the teachers and classroom volunteers still reported that even on a good day she was fidgety, and on bad ones she was practically climbing the walls. I explained that sitting in the front row typically helps children focus, but a child with an FASD can also get distracted by kids nearby. In the girl's class, the rest of the kids in the front row were working on behavioral issues, including ADHD. In this case, the girl was modeling the behavior of these classmates in an effort to make friends. I suggested we move the girl next to a model student who could maybe be her buddy or mentor, and that worked well.
DENISE:	That could prove useful, as well. Elise does tend to model other children's behavior.

Master Clinician Note:
- Example 3: Work with the educational staff to think "outside the box" when it comes to accommodations.

SOCIAL WORKER:	Educators are generally working from a menu of options when it comes to accommodations; such-and-such is suggested based on what the child's condition is. Now, this menu is fairly long, as you know, but it's still an Individualized Education Plan. It should still be geared to Elise's specific needs. Don't be afraid to suggest ideas that you've found work for her, even if they aren't "on the form." Think about what you've done with her in other environments, like at church or in other social activities.
DENISE:	Okay. Thanks for your suggestions.
SOCIAL WORKER:	You're welcome. Please call me after the meeting and let me know how it goes.
DENISE:	I will, thank you.

Refer to Part 1, Chapter 2 for additional guidance on educational accommodations for individuals with an FASD who are still in school.

Part 2: Administrator's Guide to Implementing FASD Prevention and Intervention

Introduction

This Treatment Improvement Protocol (TIP) is designed to assist not only substance abuse treatment and mental health counselors in providing FASD-informed services, but also the clinical supervisors and administrators who support the work of these professionals. The need for a TIP that addresses FASD prevention and intervention for these settings is clear:

- Individuals with an FASD experience higher rates of substance abuse and mental health issues than the general population (Streissguth et al., 1996; Streissguth & O'Malley, 2000; Astley, 2010). In addition, individuals with an FASD exhibit higher rates of life problems commonly encountered in substance abuse and mental health treatment populations, including higher risk of suicide (Huggins et al., 2008), exposure to multiple traumas throughout the lifespan (Henry, Sloane, & Black-Pond, 2007; Greenbaum et al., 2009), homelessness (Fryer, McGee, Matt, Riley, & Mattson, 2007), and increased interaction with the criminal justice system (Streissguth et al., 1996).

- According to the 2009 *National Survey on Drug Use and Health* (NSDUH), 17.1 percent of women age 18 or over in the U.S. received mental health treatment or counseling in 2009, compared to only 9.2 of men in the same age group (Center for Behavioral Health Statistics and Quality [CBHSQ], 2010), while the *Treatment Episode Data Set* (TEDS) indicates that 33.0 percent of admissions to substance abuse treatment facilities in 2011 were female, more than half of whom (50.5 percent) indicated alcohol as a primary, secondary, or tertiary substance of abuse (CBHSQ, 2013). In addition, an in-depth study of 80 birth mothers of children with FAS revealed that 97 percent had from 1 to 9 mental disorders, and the subset that successfully achieved abstinence was significantly more likely to have received treatment for their mental disorders than the subset who did not achieve abstinence (Astley et al., 2000b).

Thus, these settings are 1) likely to see a high prevalence of individuals with an FASD (and/or their parents/caregivers), and 2) provide an ideal environment for conducting interventions with women of childbearing age to prevent additional incidences of FASD.

The methods and techniques presented in this TIP are appropriate for clients in all stages of recovery and treatment. However, this TIP is not meant to create a 'one-stop shop' for FASD-informed services. An FASD is not a simple category that can be addressed with a simple, categorical response; the disorders in this spectrum cannot be cured, and clients with an FASD need specialized treatment from a variety of healthcare professionals to function at their maximum potential. At the same time, when treating a substance abuse or mental health issue with a client, the counselors' role is to:

1. Be able to recognize when a client is exhibiting a co-occurring issue (such as an FASD) that can impede treatment success;

2. Address how the physical, cognitive, and behavioral manifestations of that issue interact with treatment; and

3. Develop a collaborative treatment relationship with the other healthcare and social service professionals who do—or potentially can—provide assistance to the client to maximize that person's potential for success, both in and outside treatment.

Like any other co-occurring issue in treatment—trauma, homelessness, etc.—addressing FASD is a fundamental step toward helping the *whole* person and ensuring that he or she does not encounter treatment barriers.

Note: This Implementation Guide follows two tracks; FASD prevention, and FASD intervention. This is because this TIP promotes 1) the screening of all women of childbearing age (whether pregnant or not) in all behavioral health settings for alcohol consumption, to help prevent future incidences of FASD [FASD prevention], and 2) the development of staff skills in recognizing individuals who have or may have an FASD, to be able to more effectively tailor treatment to their needs [FASD intervention]. In Part 1 of this TIP, these topics are treated separately. In the Implementation Guide, they are discussed together, since they each represent organizational change and the core processes involved in making such changes within a program overlap significantly.

1   The Administrative Response to FASD in Behavioral Health Settings

Why SAMHSA Created an Implementation Guide as Part of This TIP

Part 1 of *Addressing Fetal Alcohol Spectrum Disorders (FASD)* provides the tools your clinicians need to begin addressing FASD prevention and intervention with clients. However, an extensive literature review suggests that without specific attention to implementation issues, these tools are likely to go unused or to be used ineffectively (Fixsen, Naoom, Blase, Friedman, & Wallace, 2005). This Implementation Guide will help you ensure that the ideas in Part 1 are put into practice in your program or agency in a way that creates value, both for your agency and your clients. Implementation will require the active support of executive administration and the expertise of clinical supervisors.

Much of the guidance provided in this Implementation Guide will be familiar to readers of TIP 48, *Managing Depressive Symptoms in Substance Abuse Clients During Early Recovery* (Center for Substance Abuse Treatment [CSAT], 2008). TIP 48 provides a useful framework for approaching organizational change, and a significant portion of that framework is reiterated here, but with some important modifications and "tweaks" that are essential to providing FASD-informed services. Another useful resource is SAMHSA's Technical Assistance Publication (TAP) 31, *Implementing Change in Substance Abuse Treatment Programs* (CSAT, 2009).

Why Address FASD Prevention and Intervention?

The value of screening women of childbearing age in behavioral health settings is clear-cut. For any woman who is or may become pregnant, protecting the health of that pregnancy (or potential pregnancy) is a fundamental health issue for the woman herself. Added to this, alcohol consumption questions are built into most forms of health screening, making exploration of this issue a professional commitment. If pregnant women are part of your client base, ignoring this issue means not fully serving the client.

The case for providing services tailored to individuals who have or may have an FASD may not be as simple, but is equally compelling. The historical perception that an FASD represents permanent brain damage, and thus these people cannot be helped in a mental health or substance abuse treatment setting is only half true: Yes, an FASD *does* represent permanent brain damage; no, it *does not* mean that these people cannot be helped, any more than being homeless or involved with the criminal justice system means an individual cannot be helped in these settings.

An FASD is a co-occurring disorder, and needs to be approached from that perspective. Families are seeking this expertise, even if they don't yet know to call it 'FASD,' and clients in need of FASD-informed services will continue to appear in your settings. There is an active movement in the mental health field toward a recovery focus and a strengths-based focus, toward meeting clients "where they are." This movement is growing in the substance abuse treatment field, as well, as are the trauma-informed and family-centered care movements. An individual who has or may have an FASD fits perfectly into any of these paradigms. Individuals with an FASD *do* want to recover, whether in substance abuse or mental health treatment; they *do* have strengths; they *do* experience trauma (at higher rates than the general population); they *do* have families; and, as with any other client, they *are* capable of responding positively when treatment is tailored to their unique needs.

The Effects of FASD on Recovery

At the same time, it cannot be ignored that clients with an FASD are likely to experience challenges to successful treatment above and beyond those experienced by clients who do not have one of these disorders. The client with an FASD may have difficulty in any or all of the following areas:

- Remembering program rules or following multiple instructions.
- Remembering and keeping appointments.
- Making appropriate decisions by themselves about treatment needs and goals.
- Appropriately interpreting social cues from treatment professionals or other clients.
- Attending (and not disrupting) group activities.
- For those accessing substance abuse treatment, staying substance-free after treatment.
- Interpreting or understanding complex meanings of language or information.

The combination of some or all of these factors may lead a counselor to assume that an individual with an FASD is resistant to treatment (and this assumption is often made). It is essential that staff be able to discriminate between a symptom of an FASD and actual treatment resistance. Clients with an FASD may fully intend to be compliant with treatment and want to do well in recovery, but lack the skills and understanding from the provider to help them meet their unique challenges while participating in a recovery program.

The Benefits to Your Program of Addressing FASD Prevention and Intervention

A growing body of evidence is demonstrating that interventions with individuals with an FASD can be effective, that this population can and does succeed in treatment when approaches are properly modified, and that these modifications can lead to reduced stress on family/caregivers as well as providers (Bertrand, 2009). Moreover, in a study of 1,400 patients with prenatal alcohol exposure, Astley (2010) found that 9.3 percent presented with no central nervous system (CNS) dysfunction, despite alcohol exposure levels as high as the 10 percent that did receive a diagnosis of FAS. The one factor that significantly differentiated the children with no CNS dysfunction (no evidence of learning or behavior problems) from those with full FAS was a stable, nurturing home environment *with intervention services.*

Addressing FASD also has the potential to enhance the treatment experience for both the individual with an FASD and those around him or her, increase retention, lead to improved outcomes, reduce the probability of relapse, increase engagement rates in aftercare services (alternately referred to as recovery support services), and reduce overall societal costs. In addition to the benefits for the client, addressing FASD as part of your program can potentially lead to increased clinical competence of your staff, an increase in appropriate referrals, increased staff retention, higher levels of staff satisfaction, reduced risk of burnout, and reduced turnover.

Addressing co-occurring disorders is also a key priority for the federal government, state governments, insurance companies, credentialing boards, and accrediting organizations. By starting now to address FASD, you will be better positioned to compete in the future treatment marketplace. Ideally, your agency can become part of the larger community of research practitioners who seek the best ways to help clients more quickly experience a higher quality of recovery. By joining with other agencies in your network, you can coordinate treatment practices and perhaps collaboratively obtain research grants. Many effective treatment practices in both the substance abuse and mental health fields, as in the field of approaches to FASD, are not yet validated through research because agencies do not fully realize the value to the greater treatment community of their unique approaches. However, the body of research around FASD is growing rapidly, and addressing FASD now positions your agency at the front end of an emerging skill area.

Most importantly, addressing FASD provides another possible route to success with a client. Individuals with an FASD are a largely hidden population, yet one that is at an increased risk of presenting in your treatment setting. For every client that did not return for additional appointments, or seemed noncompliant or resistant with no clear explanation of why, or just didn't seem to 'get it,' **a knowledge of FASD on the part of your staff can be the one additional clue that solves that puzzle and enables success for both the client and the program**.

Thinking About Organizational Change

If you have decided to implement some or all of the recommendations in *Addressing Fetal Alcohol Spectrum Disorders (FASD), Part 1*, you, your staff, your clients, and the other agencies and organizations with which you interact may require the development of new treatment protocols and policies, as well as new clinical knowledge, attitudes, and skills. These changes can be rewarding and/or frustrating. Any change in services or approaches to clients will call for a significant change in organizational culture, but will be beneficial to client well-being in the long run.

The box "Key Elements of Assessment and Planning" summarizes the key elements of organizational assessment and planning for change, topics that are discussed in greater detail in Chapter 2 of this Guide.

Key Elements of Assessment and Planning

The following five areas are critical to organizational assessment and change planning.

Current status of the organization relative to targeted change goals	Current practices, staff and administrator competencies, policies and procedures, facilities, etc., will need to be evaluated. These are similar to client assessments that determine the nature and scope of a client's issues and challenges as well as their strengths and assets.
Past experiences with change initiatives	Just as a bad experience in a previous treatment program may color a client's perception of a new program, old experiences with organizational change may affect attitudes toward new efforts. A thorough review of organizational history of change is critical to planning new organizational change.
Ongoing assessment	As in treatment, assessment is not a one-time activity, but rather an ongoing process that includes regular feedback and adjustment of your plans for organizational change and your approaches to facilitating change.
Stakeholders of all kinds	Involve as many clients, stakeholders, and community resources as possible (e.g., boards, staff, funders, clients, community representatives, 12-Step groups). These groups function best when they feel involved, and have a key role in determining how to make the recommended changes work best in daily practice (particularly staff). In addition, the plan should speak to what these groups want and what motivates them for the change: If your staff desires professional growth opportunities, change aimed at providing FASD-informed services can be linked to expanding staff capabilities. Similarly, your board's concern with expansion might be tied to the need for increased capacity if the organization is to address FASD among clients.
Clinical supervision	No stakeholder is more important than the clinical supervisor commissioned to implement the clinical mission and vision of the administrators. This individual's challenge is to help clinicians maintain a high level of best practices, to oversee the application of these practices, and to conduct process and program evaluation for quality control. Supervision should be more instructive and less crisis-driven—proactive rather than reactive—by using such strategies and resources as: • Innovative methods including live, in-session supervision, role-playing, taping, and group and peer supervision; • Regularly scheduled, ongoing clinical supervision; • Checklists and fidelity scales; • Quality skills training; and • Counselor mentoring.

An excellent resource for organizational assessment for change is the Program Change Model discussed by Lehman, Greener, & Simpson (2002; **http://forces4quality.org/sites/default/files/Tool2.1Lehman Assessing Agency Readiness for change. pdf**), and its accompanying survey, Organizational Readiness for Change (**http://www.ibr.tcu.edu/pubs/datacoll/Forms/orc-s. pdf**). Their model addresses strategies and tools for assessing institutional and personal readiness and outlines the stages of the transfer process.

Ultimately, the application of these elements may suggest that the best decision is to delay attempting a change and focus instead on organizational climate and readiness. Introducing organizational change before the groundwork has been laid—much like introducing change to a client when they are not at the right stage of readiness—can hinder later change opportunities. However, if you decide to move forward with a change plan, the box "Key Principles of Implementation" provides information on implementation.

Key Principles of Implementation

Principles for implementing the change plan are directly analogous to principles of treatment and recovery in that both are achieved in steps, making it a process rather than an outcome. The following principles of managing change are directly adapted from principles of care that are relevant to providing effective FASD-informed services.

There is no single model or approach to providing FASD-informed services, or for implementing a program of organizational change.	A preconception about how change should occur or inflexibility during the change process is likely to be counterproductive to meeting a client's treatment goals or a program's change goals. Constant vigilance and course corrections will be needed, and should be made in consultation with the same stakeholders who developed the original change plan. Periodic focus groups or meetings with staff, clients, and administration provide excellent opportunities for feedback and give all those involved a voice in the process.
A belief in your organization's ability to accomplish the change plan is fundamental.	As with counselors, an administrator's belief that change can happen (and the ability to communicate that belief) is a central component of the change process.
The change program for an organization should be individualized to accommodate the specific needs, goals, culture, and readiness-for-change of that organization.	Like any treatment plan for an individual who has or may have an FASD, it is critical to adapt and 'personalize' the plan to fit specific organizational needs and culture.
It's about maintenance.	After implementing an organizational change plan, maintenance of the changes is essential, particularly in the first year or two. Flexibility around incorporating staff and client recommendations is critical to buy-in of the change. Newly learned practices and procedures are fragile and will tend to drift. In addition, organizational change almost always brings about some degree of personnel change, which requires up-front planning for the selection and integration of new employees. Equally important, unforeseen barriers may arise.

Regular supervision and training boosters are the best insurance that behavior change will last over time. Even when the changes are institutionalized, however, a commitment to continuous quality improvement will help ensure your program's ability to respond to ongoing changes in the needs of your client population and community. |

The Challenges of Implementation

Any approach to organizational change should assume that resistance may challenge the process. Specific to FASD, some of the usual forms of staff resistance you may encounter are included below, along with suggested responses that may help staff members to see the change process in a more positive light.

It is also useful to remember that resistance can be valuable to a change effort, as it often springs from legitimate needs and/or concerns. By rolling with resistance, you can identify aspects of your change plan that warrant revisiting or revising.

At the same time, failure to implement new clinical practices often has little to do with resistance to change on the part of staff.

> *Addressing resistance directly will lessen the likelihood that opposition will spread and influence others.*
> - ATTC *Change Book*, 2nd Edition, p. 27

Failure to implement can be a result of issues such as inadequate modeling from administration, lack of follow-through, inadequate training, and many others. Even the best

Resistance	Response
I haven't learned this. When will I have time to do the training?	All changes in programming require new learning, and FASD will be no exception. However, new learning means new and expanded skill sets, which can positively impact professional development and advancement. I will work with you to adjust your caseload so that the training is possible.
How can I tell a pregnant mother not to drink? Her OBGYN/doctor says it's okay.	It is true that some doctors still suggest that the occasional drink is okay. However, the SAMHSA FASD Center for Excellence Web site (**www.fasdcenter. samhsa.gov**) contains evidence-based materials that we can use to communicate the "no safe level" message with clients.
The mother is choosing to harm her baby.	Many women are unaware of the risk of alcohol consumption during pregnancy (see previous statement). In addition, half of all U.S. pregnancies are unplanned, so the mother may not realize the potential harm she's doing. Lastly, if the mother has a problem with alcohol, her 'choice' to drink is no more a choice than it is for any other individual in substance abuse treatment.
How do I adjust this cognitive abstract program for someone who does not have the ability to understand abstract concepts?	You don't have to abandon the techniques you generally use. The FASD training will show you how to modify treatment for these individuals within the framework of your usual treatment approaches.
Why am I making exceptions for this client and not for others? This will require ongoing modification of the treatment plan.	It is better to see modifications to the treatment plan as tailoring rather than 'making exceptions,' as tailoring and ongoing modification are a necessary part of meeting clients where they are.

counselors and administrators are highly constrained by the contexts in which they work. Accordingly, implementation success requires administrators to 1) be proactive in making the new practice fit the context, and 2) create an organizational climate that encourages and supports implementation.

These two tasks are intertwining: Fitting new practices to your context requires a thorough review of your agency's current operations. Such self-examination, in turn, helps create an organizational climate of openness to new ideas and experimentation. Before implementation begins, it is important to create positive expectations among staff. Investing the time to educate staff, express support for the specific implementations, and explore potential barriers and concerns with staff can go a long way toward creating an environment of operational transparency and ensuring staff acceptance of change, especially in the early stages.

Often, the executive staff faces more immediate resistance or ambivalence because the initial groundwork was not done. Moreover, administrators have likely considered the change ideas for some time and expect staff to be at a similar level of enthusiasm and commitment to the proposal. Change is easier to make when those involved:

- Understand why the change is needed and the benefits they will realize;

- See how the new ways will integrate into and honor what has been done previously; and

- Are given motivation strategies for providing ideas and offers of assistance in implementation.

Maximizing the Fit

For a clinical innovation to take hold, it must fit with:

(1) Key characteristics of your target population and community (e.g., values, expectations);

(2) The skills, licensures, certifications, and team structures of your staff;

(3) Your program or agency's facilities and resources;

(4) Your policies and practices;

(5) Local, state, and federal regulations;

(6) Available interagency networks (e.g., needed outside resources, memoranda of understanding); and

(7) Your reimbursement procedures.

Certain kinds of mismatches will impede change. For example, no one would expect successful implementation of an innovation when staff lacks the skills to perform it. However, something as seemingly trivial as a lack of appropriate space or needed audiovisual equipment can also stall an innovation. As with many endeavors, the details are critical.

It is likely that adjustments will be needed both in your agency or program's context and in the ways that the recommendations presented in Part 1 are implemented. Part 2, Chapter 2 of this TIP provides procedures, checklists, and other tools for assessing the fit between the recommendations provided in Part 1 and your program or agency's current context, procedures, and so on. Useful though these materials are, your ultimate success in "maximizing the fit" will depend on creativity, problem-solving skills, and determination and patience in applying them.

The Stages of Organizational Change

Change in a program, just like change for a client, occurs in stages. In the early stages of implementing the recommendations in Part 1, organizations will profit from a climate that promotes:

- A willingness to take risks and try unconventional approaches;

- A willingness to tolerate some ambiguity as the fit between new practices and context evolves;

- An ability to recognize false starts and to abandon approaches that are not working;
- Transparency and inclusion when pursuing change; and
- Appreciation and reward for ideas and implementation.

As noted earlier, the later stages of implementation will be facilitated by:
- A commitment to continuous quality improvement;
- The development of structures that support and reinforce the change (e.g., standardized training for new staff, and continuing education and supervision for all staff);
- Expressions of organizational pride in accomplishment; and
- Institutionalization (in which new practices become everyday practices).

The Role of the Administrator in Introducing and Supporting New Clinical Practices

Chapter 2 of this Implementation Guide presents the tasks you will need to accomplish to implement the changes elaborated in Part 1. Important as these tasks are, successful implementation will ultimately depend on the leadership you provide as they are carried out. The box, "Key Elements of Leadership," provides a summary and leads directly into the more detailed discussions of Chapter 2 of this Implementation Guide.

Key Elements of Leadership

Commitment	If you and your administrative colleagues are not fully committed to making your agency's services more FASD-informed, meaningful change is unlikely to occur. In many ways, attempting change without the commitment of organizational leaders can be worse than no attempt to change at all. Staff will eventually "figure it out" if leaders are only giving lip-service to a new idea. This perception will undermine the current attempts at innovation and may lead to a staff that is reluctant to try new ideas.
Vision	Leadership means having a vision of how the organization will change. This vision should include explicit goals and a clear statement of how conflicts with other organizational goals will be resolved. However, a vision is more than a list of goals. It is a picture of how the organization will look when change has been accomplished—a picture you must paint with words. Developing this vision and the means to communicate it throughout an agency requires effort.
Knowledge	Leadership should include skilled and competent clinicians trained in mental health and/or substance abuse treatment who can direct and supervise services for clients with FASD-related issues. These clinicians should know and appreciate the specific roles that can be played by speech-language pathologists, occupational therapists, licensed social workers, psychologists, physicians, and other behavioral health professionals that are part of a comprehensive network of care for individuals who have or may have an FASD. They should also have an appreciation for the role that FASD can play in interfering with treatment.

Inspiration	Inspirational leaders communicate confidence in the organization's ability to change, enthusiasm and optimism about the change process, and an unwillingness to accept failure. This must be communicated to all stakeholders including current and potential clients, funders, board members, staff, community leaders, community 12-Step participants and programs, and sister agencies. Inspiration not only is a process of oral and written communication, but also involves modeling the attitudes and values you want staff and other stakeholders to adopt. Inspiration also involves getting your hands "dirty;" struggling alongside staff in the day-to-day tasks of making new ideas work.
Appraisal	Finally, leadership means an ongoing and honest appraisal of progress. As noted above and discussed further in Chapter 2, implementing the recommendations from Part 1 of this TIP will require ongoing assessments of progress, including regular formative evaluation of process and outcomes. Periodic reports on how the organization is doing can and should be developed from the assessments and evaluations. These reports should be shared with staff, as should plans for corrective action (when needed). The most effective leaders frame both good and bad news in a positive light; e.g., emphasizing the learning value of challenges and setbacks and reminding staff that it is the organization as a whole, rather than any individual, that is responsible for making change happen. This means that "we still have room to improve" is preferable to "you still have room to improve."

2 Building an FASD Prevention- and Intervention-Capable Agency

Introduction

The resources presented in this chapter have been organized into those related to organizational assessment and those related to planning and implementing organizational change. The change process in your agency or program will require creative and thoughtful adaptation and application of these resources to your specific circumstances. They should be viewed as points of departure only. You should revise or otherwise modify the materials as needed for your organization.

You may also wish to consult with colleagues who have managed organizational change in organizations similar to yours. At this point in the development of implementation strategies for human services, many excellent ideas are still to be found outside the published literature. Your colleagues may have insights or ideas that are equal to or more applicable than those presented in this Implementation Guide.

> The *Change* Book, produced by the Addiction Technology Transfer Center (ATTC) Network, provides the basis for the organizational change process presented in TIP 48 and in this TIP. The page numbers referenced in this chapter refer to the Second Edition, 2010, which can be downloaded for free from the ATTC Network (**www.attcnetwork.org**) in English or Spanish (**http://www.attcnetwork.org/explore/priorityareas/techtrans/tools/changebook.asp**).
>
> Additionally, you may wish to consult *Implementation Research: A Synthesis of the Literature* (Fixsen et al., 2005; **http://cfs.cbcs.usf.edu/_docs/publications/NIRN_Monograph_Full.pdf**). This monograph provides a valuable summary of the scientific basis for various implementation practices.
>
> Another resource is SAMHSA's TAP 31, *Implementing Change in Substance Abuse Treatment Programs* (CSAT, 2009).

Assessment and Planning Before Implementation

How Do You Decide Whether to Implement a Policy for Addressing FASD?

To determine whether it makes sense for your agency to implement the recommendations made in Part 1 of this TIP, refer to Figure 2.1.

How Do You Identify the Issue or Need?

The How-To components on the following pages provide ways to operationalize the steps presented in Figure 2.1.

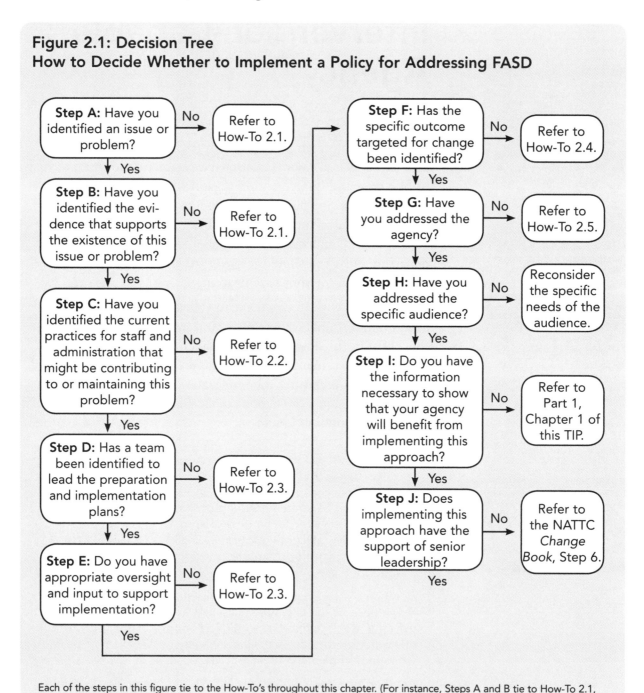

Figure 2.1: Decision Tree
How to Decide Whether to Implement a Policy for Addressing FASD

Step A: Have you identified an issue or problem? — No → Refer to How-To 2.1. / Yes ↓

Step B: Have you identified the evidence that supports the existence of this issue or problem? — No → Refer to How-To 2.1. / Yes ↓

Step C: Have you identified the current practices for staff and administration that might be contributing to or maintaining this problem? — No → Refer to How-To 2.2. / Yes ↓

Step D: Has a team been identified to lead the preparation and implementation plans? — No → Refer to How-To 2.3. / Yes ↓

Step E: Do you have appropriate oversight and input to support implementation? — No → Refer to How-To 2.3. / Yes →

Step F: Has the specific outcome targeted for change been identified? — No → Refer to How-To 2.4. / Yes ↓

Step G: Have you addressed the agency? — No → Refer to How-To 2.5. / Yes ↓

Step H: Have you addressed the specific audience? — No → Reconsider the specific needs of the audience. / Yes ↓

Step I: Do you have the information necessary to show that your agency will benefit from implementing this approach? — No → Refer to Part 1, Chapter 1 of this TIP. / Yes ↓

Step J: Does implementing this approach have the support of senior leadership? — No → Refer to the NATTC *Change Book*, Step 6. / Yes

Each of the steps in this figure tie to the How-To's throughout this chapter. (For instance, Steps A and B tie to How-To 2.1, below.)

How-To 2.1: How to Identify the Issue or Need (Figure 2.1, Steps A and B)

Research suggests that the following issues or problems may be relevant to your agency's treatment outcomes. Think about the three levels where change can occur (i.e., program/organizational, practitioner/counselor, and client/patient) when considering the following steps. Also, begin thinking about the part of the agency where you may want to implement changes first (for more information, see also the section *How Do You Decide Where To Start?* later in this chapter).

1. Individuals with an FASD are at higher risk for substance abuse and mental health issues. Determine whether clients who have or may have an FASD are being identified and effectively treated in your agency (see How-To 2.2).

2. People who present with FASD symptoms may take longer and/or require different guidelines and rules to benefit from treatment. Determine whether this is an issue for your agency. Does your program offer the option of longer treatment stays to clients who may have an FASD? Does it offer alternatives to standard policies (e.g., zero tolerance rules) for such clients? If not, how is this need addressed? What practices may need to be changed?

3. Unrecognized symptoms of an FASD result in poorer substance abuse treatment outcomes. Determine whether a goal for your agency is to improve retention rates of clients with an FASD. Determine whether a goal for your agency is to more effectively reduce the number of barriers experienced by these clients.

One aspect of the identification process is to assess the organizational capability of the agency to implement or augment a program for services to clients with an FASD.

How Do You Assess the Capacity of the Agency to Provide FASD Prevention and Intervention?

Individuals with an FASD may see themselves as not fitting in, may be hostile or act out, and may struggle with multiple directions and tasks. Is this addressed in your treatment program? For example, are people failing to make appointments with no clear explanation of why? Speaking at the wrong time during group sessions? Or consistently completing only a portion of the treatment tasks they're given? In terms of prevention, is your program serving pregnant women and/or women of childbearing age? Are these women being asked about their alcohol consumption? Are they being made aware of the risk of FASD? Assess the current capacity of your agency

How-To 2.2: How To Assess Current Capacity to Address FASD (Figure 2.1, Step C)

For each program setting consider the following questions:

1. Has a needs assessment been done to determine the needs of both the clients and the agency?

2. If FASD prevention and intervention have been identified as areas of need, are they adequately addressed in treatment plans?

3. Have key personnel looked into the literature on FASD intervention methods? Are appropriate interventions planned to treat signs of an FASD?

4. Are the FASD prevention and intervention methods already in use (if any) effective with the program's clientele?

5. Are the treatment teams interdisciplinary (e.g., psychiatrist, nurse, licensed master's level clinicians, certified counselors, clinicians, and counselors in training)? If not, your agency can still address FASD through interagency collaboration.

6. Does the supervisory staff have the knowledge, skills, and attitudes necessary to supervise or coach the line staff in addressing FASD?

7. Does the program have referral or consultation relationships with the necessary agencies and professionals (e.g., trained and licensed physicians, physical therapists, occupational therapists, neuropsychologists and speech language pathologists, prenatal care, FASD evaluation/diagnosis teams or agencies)?

Note: For more information on assessing capacity and capabilities, see Sample Policies 1–6 and Checklists 1–4.

or program to deliver FASD prevention and intervention (see How-To 2.2).

How Do You Organize a Team to Address the Problem?

Once you have identified an issue or problem, you need to create a workgroup to address the problem (see How-To 2.3).

How Do You Identify a Specific Outcome to Target for Change?

Once you've organized a workgroup to address the problem, you need to identify a specific outcome to be targeted for change (see How-To 2.4).

How Do You Decide Where to Start?

Once you've identified a specific outcome or outcomes to target for change, you will want the workgroup to assess the agency and the staff (both frontline and supervisory) to be targeted by the implementation. You will have

How-To 2.3: How to Organize a Team to Address the Problem (Figure 2.1, Steps D and E)

1. Identify one person to lead the effort. Many programs that have successfully implemented programming for individuals with an FASD were able to do so because there was one committed, passionate person willing to lead the effort, a 'champion.' This person must have the backing of senior administration and the respect of direct treatment staff.

2. Obtain the commitment of the Chief Executive Officer of the agency to articulate the vision for implementation throughout the agency and with all stakeholders (including clients).

3. Convene an implementation workgroup consisting of key leaders from different stakeholder groups; client leaders, family leaders, team leaders, clinical leaders, and program and administrative leaders. Some stakeholders will serve as ongoing members of the workgroup, while information from others may be solicited through focus groups. If your program has a residential or inpatient component, be sure to include an individual from the night staff (i.e., aide, tech, night nurse). This staff will actually have more conversations with patients than most clinical staff and are in a position to support this program through their observations and understanding.

4. Identify the program oversight committee to which the work group will report. For example, if your agency has a quality improvement committee, the work group may report its findings, recommendations, strategic plans, and modifications to that committee. This is one way to initiate and sustain implementation.

How-To 2.4: How to Identify a Specific Outcome to Target for Change (Figure 2.1, Step F)

1. Begin with the issue or problem identified in Step A of Figure 2.1, and determine a specific variable that can be measured that is directly related to improving the management of FASD. For example, in terms of prevention, the variable may be to "Add FASD awareness as an element of client education with all female clients of childbearing age, whether pregnant or not." In terms of intervention, the variable may be to "Increase staff ability to identify signs of a client who may have an FASD."

   - Identify a way to measure "identify signs of a client who may have an FASD." For example, there is a list of common physical and behavioral manifestations of FASD in Part 1, Chapter 2 of this TIP, and repeated later this chapter, that can be used as a checklist.

   - Identify a way to measure "client education with all female clients of childbearing age, whether pregnant or not." For example, tracking instances of client education on the topic of alcohol-exposed pregnancies, and/or rates of abstention among pregnant clients.

2. Measure a baseline prior to implementing FASD prevention or intervention. For example, determine how many women of childbearing age you see at your agency in a given month. In terms of intervention, review cases of client noncompliance, particularly where no specific cause of the noncompliance is known. Did these clients forget appointments? Not follow directions? Act out? Exhibit family instability and/or have a history of multiple foster care placements? These can become cues for identifying case of possible FASD in the future.

3. Identify which outcome you are most interested in measuring to determine whether implementing FASD prevention or intervention is working. For example:

   - **Intervention**
     - Number of staff trained in FASD intervention methods
     - Rates of identifying potential cases of an FASD
     - Rates of conducting FASD evaluations/assessments
     - Rates of finding/filling FASD assessment slots
     - Diagnoses achieved
     - Follow-up/Aftercare: Family stability over time
     - Multiple foster placements reduced
   - **Prevention**
     - Number of staff trained in FASD prevention
     - Implementation of alcohol screening with all women of childbearing age, whether pregnant or not
     - Treatment planning adaptation based on this screening
     - Achieving abstinence/reduction of at-risk drinking
     - Use of effective contraception by the client

an easier time implementing your plan if you start with a small program where staff members already work well with one another and believe in the new techniques. Staff members on closely knit teams work with one another's strengths and will have an easier time assigning responsibilities when it comes time to implement the practice. Alternatively, you may choose a small, core group of staff members who are ready to try new techniques and are prepared to be part of an implementation process (i.e., target early adopters across programs). These will be the first staff members trained and coached in using these techniques. Other advantages to starting small include the following:

1. It is easier to track the success of the implementation.

2. It is easier to identify and make any modifications to the techniques that may be necessary to accommodate the agency's clientele.

3. The core group members will talk about the success they are having with the techniques and get other staff interested in learning and using the techniques.

For more information on assessing your agency's readiness for implementation, see How-To 2.5.

How-To 2.5: How to Assess the Agency's Organizational Readiness for Implementation (Figure 2.1, Step G)

1. The committee assesses the agency's organizational readiness by first determining whether implementing practices to improve the management of FASD in the agency's clientele are consistent with the agency's mission statement. (See also the section *Modifying Existing Policies*, this chapter).

2. The committee determines the obstacles to implementation:
   a. Rate of staff turnover in the agency, including average longevity of clinical and support staff.
   b. Inadequate funding for training, technical assistance, and outcome measurement.
   c. Policies and procedures that would have to be changed (see Sample Policies 1–6, this chapter).
   d. Agency facilities and resources.
   e. Federal, state, and local regulations that affect the decision to implement FASD prevention and intervention (see *Addressing Relevant Regulations*, this chapter).

3. The committee determines the opportunities created by implementing FASD prevention or intervention:
   a. Increased funding.
   b. Increased collaboration with other agencies.
   c. Improved community relations and marketing opportunities.

4. The committee determines the organization's stage of change (see also the ATTC's Change Book, p. 29).

5. The committee determines where the resources will come from to provide support for the change initiative (Change Book, p. 29).

6. The committee determines what adoption of this change will mean at all levels of the organization and what the benefits are for administrators, supervisors, and counselors (Change Book, p. 29).

7. The committee determines what is already happening that might lay the foundation for the desired change (Change Book, p. 29). For example, you may already have an FASD 'champion' on your staff.

Addressing Policies and Procedures

Although varying in format and structure as a result of regulatory and organizational diversity, policies and procedures serve as the foundation of organizational practice. Planning and implementing a new program component almost always impacts existing policies and procedures, but those same policies and procedures constitute one of the most common and effective mechanisms for institutionalizing organizational practices. As such, they will need to be reviewed and adapted to be sure they are in conformance with the new program.

Modifying Existing Policies

In addition to adopting policies on addressing FASD, provider agencies might consider modifying other policies and program descriptions to provide continuity of care for (1) women who are or may become pregnant who screen positive for at-risk drinking, and (2) individuals who have or may have an FASD.

For example, each program will develop its own approach to screening and monitoring for FASD based on (a) the characteristics of its clientele; (b) its resources, especially its staff training and background; (c) legal and reimbursement considerations; and (d) other factors unique to your agency (e.g., specific arrangements worked out with referral resources or consultants, participation in clinical trials, or other external influences). Your professional input into developing the necessary policies and procedures is essential, and at a minimum there should be a protocol that stipulates:

- What standard questions a client is asked, when they are asked (by interview and/or self-report mechanisms), and when they should be repeated (especially what observations or events might trigger a

fuller evaluation for an FASD)—**These elements of the protocol should use published, reliable tools as discussed in Part 1 and the Literature Review for this TIP** (Appendix C, *Public and Professional Resources on FASD*, contains useful links to sites where tools can be accessed);

- Who can ask these questions and what training is provided or needed regarding the questions and the overall process, procedures, and policies;

- Exactly how scoring or assessment of the clients' responses will be done, including exact guidelines for the follow-up triggered by various responses;

- Where these policies and procedures fit within the agency's policies and procedures and what chain of command and communication exist;

- How long AEP screening and prevention and/or treatment modification for FASD intervention will typically take, which will help you calculate how many interventions one staff member can realistically accomplish per day, anticipate staffing requirements for the project, and project potential income (consult with your administration and billing department—billing for both Medicaid and private insurance may require an intervention of at least 15 minutes' duration);

- How personnel will obtain necessary training, forms, or materials;

- How FASD-informed prevention and/or intervention will be introduced to the client (it might be helpful to have introductory statements worked out and written down in advance, and available to all staff); and

- How FASD prevention and/or intervention will be documented, whether as written or electronic medical record documentation.

This section provides six samples of critical policies and procedures related to addressing FASD prevention and intervention within substance abuse treatment and mental health agencies. In each topic area, a policy statement and set of procedures related to the topic are presented. These sample policies can be used as presented, combined into one or more comprehensive policies, or integrated into the organization's existing policies. Each policy is divided into an example of a policy statement and a set of procedures, as the language will differ depending on whether an agency is revising policies to incorporate FASD intervention or FASD prevention.

Sample Policy 1a

Topic: Clinical staff training and competency [FASD intervention].

Policy Statement: All clinical staff will demonstrate basic competency in identifying signs of an FASD.

Procedures:

1. All clinical and support staff will participate in a 3–5 hour training session covering FASD, the impact of these disorders on treatment, retention, and outcomes, and criteria and procedures for referring individuals to services aimed at formally diagnosing and addressing FASD. (See Appendix C, *Public and Professional Resources on FASD*, for training resources.)

2. The clinical supervisor of new employees will provide site-specific information on the procedures for screening and referring individuals who exhibit signs of a possible FASD.

3. Clinical competency checklists completed at hire and annually thereafter will ensure that all clinical staff members have a basic knowledge of FASD, an understanding of strategies for assessing the significance of FASD, and an awareness of appropriate referral procedures.

Sample Policy 1b

Topic: Clinical staff training and competency [FASD prevention].

Policy Statement: All clinical staff will demonstrate basic competency in screening women of childbearing age (whether pregnant or not) for alcohol consumption.

Procedures:

1. All clinical and support staff will participate in a 3–5 hour training session covering FASD, the impact of alcohol on a fetus, and (if necessary) criteria and procedures for referring women who screen positive for at-risk drinking to appropriate services. (See Appendix C, *Public and Professional Resources on FASD*, for training resources.)

2. The clinical supervisor of new employees will provide site-specific information on the procedures for screening and referring women who screen positive for at-risk drinking.

3. Clinical competency checklists completed at hire and annually thereafter will ensure that all clinical staff members have a basic knowledge of FASD, an understanding of strategies for assessing the dangers of alcohol consumption for women of childbearing age, and an awareness of appropriate referral procedures.

Sample Policy 2a

Topic: Recruitment, training, and supervision of FASD-capable clinical staff [FASD intervention].

Policy Statement: Counselors interested in providing FASD-informed care and who possess the relevant basic counseling skills, knowledge, and attitudes (see Checklist 2, *Characteristics and Competencies of All Clinical Staff*, this chapter) will be recruited, trained, and supervised to deliver these interventions.

Procedures:

1. At least one clinical position in each program or modality of care will be designated to provide FASD-informed care.

2. Individuals exhibiting the attitudes, knowledge, skills, and job performance required to provide FASD-informed care will be identified by their clinical supervisor and designated to provide these services.

3. The counselors identified to provide FASD-informed care will receive an initial training and additional "update" training each year in some or all of the following areas (see Appendix C, *Public and Professional Resources on FASD*, for training resources):

    - Fundamentals of FASD, including the effect of alcohol on the developing fetus and typical cognitive and behavioral impact across the lifespan.
    - Summary of current literature on FASD intervention, and on scientifically validated FASD intervention approaches.
    - Adapting treatment approaches for individuals with an FASD.
    - Talking with individuals with an FASD about their diagnosis.
    - Planning for client safety.
    - Principles of trauma-informed care.
    - Providing a "hands-on hand-off" approach to outside services (i.e., not simply making a referral and assuming that the client takes the appropriate action).
    - Addressing FASD in the context of cultural competency.
    - Building client self-efficacy and self-advocacy
    - Client-centered care.
    - Motivational interviewing.
    - Targeted provider and school consultation.
    - Personal boundaries and professional ethics.
    - Termination, referral, and discharge planning.
    - Appropriate community linkages.
    - Anticipatory guidance and planning for the future.

4. Counselors providing FASD-informed care will receive clinical supervision twice monthly that includes direct observation or review of tapes of individual sessions with clients who have or may have an FASD.

5. Counselors providing FASD-informed care will meet quarterly to provide peer support, supervision, and share resources related to the management of clients who have or may have an FASD.

Sample Policy 2b

Topic: Recruitment, training, and supervision of clinical staff capable of screening women of childbearing age (whether pregnant or not) for alcohol consumption [FASD prevention].

Policy Statement: Counselors interested in providing alcohol screening and referral and who possess the relevant basic counseling skills, knowledge, and attitudes (see Checklist 2, *Characteristics and Competencies of All Clinical Staff*, this chapter) will be recruited, trained, and supervised to deliver these interventions.

Procedures:

1. At least one clinical position in each program or modality of care will be designated to provide alcohol screening to women of childbearing age.

2. Individuals exhibiting the attitudes, knowledge, skills, and job performance required to provide alcohol screening will be identified by their clinical supervisor and designated to provide these services.

3. The counselors identified to provide alcohol screening will receive an initial training and an additional update training each year in some or all of the following areas (see Appendix C, *Public and Professional Resources on FASD*, for training resources):

   - Fundamentals of FASD, including the effect of alcohol on the developing fetus and typical cognitive and behavioral impact across the lifespan.

   - Summary of current literature on FASD intervention, and on scientifically validated FASD intervention approaches.

   - Planning for client safety.

   - Principles of trauma-informed care.

   - Providing a 'hands-on hand-off' approach to outside services (i.e., not simply making a referral and assuming that the client takes the appropriate action).

   - Addressing FASD in the context of cultural competency.

   - Building client self-efficacy and self-advocacy

   - Client-centered care.

   - Motivational interviewing.

   - Targeted provider consultation.

   - Personal boundaries and professional ethics.

   - Termination, referral, and discharge planning.

   - Appropriate community linkages.

   - Anticipatory guidance and planning for the future.

4. Counselors providing alcohol screening will receive clinical supervision twice monthly that includes direct observation or review of tapes of individual sessions with female clients of childbearing age.

5. Counselors providing FASD-informed care will meet quarterly to provide peer support, supervision, and share resources related to providing alcohol screening to female clients of childbearing age.

Sample Policy 3a

Topic: Observation and referral of clients exhibiting signs of an FASD [FASD intervention].

Policy Statement: The possible presence of an FASD will be considered with all noncompliant or resistant or 'problem' clients, and possible indicators will be noted through a process of observation and interviewing. Clients exhibiting signs of a potential FASD will be referred as needed.

Procedures:

1. During intake and throughout the early stages of treatment (i.e., first month), all clients exhibiting persistent (and otherwise unexplained) noncompliance with treatment will be observed, and the individual's case history reviewed, for FASD "indicators" based on a checklist (see the *FASD 4-Digit Code Caregiver Interview Checklist* in Part 1, Chapter 2 of this TIP).

2. Individuals exhibiting signs of an FASD will either be assessed by an identified in-house team with FASD expertise or be referred to an accepted FASD evaluation agency.

3. With or without a formal diagnosis of FASD, a client exhibiting signs of an FASD will be referred to a counselor competent in providing FASD-informed care and capable of modifying treatment to account for the observed behavioral/cognitive deficits (see Sample Policy 2).

4. All screening results, consultation sessions with the clinical supervisor, and referrals (and ongoing communications) to an FASD evaluation agency will be documented in the client's record.

5. The counselor providing FASD-informed care will provide the client with an emergency contact list that includes agency personnel and emergency care providers. The client can refer to this list if he or she has treatment or safety issues outside business hours or when a counselor is not available. (See Appendix F for a *Sample Crisis/Safety Plan* that can be filled out with clients.)

Sample Policy 3b

Topic: Screening and referral of female clients of childbearing age exhibiting signs of an alcohol use/abuse [FASD prevention].

Policy Statement: All women of childbearing age (whether pregnant or not) will be screened for alcohol consumption and referred as needed.

Procedures:

1. During the intake process, all women of childbearing age will be screened for alcohol consumption.

2. Staff will be trained in using specific alcohol screening tools that are validated for use with women, such as the T-ACE or TWEAK (for pregnant women), the AUDIT-C Questionnaire (non-pregnant women), or the CRAFFT Interview or FRAMES (with adolescent and young adult clients).

3. Individuals screening positive for at-risk alcohol consumption will receive an appropriate assessment or be referred for one, to be conducted by a qualified substance abuse treatment professional.

4. Clients who are determined by a qualified substance abuse treatment professional to have an alcohol-related disorder will receive or be referred for substance abuse treatment, also to be delivered by that professional. Collaborative relationships with appropriate providers will be developed.

5. All women of childbearing age will receive FASD-related education (pamphlet, suitable Web site, etc.), whether pregnant or not and whether screening positive for at-risk alcohol consumption or not.

6. All screening results, consultation sessions with the clinical supervisor, and referrals (and ongoing communications) to a qualified substance abuse treatment professional will be documented in the client's record.

7. The counselor providing substance abuse treatment will provide the client with an emergency contact list that includes agency personnel and emergency care providers. The client can refer to this list if she has treatment issues outside business hours or when a counselor is not available. (See Appendix F for a *Sample Crisis/Safety Plan* that can be filled out with clients.)

Sample Policy 4a

Topic: Treatment planning, service recording, discharge planning, and continuity of care [FASD intervention].

Policy Statement: Management of FASD will be integrated with substance abuse/mental health services, be properly documented, and include appropriate discharge and transfer planning.

Procedures:

1. Screening and observation for signs of an FASD and—when indicators are present—strategies for addressing FASD will be included in the client's treatment plan.

2. Treatment plans incorporating FASD management will be jointly developed by the interdisciplinary team and the client within and/or across programs.

3. To minimize client confusion, the client will be provided with information about the roles and responsibilities of those delivering care.

4. Treatment plans will include referral to other community resources and peer support activities that may increase the client's self-efficacy and reduce FASD-related treatment barriers.

5. Interdisciplinary treatment update sessions including all professionals involved with the client's care should occur regularly. (The frequency of treatment plan updates should be consistent with state and organizational standards and will vary by modality of care and regulatory agency.) Ideally these would be held weekly for short-term residential treatment and monthly for long-term residential treatment and outpatient settings.

6. Services delivered by the primary counselor will be recorded in the client's record at each contact and will be available to other members of the treatment team.

7. Major changes in the client's condition or treatment compliance/success will be communicated between the primary counselor and the interdisciplinary team.

8. The checklist of FASD "indicators" (see Sample Policy 3) will be completed at the last session before termination to assist in developing the discharge plan and to be used by the quality assurance department for outcome monitoring.

9. Discharge and transfer planning will include recommendations for the client about self-care, self-advocacy, and other available FASD-informed services that are available to them.

Sample Policy 4b

Topic: Treatment planning, service recording, discharge planning, and continuity of care [FASD prevention].

Policy Statement: Treatment for at-risk alcohol consumption among all women of childbearing age (whether pregnant or not) will be integrated with substance abuse/mental health services, be properly documented, and include appropriate discharge and transfer planning.

Procedures:

1. Screening for alcohol consumption among all women of childbearing age (whether pregnant or not) and strategies for addressing the client's alcohol use will be included in the client's treatment plan.

2. Treatment plans incorporating alcohol use management will be jointly developed by the interdisciplinary team and the client within and/or across programs.

3. To minimize client confusion, the client will be provided with information about the roles and responsibilities of those delivering care.

4. Treatment plans will include referral to other community resources and peer support activities that may increase the client's self-efficacy and reduce alcohol consumption.

5. Interdisciplinary treatment update sessions including all professionals involved with the client's care should occur regularly. (The frequency of treatment plan updates should be consistent with state and organizational standards and will vary by modality of care and regulatory agency.) Ideally these would be held weekly for short-term residential treatment and monthly for long-term residential treatment and outpatient settings.

6. Services delivered by the primary counselor will be recorded in the client's record at each contact and will be available to other members of the treatment team.

7. Major changes in the client's condition or pattern of alcohol use (or simply changes in alcohol use, if this is the primary objective of treatment) will be communicated between the primary counselor and the interdisciplinary team.

8. An appropriate alcohol screening tool agreed upon by the interdisciplinary team will be completed at the last session before termination to assist in developing the discharge plan and to be used by the quality assurance department for outcome monitoring.

9. Discharge and transfer planning will include recommendations for the client about self-care, self-advocacy, and other alcohol use support services that are available to them.

Sample Policy 5a

Topic: Counselor performance appraisal [FASD intervention].

Policy Statement: Counselors capable of providing FASD-informed services will have job descriptions that include a high level of specific performance expectations related to provision of services for these clients.

Procedures:

1. Job descriptions for counselors agreeing/qualified to provide FASD intervention services may include reduced caseload and productivity expectations, particularly during an agreed-upon early stage of implementation.

2. Performance appraisal of counselors providing FASD intervention services will include demonstration of relevant core competencies (e.g., as observed directly and/or through videotaping).

3. Annual training requirements will be outlined in the job descriptions of counselors identified to provide FASD-informed services.

4. Client satisfaction surveys and outcome reports will be discussed in performance evaluations with counselors providing FASD intervention services. Such evaluations may need to occur more regularly than annually when implementing new practice.

Note: The following sample policy is potentially more relevant in mental health treatment settings than in substance abuse treatment settings, as alcohol use management services are a core competency in substance abuse treatment and presumably would not be separated out in a policy statement in this fashion.

Sample Policy 5b

Topic: Counselor performance appraisal [FASD prevention].

Policy Statement: Counselors capable of providing alcohol consumption screening for women of childbearing age (whether pregnant or not) and appropriate services/referral will have job descriptions that include a high level of specific performance expectations related to provision of services for these clients.

Procedures:

1. Job descriptions for counselors agreeing/qualified to provide FASD prevention services may include reduced caseload and productivity expectations, particularly during an agreed-upon early stage of implementation.

2. Performance appraisal of counselors providing FASD prevention services will include demonstration of relevant core competencies (e.g., as observed directly and/or through videotaping).

3. Annual training requirements will be outlined in the job descriptions of counselors identified to provide alcohol use management services.

4. Client satisfaction surveys and outcome reports will be discussed in performance evaluations with counselors providing FASD prevention services. Such evaluations may need to occur more regularly than annually when implementing new practice.

Sample Policy 6a

Topic: Evaluation of service effectiveness and quality assurance [FASD intervention].

Policy Statement: Services for addressing FASD will be reported annually through the agency's quality assurance system along with indicators of effectiveness based on client outcomes.

Procedures:

1. The agency's quality assurance program will include monitoring the implementation of policies related to FASD screening and treatment modifications, FASD evaluation referral procedures, documentation and treatment planning, and supervision of counselors providing FASD-informed services.

2. Data from admission and discharge screening of clients exhibiting FASD "indicators" (see Sample Policy 3) will be aggregated by the quality assurance coordinator for annual reporting to the agency.

3. The following overall agency performance outcomes will be reviewed annually by the management team:

   a. The proportion of clients dropping out of treatment before the third session after implementation of FASD-informed services, or appropriate length of time based on your agency's treatment schedule (it will be important to have information on the dropout rate *after* implementation to assess the impact of these services on treatment engagement and retention).

   b. The number of clients receiving FASD-informed services, as a percentage of overall client population.

   c. The number of clients referred to an FASD evaluation agency, as a percentage of overall client population.

   d. A comparison of (1) the proportion of all clients experiencing a relapse during treatment, and (2) the proportion of all clients receiving FASD-informed care that experience a relapse during treatment.

Note: As with sample policy 5b, the following sample policy is potentially more relevant in mental health treatment settings than in substance abuse treatment settings, as alcohol use management services are already a core competency in substance abuse treatment.

Sample Policy 6b

Topic: Evaluation of service effectiveness and quality assurance [FASD prevention].

Policy Statement: Services for managing alcohol use consumption among women of childbearing age (whether pregnant or not) will be reported annually through the agency's quality assurance system along with indicators of effectiveness based on client outcomes.

Procedures:

1. The agency's quality assurance program will include monitoring the implementation of policies related to alcohol use management among women of childbearing age (whether pregnant or not), substance abuse treatment referral procedures, documentation and treatment planning, and supervision of counselors providing alcohol use management services.

2. Data from admission and discharge screening of clients who are women of childbearing age and have received alcohol use management services (see Sample Policy 3) will be aggregated by the quality assurance coordinator for annual reporting to the agency.

3. The following overall agency performance outcomes will be reviewed annually by the management team:

    a. The proportion of clients who receive screening for at-risk alcohol use who subsequently drop out of treatment, as a comparison with clients who do not receive this screening and subsequently drop out of treatment.

    b. The proportion of these clients evidencing at-risk alcohol consumption at both admission and discharge.

    c. The number of clients who are women of childbearing age who receive screening for at-risk alcohol use, as a percentage of overall client population.

    d. The number of clients who are women of childbearing age who receive services for alcohol use management or a referral to a qualified substance abuse treatment professional, as a percentage of overall client population.

    e. A comparison of (1) the proportion of all clients experiencing a relapse during treatment, and (2) the proportion of all clients who are women of childbearing age and receiving alcohol-use management services that experience a relapse during treatment.

Addressing Relevant Regulations

Another aspect of assessing your agency is to determine whether implementing FASD prevention and/or intervention will conflict with the existing local and governmental regulations and standards that apply to your agency's operation.

For example, both the federal government and individual states have developed their own laws regarding the reporting of cases of known or suspected substance-exposed infants. These laws vary widely in their requirements, but are nonetheless of critical importance to any healthcare setting serving the needs of pregnant women. In addition, providing services to individuals who have or may have an FASD—a recognized disability—carries its own legal and ethical responsibilities.

The following sections discuss relevant regulatory issues related to (1) women who drink during pregnancy, and (2) individuals who have or may have an FASD.

Legal Issues Related to Women Who Drink During Pregnancy

Federal laws related to alcohol use during pregnancy tend focus on prevention and treatment of FASD rather than being punitive. State and local laws vary. Some states, such as Hawaii and Montana, have laws authorizing FASD prevention and treatment programs. Others, such as New Hampshire and Rhode Island, require that information on FASD be available to couples seeking marriage licenses. At least one state, Missouri, requires physicians to counsel pregnant patients about the dangers of alcohol use. It is important for counselors to stay abreast of state laws related to alcohol use during pregnancy and their effect on treatment and recovery.

The Administration for Children & Families, an agency within HHS, provides a searchable guide to state-level statutes regarding the reporting of substance-exposed infants (**http://www.childwelfare.gov/systemwide/laws_policies/state/**).

Custody Issues

Several states (e.g., Florida, South Carolina) do take punitive measures toward alcohol use during pregnancy, such as including prenatal alcohol exposure in their definitions of abuse or neglect. Such measures can be used to remove the child from the parent's custody. Texas allows involuntary termination of parental rights if a woman causes her child to be born addicted to alcohol (other than via a controlled substance legally obtained by the mother by prescription; Section 161.001[1-R]). Generally, a mother who abuses substances may be charged with child neglect or abuse. As a result, her children may be taken from her.

In Virginia, physicians, nurses, teachers, and other professionals are required to report certain injuries to children. For purposes of the law, "reason to suspect that a child is abused or neglected" includes a diagnosis by an attending physician within 7 days of a child's birth that the child has fetal alcohol syndrome attributable to in utero exposure to alcohol (Section 63.2-1509). One state, South Dakota, permits involuntary commitment of a pregnant woman who is drinking.

A number of experts fear that such punitive measures may discourage pregnant women with alcohol problems from seeking treatment. Many states take a more supportive approach:

- Arizona (**http://www.azleg.state.az.us/ars/36/00141.htm**)
- California (**http://law.justia.com/codes/california/2005/hsc/11998-11998.3.html**)
- Washington state (**http://apps.leg.wa.gov/RCW/default.aspx?cite=70.83C.005**)

These three states give pregnant women priority for alcohol treatment slots or otherwise provide access to treatment. Others (e.g.,

California) provide outreach or case management to pregnant women with substance abuse problems. California also may cover residential treatment for pregnant women under Medi-Cal. In addition, Iowa prohibits discrimination against pregnant women seeking alcohol treatment (**http://www.legis.state.ia.us/IACODE/2001SUPPLEMENT/125/32A.html**).

State and federal governments have established various policies in response to the risks associated with drinking during pregnancy. Among these are various arrangements to increase access to substance abuse treatment by pregnant and postpartum women. Such arrangements include state-run treatment services, funding for private providers, and mandates that such women receive a priority for available treatment. The Alcohol Policy Information System (APIS) addresses statutes and regulations mandating priority access to substance abuse treatment for pregnant and postpartum women who abuse alcohol. In addition, the SAMHSA FASD Center for Excellence Web site provides an FASD legislation report that is updated twice a year.

State statutes that remove custody from birth mothers of children with an FASD are designed to protect the children. However, the threat of losing custody can interfere with the woman's recovery, or cause her to leave prenatal care and/or treatment. The goal is to remain alcohol-free long-term and acquire parenting skills needed to retain child custody and have a healthy, intact family. When screening or referring pregnant women for substance abuse treatment, counselors will need to be familiar with the laws in his or her state and their impact on efforts at family reunification and client recovery.

Child Abuse Prevention and Treatment Act (CAPTA)

One of the most significant pieces of legislation impacting the provision of services to pregnant women is the Child Abuse Prevention and Treatment Act, or CAPTA (P.L. 93-247). Most recently reauthorized on December 20, 2010 (S 3817), CAPTA is designed to protect rather than punish women who give birth to substance-exposed infants. The intent of these reporting laws is that "The newborn and their families will be brought to the attention of the child protective agency in the community, and they will ideally receive needed services within their community" (Burke, 2007).

A new CAPTA state grant eligibility requirement modifies earlier CAPTA language that mandates identifying and making appropriate referrals by healthcare providers to child protective services—and developing service 'plans for safe care' of the child—of newborns affected by prenatal drug exposure. Added as a new category of 'referral' and 'safe care plan' requirement are newborns diagnosed with an FASD. This CAPTA amendment was not meant to cover all situations where a newborn's mother drinks alcohol during her pregnancy, but rather those where a newborn has facial characteristics, growth restriction, or other abnormalities (birth defects) caused by prenatal alcohol use.

This new CAPTA provision (and the earlier requirement regarding drug-exposed newborns) is not intended to have states make prenatal alcohol or drug exposure a category of child abuse or neglect or to make those children subjects of mandatory reporting laws. Congress carefully chose the word "referral" to avoid that. Rather, the goal is to address the safety and well-being of these children. Intervening early through safety plans that promote the health and well-being of these children will be key.

The U.S. Department of Health and Human Services (HHS) provides a comprehensive guide to the CAPTA legislation and its impact on service provision, as well as its implications for community-based family resource and supports grants (**http://www.childwelfare.gov/systemwide/laws_policies/federal/index.cfm?event=federalLegislation.viewLegis&id=142**). CAPTA is also discussed in Part 3 of this TIP, the online literature review.

Territorial and Tribal Laws

At this time, no U.S. Territories have laws related to alcohol use during pregnancy. Tribal laws vary, but the Indian Child Welfare Act (**http://www.nicwa.org/policy/law/icwa/ICWA.pdf**) requires the Indian Health Service (IHS) to make residential treatment available for pregnant women with alcohol problems. In addition, the definition of 'health promotion' in the Act includes FASD prevention. The Act also allows the IHS to make grants to tribes and tribal organizations for various FASD prevention efforts, including alcohol treatment for high-risk women. It also has provisions related to educating Native women about FASD.

Counselors working with Tribal populations will also want to consider the implications of the Tribal Law and Order Act (TLOA) of 2010 and the Indian Health Care Improvement Act (IHCIA), which was made permanent in 2010. Both seek to strengthen access to care and protection of personal rights among Tribal populations, particularly women.

Information about the TLOA can be accessed at **http://www.narf.org/nill/resources/tloa.html**.

Information about the IHCIA can be accessed at **http://www.ihs.gov/ihcia/**.

Confidentiality Issues

Laws such as the Health Insurance Portability and Accountability Act (HIPAA) may affect activities such as reporting of alcohol use during pregnancy. HIPAA has certain requirements regarding privacy and sharing of client information and records. Confidentiality laws vary by state and may affect the addiction professional's ability to share information with various social, health, and legal systems, such as child welfare agencies.

It is essential to be familiar with confidentiality laws in one's state and to consult with an attorney if necessary. Inappropriate reporting of current or previous alcohol use during pregnancy can jeopardize long-term recovery and can harm a counselor's career.

Legal Issues Related to Individuals with an FASD

The most prominent regulatory issue related to individuals who have or may have an FASD is to recognize their rights as individuals with (or potentially having) a recognized disability.

Americans with Disabilities Act Compliance in Treatment Plans

The Americans with Disabilities Act (ADA) of 1990 is a federal law that prohibits discrimination on the basis of disability in employment, state and local government, public accommodations, commercial facilities, transportation, and telecommunications. An individual with a disability is defined by the ADA as a person who has a physical or mental impairment that substantially limits one or more major life activities, a person who has a history or record of such an impairment, or a person who is perceived by others as having such an impairment. Treatment facilities cannot discriminate on the basis of a disability. Many individuals with an FASD will have cognitive disabilities that meet the definitions set forth by the ADA; in any case, such individuals should receive treatment that recognizes their condition as a disability that should not be discriminated against.

Counselors will need to incorporate accommodations for persons with an FASD into any treatment plans. For example, lighting at meetings may need to be dimmed to keep the person with an FASD from becoming overstimulated. Reading materials may need to be adapted to a lower literacy level to accommodate cognitive deficits. More information on accommodating disabilities can be found in Appendix D of TIP 29, *Substance Use Disorder Treatment for People With Physical and Cognitive Disabilities* (CSAT, 1998; **http://www.ncbi.nlm.nih.gov/books/NBK64881/**). Part 1, Chapter 2 of this TIP discusses accommodations specific to individuals who have or may have an FASD.

More information on the ADA can be found at **http://www.ada.gov/**. For technical assistance related to ADA requirements, visit **http://www.ada.gov/taprog.htm** or contact SAMHSA's FASD Center for Excellence toll-free at 1-866-STOPFAS or by visiting **www.fasdcenter.samhsa.gov**.

Addressing Staff Competence

Where Is the Clinical Expertise in Your Agency?

Change in clinical practice is best facilitated by assessing the skills of well-trained and experienced clinicians and targeting them for training and/or enlisting them in helping less skilled counselors facilitate change. Two clinical management structures are described here—interdisciplinary teams and traditional clinical supervisors.

Interdisciplinary teams are one effective way to ensure that the expertise for providing FASD-informed treatment is available in your agency (Clarren & Astley, 1997; Clarren et al., 2000). If you have interdisciplinary teams in your program, the teams assume the responsibility of tailoring interventions to an individual client's needs in a way that addresses FASD seamlessly. Such teams provide ongoing support, education, and treatment planning assistance for all staff. Teamwork creates an enriched environment for implementing FASD-informed techniques.

If your agency has an interdisciplinary team format for responding to other issues, this may be adapted to FASD. With an interdisciplinary team, you have an advanced level of capability for addressing FASD prevention or intervention in clients with substance use or mental disorders. This assumes that the more experienced and skilled members of the team have the knowledge, skills, and attitudes required to apply FASD-informed interventions and to supervise and coach application of an intervention for other counselors.

Many treatment agencies do not have interdisciplinary teams and instead rely on the expertise of *clinical supervisors* to evaluate and support the work of line staff. Clinical supervisors must have the knowledge, skills, and abilities required to apply an intervention and be able to demonstrate the intervention before they can coach others to perform it. The supervisors must also have the time to supervise and coach the staff. If this describes the supervisors in the setting where you work, you have an intermediate capability to provide FASD-informed care. If the supervisors have not yet reached this level, then you have a beginning capability for implementing FASD-informed care and must develop a plan to build the resources necessary to increase capacity.

The Frontline Staff and Clinical Supervisors
Once you've assessed the agency, you may want to assess the staff who will actually implement the change (see How-To 2.6).

Staff Qualifications and Competencies
As a part of implementing FASD-informed services, a number of process-oriented tasks

---

How-To 2.6: How to Assess the Frontline Staff and Clinical Supervisors for Change (Figure 2.1, Step H)

The committee determines the specific program and staff members who will be the first to implement change.

1. Are there incentives/organizational supports for change (ATTC Change Book, p. 29)?

2. What are the barriers to change (ATTC Change Book, p. 28)?

3. At what stage of change is the program staff (ATTC Change Book, p. 29)?

4. How will staff practice be affected (ATTC Change Book, p. 29)?

5. What additional support will staff need (ATTC Change Book, p. 29)?

6. Does staff have the prerequisite knowledge, attitudes, and skills?

7. What training and continuing resources are necessary to provide the core intervention components?

See also Sample Policies 1–6 and Checklists 1–4 in this chapter for additional information to be used in assessing staff readiness. See Appendix C, *Public and Professional Resources on FASD*, for links to training resources.

should be completed, including an assessment of initial staff competence, education and training, development of skills and resources, and supervision. These considerations are relevant not only to the counselors' ability to deliver the services but also to clinical supervisors, other clinical staff, and support staff responsible for recording and billing services.

Compared with those providing support services, however, the required level of knowledge and skill is significantly different for those directly involved in clinical care. For this reason, the attitudes, knowledge, and skills required to provide FASD-informed services are separated into four categories:

1. Administrative and support staff

2. All clinical staff

3. Counselors designated to provide FASD-informed services

4. Clinical supervisors overseeing the counselors who provide these services

The four checklists that follow serve two purposes. First, they can be used to assess staff and organizational readiness to implement or sustain FASD-informed services. Second, they can be used to identify gaps in training and supervision to be addressed with individuals or groups.

Addressing Gaps in Staff Capacity to Deliver Services

Not all clinical staff are ready, willing, or able to address co-occurring issues such as FASD. The clinical supervisor is charged with helping staff and administration differentiate the level

---

Checklist 1: Characteristics and Competencies of Administrative and Support Staff

Attitudes

_____Integrating FASD-informed care is important for promotion of the agency mission.

_____FASD prevention and intervention constitute valid and important experiences for our clients and deserve and require specialized attention.

Knowledge

_____Recognizes the relationship between FASD-informed care and treatment effectiveness.

_____Recognizes how provision of FASD-informed services fits in the mission and goals of the organization.

_____Is familiar with the policies and procedures related to recording and billing services for FASD-informed services.

_____Recognizes the distinction between a person formally diagnosed with FAS/pFAS/ARND and the general signs of an FASD in an individual.

_____Knows the agency's policies and procedures on providing FASD-informed services as they relate to the specific position (e.g., administrative staff in clinical records are familiar with documentation requirements for these services, and the finance staff are knowledgeable about how services are defined for billing purposes).

_____Understands the role of self-help and support groups in recovery and how those groups can support the goals of the program in providing FASD-informed care.

Skills

_____Communicates to the public the role of specialized services related to FASD prevention/intervention.

_____Identifies the 'indicators' of an FASD listed in the screening policy and procedure (see Sample Policy 3).

_____Administers FASD screening and observation properly.

_____Conducts basic client education session on the relationship between substance abuse/mental health issues and FASD.

_____Conducts basic client education sessions with all female clients of childbearing age (whether pregnant or not) on the relationship between alcohol use during pregnancy and the risk of an FASD.

_____Collaborates with other team members on treatment and discharge planning.

_____Conducts a suicide risk screening.

Checklist 2: Characteristics and Competencies of All Clinical Staff

Attitudes

_____Integrating FASD-informed care is important for promotion of the agency mission.

_____FASD prevention and intervention constitute valid and important experiences for our clients and deserve and require specialized attention.

_____Clients have a central role in creating and shaping their treatment goals.

_____Substance abuse/mental health issues and FASD can be both interrelated and independent; resolving one set of concerns may not lead to resolution of the other set of concerns without specialized treatment.

_____There is no one "right" approach to addressing FASD in our clients.

_____Individual sessions can be particularly valuable for clients who have or may have an FASD and can provide an effective adjunct to group treatment.

Knowledge

_____Recognizes the relationship between FASD-informed care and treatment effectiveness.

_____Recognizes how provision of FASD-informed services fits in the mission and goals of the organization.

_____Recognizes the distinction between a person formally diagnosed with FAS/pFAS/ARND and the general signs of an FASD in an individual.

_____Knows the agency's policies and procedures on addressing FASD prevention/intervention.

_____Recognizes the interrelationship between substance abuse/mental health issues and FASD.

Skills

_____Communicates to the public the role of specialized services related to FASD prevention/intervention.

_____Identifies the 'indicators' of an FASD listed in the screening policy and procedure (see Sample Policy 3).

_____Administers FASD screening and observation properly.

_____Conducts basic client education session on the relationship between substance abuse/mental health issues and FASD.

_____Conducts basic client education sessions with all female clients of childbearing age (whether pregnant or not) on the relationship between alcohol use during pregnancy and the risk of an FASD.

_____Collaborates with other team members on treatment and discharge planning.

_____Conducts a suicide risk screening.

Checklist 3: Characteristics and Competencies of All Clinical Staff

Attitudes

_____Integrating FASD-informed care is important for promotion of the agency mission.

_____FASD prevention and intervention constitute valid and important experiences for our clients and deserve and require specialized attention.

_____Clients have a central role in creating and shaping their treatment goals.

_____Substance use/mental health issues and FASD can be both interrelated and independent; resolving one set of concerns may not lead to resolution of the other set of concerns without specialized treatment.

_____There is no one 'right' approach to addressing FASD in our clients.

_____Individual sessions can be particularly valuable for clients who have or may have an FASD and can provide an effective adjunct to group treatment.

_____Resistance to change from clients is surmountable within the influence of the counseling relationship.

_____The client is an integrated whole rather than one or more diagnoses or sets of symptoms.

_____A desire exists to deliver services to clients who have or may have an FASD along with a substance abuse/mental health issue.

_____A desire exists to deliver FASD-informed care to female clients of childbearing age (whether pregnant or not).

Checklist 3: Characteristics and Competencies of All Clinical Staff

Knowledge

_____Recognizes the relationship between FASD-informed care and treatment effectiveness.

_____Recognizes how provision of FASD-informed services fits in the mission and goals of the organization.

_____Recognizes the distinction between a person formally diagnosed with FAS/pFAS/ARND and the general signs of an FASD in an individual.

_____Demonstrates a nuanced understanding of the relationship between substance use/mental health issues and FASD.

_____Recognizes the distinctions among screening, assessment, and diagnosis of an FASD.

_____Knows the common approaches to addressing FASD in substance abuse/mental health treatment settings including motivational interviewing, accommodations, parent/personal navigator, and the importance of coordinated care.

_____Recognizes how FASD presents in ethnic and other cultural groups encountered in the agency.

_____Knows community resources (particularly substance abuse/mental health, primary care, FASD service providers, school contacts when applicable, family/caregiver navigators).

_____Understands how 12-Step and other mutual-help support programs can support someone with an FASD.

_____Is aware of the role of transference and countertransference in the counseling relationship.

_____Recognizes the role of religion and spirituality in promoting recovery for some clients.

_____Knows how to learn more about FASD intervention methods.

Skills

_____Communicates to the public the role of specialized services related to FASD prevention/intervention.

_____Identifies the "indicators" of an FASD listed in the screening policy and procedure (see Sample Policy 3).

_____Administers FASD screening and observation properly.

_____Conducts basic client education session on the relationship between substance abuse/mental health issues and FASD.

_____Conducts basic client education sessions with all female clients of childbearing age (whether pregnant or not) on the relationship between alcohol use during pregnancy and the risk of an FASD.

_____Collaborates with other team members on treatment and discharge planning.

_____Conducts a suicide risk screening.

_____Exhibits evidence-based thinking (tailoring approach to service based on clinical experience, client characteristics, knowledge of field, consultation with supervisor, constraints, and resources available).

_____Uses clinical supervision effectively.

_____Demonstrates empathic listening skills and reflection.

_____Demonstrates competency in common approaches to addressing FASD (e.g., motivational interviewing, accommodations, parent/personal navigator, coordinated care).

_____Displays confidence in ability to provide FASD-informed services.

_____Acts as a role model for a balanced, healthy lifestyle.

_____Exhibits advanced skills in dealing with resistance to change through non-confrontational approaches.

_____Identifies and responds to variations in learning styles among clients.

_____Demonstrates the ability to quickly establish a therapeutic alliance with the client: treating the client with respect, communicating a nonjudgmental attitude, listening reflectively, setting appropriate limits, being sensitive to culture and value contexts, and acting as a role model.

_____Is comfortable with and able to resolve conflict.

_____Is able to prepare clients for discharge.

Checklist 4: Characteristics and Competencies of Clinical Supervisors

Attitudes

_____Substance abuse counselors have the basic characteristics needed to provide FASD prevention/intervention.

_____Clinical supervision extends beyond talking about treatment to observing and coaching counselors directly.

Knowledge

_____Possesses all of the knowledge areas listed on Checklist 3.

_____Is knowledgeable of the role of clinical supervision.

_____Recognizes the limits and opportunities related to the role of counselors with specialized training in FASD-informed services and supports training for counselors as needed.

_____Can determine when a client who has or may have an FASD needs additional skills and services beyond the qualifications of currently-staffed counselors.

_____Is trained to screen and observe for "indicators" of an FASD.

_____Is aware of the role of transference and countertransference in the counseling and supervisory relationship.

_____Recognizes resistance to change among clinical staff and is knowledgeable of strategies to address resistance.

_____Is aware of change processes, process steps and strategies for supporting them.

_____Possesses knowledge of the FASD intervention literature and scientifically-validated intervention techniques.

Counseling Skills

_____Possesses all of the skills listed on Checklist 3.

Supervisory Skills

_____Articulates his or her approach and philosophy to clinical supervision as it relates to clinical supervision approaches described in the literature.

_____Identifies and responds to variations in learning styles among counselors.

_____Is comfortable with and able to resolve conflict among team members.

_____Models advanced counseling skills including development of therapeutic alliance, preparing clients for discharge, and dealing with client resistance.

_____Uses direct observation or taping to conduct supervisory sessions.

_____Is able to teach and model skills for providing FASD-informed services.

_____Is able to determine when referral for a formal FASD assessment is required, and facilitate such a referral.

_____Provides incentives through encouragement and support for counselors to enhance skills in providing FASD-informed services.

_____Conducts competency assessment of counselors' skills in providing FASD-informed services.

_____Shows how to learn more about FASD intervention methods.

of new knowledge, attitudes, and skills needed to help counselors and support staff address co-occurring substance use/mental health disorders and FASD prevention and intervention. The characteristics and competencies checklists presented above outline the qualifications needed at various levels or in agencies wishing to provide FASD-informed services in clients with substance use or mental disorders. However, gaps may exist; staff may be lacking in various areas and require additional training and support. In this instance, the implementation workgroup described in earlier sections may be commissioned to identify these gaps and to develop plans to provide specific training and support to individual staff members on an as-needed basis.

In addition to developing individualized plans to develop attitudes, skills, and knowledge, a number of organizational approaches can be used both to reinforce the change and to overcome resistance to change. _The Change Book_ (ATTC, Second Edition 2010) offers valuable suggestions on addressing resistance to change (particularly pp. 27–28). These include such strategies as openly discussing staff feelings related to the change, celebrating victories, promoting feedback about the change as a vehicle to improve the process, being realistic about goals, identifying and using the change leaders in promoting the change, and providing training related to the change.

Approaches to Staff Training

It is recommended that training aimed at developing the basic attitudes, knowledge, and skills for delivering FASD-informed care be provided to all agency staff as part of implementation. It is important for clinical staff to see the link between the change and organizational leadership. Thus, administrators need to attend these sessions to personally provide the vision of the organization. In addition to training current staff, it is important to consider the ways in which the organization can communicate the vision to new staff. This may be most efficiently accomplished by using existing vehicles, such as new staff orientation and training sessions and worksite orientation procedures.

Training of all clinical staff members on attitudes, knowledge, and skills specific to their positions can be conducted by administrative or clinical supervisors. Again, it is important to communicate the commitment of leadership to integrating FASD-informed services. In addition, it is recommended that training sessions provide practice in the skill areas outlined in Checklist 3. To reinforce the importance of the need to provide FASD-informed services, clinical and administrative supervisors are advised to incorporate didactic education, identification of incompatible attitudes, and coaching on the skills needed to implement the policies within existing supervision sessions and team meetings. In short, the agency's vision and commitment to addressing FASD must inform all clinical interactions between supervisors and counselors.

Figure 2.2 provides a list of recommended credentials for trainers; Appendix C, *Public and Professional Resources on FASD*, lists resources for FASD prevention and intervention training. How-To's 2.7 and 2.8 discuss the process of selecting a trainer, and how to continue the learning after the initial training is completed.

Figure 2.2
Recommended Credentials for Individuals Providing Training in FASD

- Advanced education in counseling, social work, or psychology.
- Minimum of 5 years' experience delivering substance abuse and/or mental health treatment.
- Being a qualified/experienced FASD Trainer.
- Understanding of commitment to preparing counselors to provide FASD-informed services.
- Possessing skills and experience in motivational interviewing, care coordination, and accommodations to address FASD.
- Meeting all certification or licensure qualifications and competencies for clinical supervisors.
- Knowledge of the FASD intervention literature and scientifically-validated intervention techniques.

How-To 2.7: How to Select a Trainer

Qualifications to look for in a trainer include the following:

1. Experience working with the clientele being served.

2. Ability to demonstrate the techniques as needed in role-play with staff or in-vivo (if possible).

3. Ability to address the types of challenging cases frontline staff encounter and how to work with challenging clients.

4. Understanding of the obstacles and challenges with which the frontline staff and the clinical supervisors are dealing.

5. Respectful attitude toward the clinical staff.

6. Models the principles and strategies of the intervention with the participants.

7. Ability to maintain and modify the technique for the treatment setting, willingness to review transcripts or tapes of actual sessions, and willingness to consult on the phone.

8. Willingness to accept specific training objectives to target specific staff skill sets in a case review format.

9. Knowledge of tested methods of FASD intervention and intervention literature.

See Appendix C, *Public and Professional Resources on FASD*, for links to organizations that can provide training and/or trainers. The SAMHSA FASD Center for Excellence, the National Organization on FAS (NOFAS), the Minnesota Organization on FAS (MOFAS), and the CDC's Regional Training Centers (RTCs) are good starting points.

How-To 2.8: How to Continue the Learning After the Initial Training is Completed

1. Assess the staff's knowledge, abilities, and skills with the core components of the techniques.

2. Check to see that staff continue to reframe the issues of individuals with FASD as being due (in part) to underlying neurological impairment.

3. Emphasize mastery of the underlying principles of the interventions. Always give feedback on how well staff members are doing with interventions and provide advice on simple ways to improve practice.

4. Emphasize mastery of the common techniques across approaches (e.g., motivational inter-viewing, case coordination, accommodations, establishing boundaries, strengths-based approaches).

5. When staff members have the basics, let them choose the approach they want to focus on next (e.g., behavioral, cognitive, beliefs, affective, family-systems, solution-focused).

6. Explore with staff members their interest in learning specific validated FASD intervention methods.

Addressing Community Relationships

How Do You Develop Referral Relationships?

Access to a range of other health and social resources is essential to quality care in substance abuse and mental health treatment settings, particularly for clients who have or may have an FASD. Agencies to which staff might refer can be screened using the following variables:

- Willing to accept referral of clients who have or may have an FASD.

- Sensitive to substance use or mental health issues.

- Able and willing to work with agencies such as ours, including regular review/discussion of any collaborative issues.

- No or low funding impediments to working collaboratively.

- Good professional reputation in the community.

- Sufficient funding to address the needs of clients we are referring.

- Willing to cross-train with our staff.

- Existing personal relationship with the referral agency.

Also, it is preferable if certain FASD capabilities are present in any agency to which you refer:

- Individualized service planning.
- Acceptance of disability.
- Recognition of strengths.
- Incorporating individual behaviors.
- More active involvement (transportation, personally ensuring client 'hand-off,' follow up, etc.).
- Services available to child and Mom (when the FASD is intergenerational).
- Flexibility in programming (modifications will be necessary; are they willing to make them?).

How Do You Develop Relationships With the 12-Step Community?

It is useful to have the program's policy and procedures manual reflect an understanding of the essential role that 12-Step programs play in the treatment of clients with substance abuse complicated by FASD. Mental health personnel need to be sensitive and competent in integrating the principles and practices of self-help programs into the clinical process. This requires knowledge of the underlying philosophy of the 12-Step model, and an understanding of how the programs function and are structured. In like manner, counselors practicing from a 12-Step facilitation model need to appreciate how principles and practices are linked to sound counseling.

For example, the use of slogans as a form of cognitive restructuring and debate is helpful to most clients. The use of structured practices like daily meetings, sponsor contact, and reading self-help group literature can help create alternate forms of reward, relief, and life-management. The policy should recognize barriers to individuals with an FASD accessing and using 12-Step programs, including:

- Whether the individual being referred requires a navigator to help them find meetings, attend them regularly and on-time, and participate appropriately;

- Insufficient social communication and social awareness skills on the part of the individual being referred; and

- Potential exploitation of the individual by other members of the group.

How Do You Find and Use Behavioral Health Resources in the Community?

Most substance abuse and mental health programs can benefit from consulting relationships with physicians, psychologists, social workers, and other community medical, rehabilitation, social service, and mental health providers who have specialized knowledge and resources in addressing the needs of clients who have or may have an FASD. As indicated in Part 1, Chapter 2 in the table titled *In-House FASD Assessment: An Ideal Core Team*, important professional areas to focus on in building relationships include neuropsychology and speech language pathology, occupational therapy, physical therapy, and a primary care physician.

These professionals can provide adjunct resources for such issues as difficult assessments and differential diagnosis, placement in appropriate treatment programs and/or support groups, medical management of co-occurring chronic medical conditions, specialized psychopharmacological services for clients with an FASD, discharge planning, and family services.

Finding and using these resources may be different from finding and using referral resources. Understanding the services that can be provided, fees for service, whether the service can be provided in the treatment program or whether the client must travel to a remote site, and the processes for reporting results of evaluations are some of the issues that need to be considered in using community resources. Generally, unlike referral resources, community resources will not have a formalized contract or agreement with the treatment program. Therefore, issues of confidentiality and information reporting will need to be explored.

Addressing Financial Considerations

Billing

Integration of FASD-informed services is intended to enhance treatment outcomes and, because these services are delivered by licensed and/or certified counselors who are *modifying* or offering *tailored* treatment, rather than changing the focus of treatment, such services are likely to be reimbursable under the client's primary treatment diagnosis. In this case, individual sessions that incorporate accommodations for FASD may be billed as individual counseling, psychotherapy (interactive or regular), or family therapy associated with the primary diagnosis. Organizations are advised to clarify this with state, county, federal, and private funding sources and to identify the specific procedures required to facilitate billing. Financial considerations also reinforce the need for support staff responsible for billing to understand how these services are delivered and their relationship to the primary diagnosis.

For organizations reimbursed based on case or capitated rates, reimbursement is not likely to change. Services that incorporate FASD are likely to be viewed by managed care organizations or funding agencies as value-added or optional services and thus included in established rates of reimbursement. Although incorporating FASD-informed services is not likely to increase reimbursement rates, it may improve performance on contractually mandated outcomes such as treatment engagement, retention, and effectiveness.

In their document *Operational Standards for Mental Health, Intellectual/Developmental Disabilities, and Substance Abuse Community Services Providers* (2011), the state of Mississippi has developed operational standards that can help define and inform a state reimbursement system. They are reprinted in full in Appendix H, *Operational Standards for Fetal Alcohol Spectrum Disorders (FASD): A Model*. In addition, Part 3 of this TIP, the online literature review (**http://store.samhsa. gov/home**), contains a discussion of reimbursement codes related to FASD, as well as the implications of the Patient Protection and Affordable Care Act.

Sources of Funding

Most of the costs of implementing FASD-informed services occur early in the process of implementation, so local foundations are potential sources of funding. A one-time cost of training and knowledge dissemination to staff offers a discrete, relatively low-cost, and an attractive opportunity for local foundations to contribute to improving treatment outcomes. Applying collaboratively with other agencies demonstrates established partnerships, and should be pursued where possible. The Council on Foundations (**www.cof.org**) is an excellent starting point for identifying foundations near you and researching their missions. Other potential sources of funding include traditional state and federal grants and contracts, direct charges for services from third-party payors, and client fees for service.

Additionally, if the services provided are innovative (addressing FASD is an emerging area of care), agencies should consider partnering with social and psychological researchers at a local university to obtain research funds to support clinical efforts. Such research efforts can have many beneficial secondary effects for agency status in the community, such as developing alternative sources of funding, partnering with new groups interested in substance abuse or mental health issues in the community and/or creating learning communities, as well as providing funds for the identified project.

Addressing Continuity and Fidelity

For FASD-informed services to be fully adopted, the importance of these services will need to be consistently communicated. Policies, mission statements, program descriptions, clinical and administrative training, team meetings, and clinical supervision sessions are all useful avenues for communicating the organization's commitment to delivering FASD-informed care (see Figure 2.3). If not formally revised, these policies should at least be reviewed to ensure that they are broad enough to encompass FASD-informed services.

Implementing the Intervention With Fidelity
When implementing any intervention, it is important to identify the active elements that characterize that specific intervention. Ensuring that a new intervention is being implemented with fidelity, as distinguished from standard practice, allows administrators

---

Figure 2.3 Avenues for Communicating Organizational Commitment to Delivering Services to Address FASD

- Mission and vision statements
- Strategic plans
- Annual goals
- Program descriptions
- Treatment philosophy statements
- Policies and procedures
- Training sessions
- Team meetings
- Clinical supervision
- Management meetings
- Quality assurance plans
- Employee newsletters
- Electronic communication vehicles including e-mail and Intranet

to more easily determine whether the new intervention is responsible for changes in expected outcomes.

For FASD-informed care, fidelity can present challenges. Behavioral health fields are encouraged by federal agencies and funding organizations to use evidence-based approaches that have not been developed for, or accommodated to, FASD. Evidence-based approaches specifically tailored for FASD are, for now, limited, though some that have been developed and tested do have built-in fidelity monitoring mechanisms.

Fortunately, the FASD evidence base is growing rapidly. There are several scientifically validated interventions now available. There is also expert clinical consensus and publications using systematic research review and synthesis that provide support for the interventions recommended in this TIP (e.g., Adubato & Cohen, 2011).

There is also precedent for tailoring interventions. For example, the past decade has brought methods for inclusion of trauma and other co-occurring disorders into treatment provision and planning into mental health and substance abuse treatment. This could be considered 'trauma-informed' care. Established practice (e.g., cognitive behavioral therapy, or CBT) has been altered and improved by informing standard care with methods to respond to these issues (e.g., trauma-focused CBT). The strategies that have been used to modify or transform practice with these issues in mind can be used by agencies to create FASD-informed care while still maintaining fidelity of existing practices.

To create FASD-informed care and demonstrate fidelity, agencies are encouraged to:

- Access reliable FASD prevention and intervention training (training resources provided in Appendix C).

- Use this TIP and/or other manualized approaches for FASD-informed care. Suggested resources for other manualized approaches include:
  - The SAMHSA FASD Center for Excellence (primarily FASD intervention)
  - The CDC (FASD prevention and intervention approaches)
  - (**http://www.cdc.gov/ncbddd/fasd/training.html**)
- Use checklists provided in this Implementation Guide to conduct process and outcome measurement.
  - If available, use fidelity checklists for other manualized approaches for FASD-informed care (be sure that fidelity checklists describe the active elements of an intervention and define them in behavioral terms).
- Where possible, and if not cost-prohibitive, bolster use of checklist(s) with direct observation of new clinical activities.

Some issues to be solved when implementing intervention fidelity monitoring:
- Which staff members measure specific parts of the checklist(s)?
- How are results conveyed to staff?
- How does a program define an acceptable fidelity score?
- How are positive results of the efforts measured by the checklist rewarded?
- What actions need to be taken if there is poor fidelity to program elements and goals?
- How are elements of checklist(s) updated over time, and when program changes occur?

Appendix A—Bibliography

[NOTE: Part 3 of this TIP, the online Literature Review, contains its own separate reference list.]

Aase, J. M., Jones, K. L., & Clarren, S. K. (1995). Do we need the term FAE? *Pediatrics*, 95(3), 428-430.

Abel, E. L., & Sokol, R. J. (1987). Incidence of fetal alcohol syndrome and economic impact of FAS-related anomalies: Drug alcohol syndrome and economic impact of FAS-related anomalies. *Drug and Alcohol Dependency*, 19(1), 51-70.

Abel, E. L., & Sokol, R. J. (1991). A revised conservative estimate of the incidence of FAS and its economic impact. *Alcoholism: Clinical and Experimental Research*, 15(3), 514-524.

Addiction Technology Transfer Center. (2004). *The change book: A blueprint for technology transfer.* (2nd ed.). Kansas City, MO: Addiction Technology Transfer Center.

Adubato, S. A., & Cohen, D. E. (2011). *Prenatal alcohol use and Fetal Alcohol Spectrum Disorders: Diagnosis, assessment and new directions in research and multimodal treatment.* Oak Park, IL: Bentham Science Publishers.

Amendah, D. D., Grosse, S. D., & Bertrand, J. (2010). Medical expenditures of children in the United States with Fetal Alcohol Syndrome. *Neurotoxicology and Teratology*, 33(2), 322-324.

American Psychiatric Association. (2000). *Diagnostic and statistical manual of mental disorders, fourth edition, text revision.* Washington DC: American Psychiatric Association.

Anderson, J. E., Ebrahim, S., Floyd, L., & Atrash, H. (2006). Prevalence of risk factors for adverse pregnancy outcomes during pregnancy and the preconception period—United States, 2002-2004. *Maternal & Child Health Journal*, 10(1), 101-106.

Andrew, G. (2011). Diagnosis of FASD: An overview. In E. P. Riley, S. Clarren, J. Weinberg, & E. Jonsson (Eds.). *Fetal Alcohol Spectrum Disorder: Management and policy perspectives of FASD* (pp. 127-148). Weinheim, Germany: Wiley-Blackwell.

Anthony, E. K., Austin, M. J., & Cormier, D. R. (2010). Early detection of prenatal substance exposure and the role of child welfare. *Children and Youth Services Review*, 32, 6-12.

Astley, S. J. (2004a). Fetal Alcohol Syndrome prevention in Washington State: Evidence of success. *Paediatric and Perinatal Epidemiology*, 18, 341-355. Accessed July 1, 2012 at **http:// depts.washington.edu/fasdpn/htmls/literature.htm**.

Astley, S. J. (2004b). *Diagnostic guide for Fetal Alcohol Spectrum Disorders: The 4-Digit Diagnostic Code*, Third Edition. Seattle, WA: University of Washington. Accessed July 1, 2012 at **http:// depts.washington.edu/fasdpn/htmls/literature.htm**.

Astley, S. J. (2010). Profile of the first 1,400 patients receiving diagnostic evaluations for Fetal Alcohol Spectrum Disorder at the Washington State Fetal Alcohol Syndrome Diagnostic and Prevention Network. *Canadian Journal of Clinical Pharmacology, 17*(1), e132-64. Accessed July 1, 2012 at **http://depts.washington.edu/fasdpn/htmls/literature.htm**.

Astley, S. J. (2011). Diagnosing Fetal Alcohol Spectrum Disorders (FASD). In S. A. Adubato & D. E. Cohen (Eds.). *Prenatal alcohol use and Fetal Alcohol Spectrum Disorders: Diagnosis, assessment and new directions in research and multimodal treatment* (pp. 3-29). Oak Park, IL: Bentham Science Publishers. Accessed July 1, 2012 at **http://depts.washington.edu/ fasdpn/htmls/literature.htm**.

Astley, S. J., Aylward, E. H., Olson, H. C., Kerns, K., Brooks, A., Coggins, T. E.,…Richards, T. (2009b). Functional magnetic resonance imaging outcomes from a comprehensive magnetic resonance study of children with Fetal Alcohol Spectrum Disorders. *Journal of Neurodevelopmental Disorders, 1*(1), 61-80. Accessed July 1, 2012 at **http://depts.washington. edu/fasdpn/htmls/literature.htm**.

Astley, S. J., Bailey, D., Talbot, C., & Clarren, S. K. (2000a). FAS primary prevention through FAS diagnosis: Part I. Identification of high-risk birth mothers through diagnosis of their children. *Alcohol & Alcoholism, 35*(5), 499-508. Accessed July 1, 2012 at **http://depts. washington.edu/fasdpn/htmls/literature.htm**.

Astley, S. J., Olson, H. C., Kerns, K., Brooks, A., Aylward, E., Coggins, T. E.,…Richards, T. (2009a). Neuropsychological and behavioral outcomes from a comprehensive magnetic resonance study of children with fetal alcohol spectrum disorders. *Canadian Journal of Clinical Pharmacology, 16*(1), e178-201. Accessed July 1, 2012 at **http://depts.washington.edu/fasdpn/htmls/literature.htm**.

Astley, S. J., Bailey, D., Talbot, C., & Clarren, S. K. (2000b). Fetal Alcohol Syndrome (FAS) primary prevention through FAS diagnosis: II. A comprehensive profile of 80 birth mothers of children with FAS. *Alcohol & Alcoholism, 35*(5), 509-519. Accessed January 13, 2014 at **http://depts.washington.edu/fasdpn/htmls/literature.htm**.

Astley, S. J., Stachowiak, J., Clarren, S. K., & Clausen, C. (2002). Application of the Fetal Alcohol Syndrome facial photographic screening tool in a foster care population. *The Journal of Pediatrics, 141*(5), 712-717. Accessed July 1, 2012 at **http://depts.washington.edu/fasdpn/htmls/literature.htm**.

Baxter, S. L. (2000). Adapting talk therapy for individuals with FAS/E. In J. Kleinfeld, B. Morse, B., & S. Wescott (Eds.), *Fantastic Antone Grows Up* (pp. 169-191). Fairbanks: University of Alaska Press.

Bays, J. (1992). The care of alcohol- and drug-affected infants. *Pediatric Annals, 21*, 485-495.

Bertrand, J. (2009). Interventions for children with Fetal Alcohol Spectrum Disorders (FASDs): Overview of findings for five innovative research projects. *Research in Developmental Disabilities 30*(5), 986-1006.

Bertrand, J., Floyd, R. L., Weber, M. K., O'Connor, M., Riley, E. P., Johnson, K. A., & Cohen, D. E. (2004). *National Task Force on Fetal Alcohol Syndrome and Fetal Alcohol Effect. Fetal Alcohol Syndrome: Guidelines for referral and diagnosis*. Atlanta, GA: Centers for Disease Control and Prevention.

Bishop, S., Gahagan, S., & Lord, C. (2007). Re-examining the core features of Autism: A comparison of Autism Spectrum Disorder and Fetal Alcohol Spectrum Disorder. *Journal of Child Psychology & Psychiatry, 48*(11), 1111-1121.

Blacher, J., & Baker, B. L. (2007). Positive impact of intellectual disability on families. *American Journal on Mental Retardation, 112*(5), 330-348.

Bobo, J. K., Klepinger, D. H., & Dong, F. B. (2007). Identifying social drinkers like to consume alcohol during pregnancy: Findings from a prospective cohort study. *Psychological Reports, 101*, 857-870.

Bonthius, D. J., & West, J. R. (1988). Blood alcohol concentration and microencephaly: A dose-response study in the neonatal rat. *Teratology, 37*(3), 223-231.

Boyce, M. C. (2010). A better future for baby: Stemming the tide of Fetal Alcohol Syndrome. *The Journal of Family Practice, 59*(6), 337-345.

Bradley, K. A., Bush, K. R., Epler, A. J., Dobie, D. J., Davis, T. M., Sporleder, J. L.,… Kivlahan, D. R. (2003). Two brief alcohol-screening tests From the Alcohol Use Disorders Identification Test (AUDIT): Validation in a female Veterans Affairs patient population. *Archives of Internal Medicine, 163*(7), 821-829.

Bradley, K. A., Bush, K. R., McDonell, M. B., Malone, T., & Fihn, S. D. (1998). Screening for problem drinking: Comparison of CAGE and AUDIT. Ambulatory Care Quality Improvement Project (ACQUIP). Alcohol Use Disorders Identification Test. *Journal of General Internal Medicine, 13*(6), 379–388.

Bradley, K. A., DeBenedetti. A. F., Volk, R. J., Williams, E. C., Frank, D., & Kivlahan, D. R. (2007). AUDIT-C as a brief screen for alcohol misuse in primary care. *Alcoholism: Clinical and Experimental Research, 31*(7), 1-10.

Brown, N. N., Gudjonsson, I., & Connor, P. (2011). Suggestibility and Fetal Alcohol Spectrum Disorders: I'll tell you anything you want to hear. *Journal of Psychiatry & Law, 39*, 39-71.

Burden, M. J., Jacobson, S. W., Sokol, R. J., & Jacobson, J. L. (2005). Effects of prenatal alcohol exposure on attention and working memory at 7.5 years of age. *Alcoholism: Clinical and Experimental Research, 29*(3), 443-452.

Burke, K. D. (2007). Substance-expose newborns: Hospital and child protection responses. *Children and Youth Services Review, 29*(12), 1503-1519.

Burke, B. L., Arkowitz, H., & Menchola, M. (2003). The efficacy of motivational interviewing: a meta-analysis of controlled clinical trials. *Journal of Consulting and Clinical Psychology, 71*, 843-861.

Bush, K., Kivlahan, D. R., McDonell, M. B., Fihn, S. D., & Bradley, K. A. (1998). The AUDIT alcohol consumption questions (AUDIT-C): An effective brief screening test for problem drinking. *Archives of Internal Medicine, 158*(16), 1789-195.

Caetano, R. (2010). Epidemiology of drinking among women of childbearing age and approaches to FAS prevention. Presentation to the Building FASD State Systems Conference, Nashville, TN, May 6, 2010. Center for Substance Abuse Treatment Prevention.

Center for Behavioral Health Quality and Statistics. (2010). *Results from the 2009 National Survey on Drug Use and Health (NSDUH): Mental Health Findings*. Rockville, MD: Substance Abuse and Mental Health Services Administration. Accessed September 1, 2013 at **http://www.samhsa.gov/data/NSDUH/2k9NSDUH/MH/2K9MHResults.htm**.

Center for Behavioral Health Quality and Statistics. (2013). Treatment Episode Data Set (TEDS): 2001-2011. *National Admissions to Substance Abuse Treatment Services*. Rockville, MD: Substance Abuse and Mental Health Services Administration. Accessed September 1, 2013 at **http://www.samhsa.gov/data/2k13/TEDS2011/TEDS2011N.pdf**.

Centers for Disease Control and Prevention. (2002). Alcohol use among women of childbearing age—United States, 1991-1999. *Morbidity and Mortality Weekly Report: Surveillance Summaries, 51*, 273-276.

Centers for Disease Control and Prevention. (2010). *Autism Spectrum Disorders*. Accessed September 30, 2011 at **http://www.cdc.gov/ncbddd/autism/data.html**.

Center for Substance Abuse Treatment. (1999). *Enhancing motivation for change in substance abuse treatment*. Treatment Improvement Protocol (TIP) Series 35. DHHS Publication No. (SMA) 01-3519. Rockville, MD: Substance Abuse and Mental Health Services Administration.

Center for Substance Abuse Treatment. (2009). *Implementing change in substance abuse treatment programs.* Technical Assistance Publication Series 31. HHS Publication No. (SMA) 09-4377. Rockville, MD: Substance Abuse and Mental Health Services Administration.

Center for Substance Abuse Treatment. (2008). *Managing depressive symptoms in substance abuse clients during early recovery.* Treatment Improvement Protocol (TIP) Series 48. DHHS Publication No. (SMA) 08-4353. Rockville, MD: Substance Abuse and Mental Health Services Administration.

Chang, G. (2001). Alcohol screening instruments for pregnant women. *Alcohol Research & Health, 25*(3), 204-209.

Chang, G., McNamara, T. K., Orav, E. J., Koby, D., Lavigne, A., Ludman, B.,…Wilkins-Haug, L. (2005). Brief intervention for prenatal alcohol use: A randomized trial. *Obstetrics & Gynecology, 105*(5-1), 991-998.

Chang, G., Wilkins-Haug, L., Berman, S., & Goetz, M. A. (1999). The TWEAK: Application in a prenatal setting. *Journal of Studies on Alcohol, 60*(3), 306–309.

Chapman, S., Borland, R., Scollo, M., Brownson, R. C., Dominello, A., & Woodward, S. (1999). The impact of smoke-free workplaces on declining cigarette consumption in Australia and the United States. *American Journal of Public Health, 89*(7), 1018-1023.

Chavez, G. F., Cordero, J. F., & Becerra, J. E. (1988). Leading major congenital malformations among minority groups in the United States, 1981-1986. *Morbidity and Mortality Weekly Report, 37*(3), 17-24.

Cherpitel, C. J., Korcha, R. A., Moskalewicz, J., Swiatkiewicz, G., Ye, Y., & Bond, J. (2010). Screening, Brief Intervention, and Referral to Treatment (SBIRT): 12-Month outcomes of a randomized controlled clinical trial in a Polish emergency department. *Alcoholism: Clinical & Experimental Research, 34*(11), 1922-1928.

Chiodo, L. M., Janisse, J., Delaney-Black, V., Sokol, R. J., & Hannigan, J. (2009). A metric of maternal prenatal risk drinking predicts neurobehavioral outcomes in preschool children. *Alcoholism: Clinical and Experimental Research, 33*(4), 634-644.

Chudley, A. E., Conry, J., Cook, J. L., Loock, C., Rosales, T., & LeBlanc, N. (2005). Fetal Alcohol Spectrum Disorder: Canadian guidelines for diagnosis. *Canadian Medical Association Journal, 172*(5), S1-S21.

Clark, E., Lutke, J., Minnes, P., & Quellette-Kuntz, H. (2004). Secondary disabilities among adults with Fetal Alcohol Spectrum Disorder in British Columbia. *Journal of FAS International, 2*(e13), 1-12.

Clarren, S. K., & Astley, S. J. (1997). The development of the Fetal Alcohol Syndrome Diagnostic and Prevention Network in Washington State. In A. Streissguth and J. Kanter (Eds.), *The Challenge of Fetal Alcohol Syndrome: Overcoming Secondary Disabilities* (pp. 40-51). Seattle, WA: University of Washington Press. Accessed July 1, 2012 at **http://depts. washington.edu/fasdpn/htmls/literature.htm**.

Clarren, S. K., Astley, S. J., Gunderson, V. M., & Spellman, D. (1992). Cognitive and behavioral deficits in nonhuman primates associated with very early embryonic binge exposures to ethanol. *The Journal of Pediatrics, 121*(5), 789-796. Accessed July 1, 2012 at **http://depts. washington.edu/fasdpn/htmls/literature.htm**.

Clarren, S. K., Carmichael-Olson, H., Clarren, S. G. B., & Astley, S. J. (2000). A child with Fetal Alcohol Syndrome. In: M. J. Guralnick (Ed.), *Handbook of Clinical Assessment for Young Children with Developmental Disabilities* (pp. 307-326). Baltimore, MD: Paul H. Brookes. Accessed July 1, 2012 at **http://depts.washington.edu/fasdpn/htmls/literature.htm**.

Clarren, S. K., & Smith, D. W. (1978). The Fetal Alcohol Syndrome. *New England Journal of Medicine, 298*(19), 1063-1067.

Coles, C. D. (1999). Intervening with children with FAS and ARND: Where do we start? In Centers for Disease Control and Prevention (Eds.), *Intervening with Children Affected by Prenatal Alcohol Exposure: Proceedings of a Special Focus Session of the Interagency Coordinating Committee on Fetal Alcohol Syndrome; September 10-11, 1998* (pp. 103-115). Chevy Chase, MD: National Institute of Alcohol Abuse and Alcoholism.

Coles, C. D., Kable, J. A., & Taddeo, E. (2009). Math performance and behavioral problems in children affected by prenatal alcohol exposure: Intervention and follow-up. *Journal of Developmental Disabilities, 28*(5), 518-530.

Coe, J., Sidders, J., Riley, K., Waltermire, J., & Hagerman, R. (2001). A survey of medication responses in children and adolescents with Fetal Alcohol Syndrome. *Mental Health Aspects of Developmental Disabilities, 4*(4), 148-155.

Committee on Ethics. (2008). *ACOG Committee Opinion Number 422: At-Risk Drinking and Illicit Drug Use: Ethical Issues in Obstetric and Gynecologic Practice (December 2008)*. Washington, DC: American College of Obstetricians and Gynecologists.

Connor, P. D., & Streissguth, A. P. (1996). Effects of prenatal exposure to alcohol across the lifespan. *Alcohol Health and Research World, 20*, 170-174.

De Bellis, M., & Thomas, L. (2003). Biologic findings of post-traumatic stress disorder and child maltreatment. *Current Psychiatry Repots, 5*, 108-117.

De Vos, G. (2003). *Women, justice and Fetal Alcohol Syndrome & Fetal Alcohol Effects: Defining the needs of the Elizabeth Fry Society to enhance work with women affected by FAS/E*. Manitoba, AB: University of Manitoba.

Denys, K., Rasmussen, C., & Henneveld, D. (2011). The effectiveness of a community-based intervention for parents with FASD. *Community Mental Health Journal, 47*(2), 209-219.

DiClemente, C. C. (1991). Motivational interviewing and stages of change. In W. R. Miller & S. Rollnick (Eds.), *Motivational Interviewing: Preparing People to Change Addictive Behaviors* (pp. 191- 206). New York: Guilford.

Division of Women's Health Issues. (2006). *Drinking and reproductive health: A Fetal Alcohol Spectrum Disorders prevention tool kit.* Washington, DC: American College of Obstetricians and Gynecologists.

Dum, M., Sobell, L. C., Sobell, M. B., Heinecke, N., Voluse, A., & Johnson, K. (2009). A Quick Drinking Screen for identifying women at risk for an alcohol-exposed pregnancy. *Addictive Behaviors, 34,* 714-716.

Elder, R. W., Lawrence, B., Ferguson, A., Naimi, T. S., Brewer, R. D., Chattopadhyay, S. K.,... Task Force on Community Preventive Services. (2010). The effectiveness of tax policy interventions for reducing excessive alcohol consumption and related harms. *American Journal of Preventive Medicine 38*(2), 217-229.

Ethen, M. K., Ramadhani, T. A., Scheuerle, A. E., Canfield, M. A., Wyszynski, D. F., Druschel, C. M.,...National Birth Defects Prevention Study. (2009). Alcohol consumption by women before and during pregnancy. *Maternal and Child Health Journal, 13*(2), 274-285.

Fabian, E., Ethridge, G., & Beveridge, S. (2009). Differences in perceptions of career barriers and supports for people with disabilities by demographic background and case status factor. *Journal of Rehabilitation, 75*(1), 41-49.

Fast, D. K., Conry, J., & Loock, C. (1999). Identifying Fetal Alcohol Syndrome among youth in the criminal justice system. *Journal of Developmental and Behavioral Pediatrics, 20*(5), 370-372.

Feldman, H. S., Jones, K. L., Lindsay, S., Slymen, D., Klonoff-Cohen, H., Kao, K...Chambers, C. (2012). Prenatal alcohol exposure patterns and alcohol-related birth defects and growth deficiencies: A prospective study. *Alcoholism: Clinical and Experimental Research, 36*(4), 670-676.

Finer, L., & Henshaw, S. (2006). *Estimates of abortion incidence 2001-2003.* New York: Guttmacher Institute.

Fixsen, D. L., Naoom, S. F., Blase, K. A., Friedman, R. M., & Wallace, F. (2005). *Implementation research: A synthesis of the literature.* Tampa, FL: University of South Florida, Louis de la Parte Florida Mental Health Institute, The National Implementation Research Network (FMHI Publication #231).

Fleming, M. F., Barry, K. L., Manwell, L. B., Johnson, K., & London, R. (1997). Brief physician advice for problem alcohol drinkers: A randomized controlled trial in community-based primary care practices. *The Journal of the American Medical Association, 277*(13), 1039-1045.

Floyd, R. L., Sobell, M., Velasquez, M. M., Ingersoll, K., Nettleman, M., Sobell, L.,...Project CHOICES Efficacy Study Group. (2007). Preventing alcohol-exposed pregnancies: A randomized controlled trial. *American Journal of Preventive Medicine, 32*(1), 1-10.

Floyd, R. L., Weber, M. K., Denny, C., & O'Connor, M. J. (2009). Prevention of Fetal Alcohol Spectrum Disorders. *Developmental Disabilities Research Reviews, 15,* 193-199.

Frank, D., Debenedetti, A. F., Volk, R. J., Williams, E. C., Kivlahan, D. R., & Bradley, K. A. (2008). Effectiveness of the AUDIT-C as a screening test for alcohol misuse in three racial/ethnic groups. *Journal of General Internal Medicine, 23*(6), 781-787.

Freunscht, I., & Feldmann, R. (2011). Young adults with Fetal Alcohol Syndrome (FAS): social, emotional and occupational development. *Klinische Pädiatrie, 223*(1), 33-7.

Fryer, S. L., McGee, C. L., Matt, G. E., Riley, E. P., & Mattson, S. N. (2007). Evaluation of psychopathological conditions in children with heavy prenatal alcohol exposure. *Pediatrics, 119*(3), e733-e741.

Gobelet, C., Luthi, F., Al-Khodairy, A., & Chamberlain, M. (2007). Vocational rehabilitation: A multidisciplinary intervention. *Disability and Rehabilitation, 29*(17), 1405-1410.

Goodacre, K., & Mercer, E. D. (1965). *Guide to the Middlesex Sessions Records, 1549-1889.* Middlesex, England: Greater London Record Office.

Goodlett, C. R. (2010). Fetal Alcohol Spectrum Disorders: New perspectives on diagnosis and intervention. *Alcohol, 44,* 579-582.

Grant, T. M. (2011). Preventing FASD: The Parent-Child Assistance Program (PCAP) intervention with high-risk mothers. In: Riley, E. P., Clarren, S., Weinberg, J., & Jonsson, E. (Eds.). *Fetal Alcohol Spectrum Disorder: Management and policy perspectives of FASD* (pp. 193-206). Weinheim, Germany: Wiley-Blackwell.

Grant, T., Ernst, C., Streissguth, A., & Porter, J. (1997). An advocacy program for mothers with FAS/FAE. In A. Streissguth, & J. Kanter (Eds.), *The Challenge of Fetal Alcohol Syndrome: Overcoming Secondary Disabilities* (pp. 102-112). Seattle: University of Washington Press.

Grant, T. M., Ernst, C. C., Streissguth, A., & Stark, K. (2005). Preventing alcohol and drug exposed births in Washington state: Intervention findings from three Parent-Child Assistance Program sites. *The American Journal of Drug and Alcohol Abuse, 31,* 471-490.

Grant, T., Huggins, J., Connor, P., Pedersen, J., Whitney, N., & Streissguth, A. (2004). A pilot community intervention for young women with Fetal Alcohol Spectrum Disorders. *Community Mental Health Journal, 40*(6), 499-511.

Green, C. R., Mihic, A. M., Armstrong, I. T., Nikkel, S. M., Stade, B. C., Rasmussen, C., Reynolds, J. N. (2009a). Executive function deficits in children with Fetal Alcohol Spectrum Disorders (FASD) measured using the Cambridge Neuropsychological Tests Automated Batter (CANTAB). *Journal of Child Psychology & Psychiatry, 50*(6), 688-697.

Green, C. R., Mihic, A. M., Brien, D. C., Armstrong, I. T., Nikkel, S. M., Stade, B. C.,… Reynolds, J. N. (2009b). Oculomotor control in children with Fetal Alcohol Spectrum Disorders assessed using a mobile eye-tracking laboratory. *European Journal of Neuroscience, 29,* 1302-1309.

Greenbaum, R. L., Stevens, S. A., Nash, K., Koren, G., & Rovet, J. (2009). Social cognitive and emotion processing abilities of children with Fetal Alcohol Spectrum Disorders: A comparison with Attention Deficit Hyperactivity Disorder. *Alcoholism: Clinical & Experimental Research, 33*(10), 1656-1670.

Greenspan, S. (2009). Foolish action in adults with intellectual disabilities: The forgotten problem of risk unawareness. In L.M. Glidden (Ed.), *International review of research in mental retardation* (vol. 36, pp. 147-194). New York, NY: Elsevier.

Guerri, C., Bazinet, A., & Riley, E. P. (2009). Foetal Alcohol Spectrum Disorders and alterations in brain and behavior. *Alcohol and Alcoholism, 44*(2), 108-114. Accessed December 2, 2011 at **http://alcalc.oxfordjournals.org/content/44/2/108.long**.

Hankin, J. R., Firestone, I. J., Sloan, J. J., Ager, J. W., Sokol, R. J., & Martier, S. S. (1996). Heeding the alcoholic beverage warning label during pregnancy: Multiparae versus nulliparae. *Journal of Studies on Alcohol and Drugs, 57*(2), 171-177.

Harden, B. J. (2004). Safety and stability for foster children: A developmental perspective. *Future of Children, 14*(1), 30-47.

Harwood, H. J., & Napolitano, D. M. (1985). Economic implications of the Fetal Alcohol Syndrome. *Alcohol Health & Research World, 10*(1), 38-43 and 74-75.

Henry, J., Sloane, M., & Black-Pond, C. (2007). Neurobiology and neurodevelopmental impact of childhood traumatic stress and prenatal alcohol exposure. *Language, Speech and Hearing Services in Schools, 38*(2), 99-108.

Hicks, M., & Tough, S. (2009). The importance of complete abstinence from alcohol before and during pregnancy: Enough evidence for justification? *Expert Review of Obstetrics & Gynecology, 4*(4), 401-414.

Higgins-Biddle, J., Hungerford, D., & Cates-Wessel, K. (2009). *Screening and brief interventions (SBI) for unhealthy alcohol use: A step-by-step implementation guide for trauma centers.* Atlanta: Centers for Disease Control and Prevention, National Center for Injury Prevention and Control.

Hoyme, H. E., May, P. A., & Kalberg, W. O. (2005). A practical clinical approach to the diagnosis of Fetal Alcohol Spectrum Disorders: Clarification of the 1996 Institute of Medicine criteria. *Pediatrics, 115*, 39-47.

Hser, Y., Grella, C., Evans, E., & Huang, Y. (2006). Utilization and outcomes of mental health services among patients in drug treatment. *Journal of Addictive Diseases, 25*(1), 73-85.

Huggins, J. E., Grant, T., O'Malley, K., & Streissguth, A. (2008). Suicide attempts among adults with Fetal Alcohol Spectrum Disorders: Clinical considerations. *Mental Health Aspects of Developmental Disabilities, 11*(2), 33-42.

Institute of Health Economics. (2009). *Fetal Alcohol Spectrum Disorders (FASD): Across the lifespan*. Proceedings from a Consensus Development Conference. Alberta, CA: Institute of Health Economics.

Interagency Coordinating Committee on FASD. (2011). *Consensus Statement: Recognizing Alcohol-Related Neurodevelopmental Disorder (ARND) in Primary Health Care of Children*. Proceedings from a Consensus Development Conference. Rockville, MD: Interagency Coordinating Committee on FASD.

Jirikowic, T., Gelo, J., & Astley, J. (2010). Children and youth with Fetal Alcohol Spectrum Disorders: Summary of intervention recommendations after clinical diagnosis. *Intellectual and Developmental Disabilities, 48*(5), 330-344. Accessed July 1, 2012 at http://depts.washington.edu/fasdpn/htmls/literature.htm.

Jirikowic, T., Kartin, D., & Olson, H. C. (2008). Children with Fetal Alcohol Spectrum Disorders: A descriptive profile of adaptive function. *Canadian Journal of Occupational Therapy, 75*(4), 236-246.

Jones, K. L., & Smith, D. W. (1973). Recognition of fetal alcohol syndrome in early infancy. *Lancet, 2*, 999-1001.

Jones, K., Smith, D. W., Ulleland, C., & Streissguth, A. (1973). Pattern of malformation in offspring of chronic alcoholic mothers. *Lancet, 1*, 1267-1271.

Kalberg, W. O., Provost, B., Tollison, S. J., Tabachnick, B. G., Robinson, L. K., Hoyme, H. E., …May, P. A. (2006). Comparison of motor delays in young children with Fetal Alcohol Syndrome to those with prenatal alcohol exposure and with no prenatal alcohol exposure. *Alcoholism: Clinical and Experimental Research, 30*(12), 2037–2045.

Kellerman, T. (2005). Recommended assessment tools for children and adults with confirmed or suspected FASD.

Kellerman, T. (2003). External brain. Accessed October 6, 2011 at **http://come-over.to/FAS/externalbrain.htm**.

Ker, K., & Chinnock, P. (2008). Interventions in the alcohol server setting for preventing injuries. *Cochrane Database of Systematic Reviews, Issue 3*, article number CD005244.

Knight, J. R., Sherritt, L., Shrier, L. A., Harris, S. K., & Chang, G. (2002). Validity of the CRAFFT substance abuse screening test among adolescent clinic patients. *Archives of Pediatrics & Adolescent Medicine, 156*(6), 607-614.

Knight, J. R., Shrier, L. A., Bravender, T. D., Farrell, M., Vander Bilt, J., & Shaffer, H. J. (1999). A new brief screen for adolescent substance abuse. *Archives of Pediatrics & Adolescent Medicine, 153*(6), 591-596.

Kodituwakku, P. W. (2007). Defining the behavioral phenotype in children with Fetal Alcohol Spectrum Disorders: A review. *Neuroscience and Biobehavioral Reviews, 31*, 192–201.

Kodituwakku, P. W., Handmaker, N. S., Cutler, S. K., Weathersby, E. K., & Handmaker, S. D. (1995). Specific impairments in self-regulation in children exposed to alcohol prenatally. *Alcoholism: Clinical and Experimental Research, 19*, 1558-1564.

Kodituwakku, P., Kalberg, M., & May, P. (2001). The effects of prenatal alcohol exposure on executive functioning. *Alcohol Res Health, 25*, 192-198.

Kodituwakku, P. W., & Kodituwakku, E. L. (2011). From research to practice: An integrative framework for the development of interventions for children with Fetal Alcohol Spectrum Disorders. *Neuropsychology Review, 21*(2), 204-223.

Kutner, M. (2006). Health literacy of America's adults. Presentation to the Meeting of the Minds II Symposium, Sacramento, CA, November 30, 2006. American Institutes of Research.

Kvigne, V. L., Leonardson, G. R., Borzelleca, J., Brock, E., Neff-Smith, M., & Welty, T. K. (2003). Characteristics of mothers who have children with Fetal Alcohol Syndrome or some characteristics of Fetal Alcohol Syndrome. *The Journal of the American Board of Family Medicine, 16*, 293-303.

Lee, K. T., Mattson, S. N., & Riley, E. P. (2004). Classifying children with heavy prenatal alcohol exposure using measures of attention. *Journal of the International Neuropsychological Society, 10*, 271-277.

Lehman, W. E. K., Greener, J. M., & Simpson, D. D. (2002). Assessing organizational readiness for change. *Journal of Substance Abuse Treatment 22*(4), 197-209.

Lemoine, P., Harousseau, H., Borteyni, J., & Menuet, J. (1968). Les enfants des parents alcooliques: anomolies observees a propos de 127 cas [The children of alcoholic parents: anomalies observed in 127 cases]. *Quest Medical, 25*, 476-482.

Leon, L., & Matthews, L. (2010). Self-esteem theories: Possible explanations for poor interview performance for people experiencing unemployment. *Journal of Rehabilitation, 76*(1), 41-50.

Leonardson, G. R., Loudenburg, R., & Struck, J. (2007). Factors predictive of alcohol use during pregnancy in three rural states. *Behavioral and Brain Functions, 3*, 8. Accessed June 13, 2011 at **http://www.behavioralandbrainfunctions.com/content/3/1/8**.

Liechty, J. M. (2011). Health literacy: Critical opportunities for social work leadership in health care and research. *Health & Social Work, 36*(2), 99-107.

Lupton, C., Burd, L., & Harwood, R. (2004). Cost of fetal alcohol spectrum disorders. *American Journal of Medical Genetics, 127C*(671), 42-50.

MacKinnon, D. P., Nohre, L., Pentz, M. A., & Stacy, A. W. (2000). The alcohol warning and adolescents: 5-year effects. *American Journal of Public Health, 90*(10), 1589-1594.

Madras, B. K., Compton, W. M., Avula, D., Stegbauer, T., Stein, J. B., & Clark, H. W. (2009). Screening, brief interventions, referral to treatment (SBIRT) for illicit drug and alcohol use at multiple healthcare sites: Comparison at intake and 6 months later. *Drug and Alcohol Dependence, 99*(1-3), 280-295.

Malbin, D. (1993). *Fetal Alcohol Syndrome Fetal Alcohol Effects: Strategies for professionals.* Center City, MN: Hazelden Educational Materials.

Manwell, L. B., Fleming, M. F., Mundt, M. P., Stauffacher, E. A., & Barry, K. L. (2002). Treatment of problem alcohol use in women of childbearing age: Results of a brief intervention trial. *Alcoholism: Clinical and Experimental Research, 24*, 1517–1524.

Marlatt, G. A., & Witkiewicz, K. (2002). Harm reduction approaches to alcohol use: Health promotion, prevention, and treatment. *Addictive Behaviors, 27*, 867-886.

Mattson, S. N., Crocker, N., & Nguyen, T. T. (2011). Fetal Alcohol Spectrum Disorders: Neuropsychological and behavioral features. *Neuropsychology Review, 21*, 81-101.

Mattson, S. N., Roesch, S. C., Fagerlund, A., Autti-Ramo, I., Jones, K. L., May, P. A., Adnams CM, Konovalova V, Riley EP, & the Collaborative Initiative on Fetal Alcohol Spectrum Disorders (CIFASD). (2010). Toward a neurobehavioral profile of Fetal Alcohol Spectrum Disorders. *Alcoholism: Clinical and Experimental Research, 34*(9), 1640–1650.

Mattson, S. N., Schoenfeld, A. M., & Riley, E. P. (2001). Teratogenic effects of alcohol on brain and behavior. *Alcohol Research and Health, 25*(3), 185-191.

May, P. A., Gossage, J. P., Brooke, L. E., Snell, C. L., Marais, A., Hendricks, L. S.,…Viljoen, D. L. (2005). Maternal risk factors for Fetal Alcohol Syndrome in the Western Cape Province of South Africa: A population-based study. *American Journal of Public Health, 95*(7), 1190-1199.

May, P. A., Gossage, J. P., Kalberg, W. O., Robinson, L. K., Buckley, D., Manning, M., & Hoyme, H. E. (2009). Prevalence and epidemiologic characteristics of FASD from various research methods with an emphasis on recent in-school studies. *Developmental Disabilities Research Reviews, 15*(3), 176-192.

McGee, C., Fryer, S., Bjorquist, O., Mattson, S., & Riley, E. (2008). Deficits in social problem solving in adolescents with prenatal exposure to alcohol. *The American Journal of Drug and Alcohol Abuse, 34*, 423-431.

McGinty, K., Worthington, R., & Dennison, W. (2008). Patient and family advocacy: Working with individuals with comorbid mental illness and developmental disabilities and their families. *Psychiatric Quarterly, 79*(3), 193-203.

Merrick, J. Merrick, E., Morad, M., & Kandel, I. (2006). Fetal Alcohol Syndrome and its long-term effects. *Minerva Pediatrica, 58*(3), 211-218.

Migliore, A., Grossi, T., Mank, D., & Rogan, P. (2007). Integrated employment or sheltered workshops: Preference of adults with intellectual disabilities, their families, and staff. Journal of *Vocational Rehabilitation, 26*, 5-19.

Migliore, A., Grossi, T., Mank, D., & Rogan, P. (2008). Why do adults with intellectual disabilities work in sheltered workshops? *Journal of Vocational Rehabilitation, 28*, 29-40.

Miller, W. R., & Rollnick, S. (2002). *Motivational interviewing: Preparing people for change.* (2nd ed.) New York, NY: Guildford Press.

Miller, W. R., & Sanchez, V. C. (1994). Motivating young adults for treatment and lifestyle change. In G. Howard (Ed.), *Issues in Alcohol Use and Misuse By Young Adults.* (pp. 55–82). Notre Dame, IN: University of Notre Dame Press.

Millon, T., Millon, C., & Davis, R. (1993). *Millon Adolescent Clinical Inventory & (MACI) Manual.* Minneapolis: NCS Assessments & NCS Pearson, Inc.

Moore, T. E., & Green, M. (2004). Fetal Alcohol Spectrum Disorder (FASD): A need for closer examination by the criminal justice system. *Criminal Reports, 19*(1), 99-108.

Moore, E. S., Ward, R. E., Rogers, J. L., Mattson, S. N., Autti-Rämö, I, Fagerlund, A,…the CIFASD. (2009). Identification of prenatal alcohol exposure using combined 3D facial imaging and neurobehavioral data. Presented at the Research Society on Alcoholism meeting, San Diego, June 2009. *Alcoholism: Clinical and Experimental Research, 33*, Supplement S1, 39A.

Morleo, M., Woolfall, K., Dedman, D., Mukherjee, R., Bellis, M. A., & Cook, P. A. (2011). Under-reporting of Foetal Alcohol Spectrum Disorders: An analysis of hospital episode statistics. *BMC Pediatrics, 11*, 14.

Morse, B. A., & Hutchins, E. (2000). Reducing complications from alcohol use during pregnancy through screening. *Journal of the American Medical Women's Association, 55*(4), 225-227, 240.

Moseley, L., & Gradisar, M. (2009). Evaluation of a school-based intervention for adolescent sleep problems. *Sleep, 32*(3), 334-341.

Murphy, N, & Elias, E. (2006). Sexuality of children and adolescents with developmental disabilities. *Pediatrics, 118*(1), 398-403.

Nanson, J. L., & Hiscock, M. (1990). Attention deficits in children exposed to alcohol prenatally. *Alcoholism: Clinical and Experimental Research, 14*, 656-661.

National Center for Birth Defects and Developmental Disabilities. (2005). *Fetal Alcohol Syndrome: Guidelines for referral and diagnosis.* Washington, DC: Centers for Disease Control and Prevention.

National Highway Traffic Safety Administration. (2007). *Fatality Analysis Reporting System (FARS).* Washington, DC: U.S. Department of Transportation.

National Institute on Alcohol Abuse and Alcoholism. (2000). *10th special report to the U.S. Congress on alcohol and health.* Washington, DC: U.S. Department of Health and Human Services.

National Institute on Alcohol Abuse and Alcoholism. (2004). NIAAA Council Approves Definition of Binge Drinking. *NIAAA Newsletter,* Winter 2004 No.3.

National Institute on Alcohol Abuse and Alcoholism. (2005). Brief Interventions. *NIAAA Alcohol Alert,* July 2005 No.66.

National Institute on Alcohol Abuse and Alcoholism. (2007). *Helping patients who drink too much: A clinician's guide.* Washington, DC: U.S. Department of Health and Human Services.

Neely-Barnes, S., Graff, J. C., Marcenko, M., & Weber, L. (2008). Family decision-making: Benefits to persons with developmental disabilities and their family members. *Journal of Intellectual and Developmental Disability,* 46(3), 93-105.

Noland, J. S., Singer, L. T., Arendt, R. E., Minnes, S., Short, E. J., & Bearer, C. F. (2003). Executive functioning in preschool-age children prenatally exposed to alcohol, cocaine, and marijuana. *Alcoholism: Clinical and Experimental Research, 27*(4), 647-656.

O'Connor, M. J., Shah, B., Whaley, S., Cronin, P., Gunderson, B., & Graham, J. (2002). Psychiatric illness in a clinical sample of children with prenatal alcohol exposure. *The American Journal of Drug and Alcohol Abuse, 28*(4), 743-754.O'Connor, M. J., & Whaley, S. E. (2007). Brief intervention for alcohol use by pregnant women. *American Journal of Public Health, 97*(2), 252-258.

Office of Applied Studies. (2006). *Treatment Episode Data Set (TEDS), 2006.* Rockville, MD: Substance Abuse and Mental Health Services Administration.

Office of Applied Studies. (2009). *The NSDUH Report: Substance Use Among Women During Pregnancy and Following Childbirth (May 21, 2009).* Rockville, MD: Substance Abuse and Mental Health Services Administration.

Office of Applied Studies. (2009). *National Survey on Drug Use and Health (NSDUH), 2002–2009.* Rockville, MD: Substance Abuse and Mental Health Services Administration.

Office of Applied Studies. (2011). *Results from the 2010 National Survey on Drug Use and Health: Summary of National Findings.* NSDUH Series H-41, HHS Publication No. (SMA) 11-4658. Rockville, MD: Substance Abuse and Mental Health Services Administration.

Office of the Surgeon General. (2005). *U.S. Surgeon General releases advisory on alcohol use in pregnancy.* Rockville, MD: U.S. Department of Health and Human Services.

O'Leary, C. (2005). Fetal Alcohol Syndrome. In: Developmental Disability Steering Group (Ed.), *Management Guidelines: Developmental Disability.* Melbourne: Therapeutic Guidelines Limited.

Olivan, G. G. (2005). What can be done to prevent violence and abuse of children with disabilities? [Article in Spanish] *Anales de Pediatria, 62*(2), 153-157.

Olson, H. C., Jirikowic, T., Kartin, D., & Astley, S. (2007). Responding to the challenge of early intervention for Fetal Alcohol Spectrum Disorders. *Infants & Young Children 20*(2), 172-189. Accessed July 1, 2012 at **http://depts.washington.edu/fasdpn/htmls/literature.htm**.

Olson, H. C., & Montague, R. M. (2011). An innovative look at early intervention for children affected by prenatal alcohol exposure. In S. Adubato & D. Cohen (Eds.), *Prenatal alcohol use and FASD: A model standard of diagnosis, assessment and multimodal treatment* (pp. 64-107). Oak Park, IL: Bentham Science Publishers.

Olson, H. C., O'Connor, M. J., & Fitzgerald, H. E. (2001). Lessons learned from study of the developmental impact of parental alcohol use. *Infant Mental Health Journal, 22*(3), 271-290.

Olson, H. C., Oti, R., Gelo, J., & Beck, S. (2009). "Family Matters:" Fetal Alcohol Spectrum Disorders and the family. *Developmental Disabilities Research Reviews, 15*, 235-249. Accessed July 1, 2012 at **http://depts.washington.edu/fasdpn/htmls/literature.htm**.

Olson, H. C., Rudo-Stern, J., & Gendler, B. (2011). Supporting parents of children with fetal alcohol spectrum disorders, and young children with significant prenatal alcohol exposure. In: R. E. Tremblay, M. Boivin, R. D. V. Peters, & G. Barr (Eds.), *Encyclopedia on Early Childhood Development* (online, pp. 1-10). Montreal, Quebec: Centre of Excellence for Early Childhood Development and Strategic Knowledge Cluster on Early Child Development. Accessed July 5, 2012 at **http://www.child-encyclopedia.com/documents/Olson-Rudo-Stern-GendlerANGxp1.pdf**.

O'Malley, K. D., & Hagerman, R. J. (1999.) Developing clinical practice guidelines for pharmacological interventions with alcohol-affected children. In Centers for Disease Control and Prevention (Eds.), *Intervening with Children Affected by Prenatal Alcohol Exposure: Proceedings of a Special Focus Session of the Interagency Coordinating Committee on Fetal Alcohol Syndrome; September 10-11, 1998* (pp. 145-177). Chevy Chase, MD: National Institute of Alcohol Abuse and Alcoholism.

Oscar-Berman, M., & Marinlovic, K. (2003). Alcoholism and the brain: An overview. *Alcohol Research & Health, 27*(2), 125–133.

Page, K. (2001). Fetal Alcohol Spectrum—The hidden epidemic in our courts. *Juvenile and Family Court Journal, 52*(4), 21-32.

Page, K. (2002). The invisible havoc of prenatal alcohol damage. *Journal of the Center for Families, Children & the Courts, 4*, 67-90.

Paley, B., & O'Connor, M. J. (2009). Intervention for individuals with Fetal Alcohol Spectrum Disorders: Treatment approaches and case management. *Developmental Disabilities Research Reviews, 15*, 258-267.

Parker, R. M., Ratzan, S. C., & Lurie, N. (2003). Health literacy: A policy challenge for advancing high-quality health care. *Health Affairs, 22*(4), 147-153.

Parker R. N., Saltz, R. F., & Hennessy, M. (1994). The impact of alcohol beverage container warning labels on alcohol-impaired drivers, drinking drivers and the general population in northern California. *Addiction, 89*, 1639-1651.

Payne, J. M., France, K. E., Henley, N., D'Antoine, H. A., Bartu, A. E., O'Leary, C. M.,… Geehoed, E. (2011). RE-AIM evaluation of the Alcohol and Pregnancy Project: Educational resources to inform health professionals about prenatal alcohol exposure and Fetal Alcohol Spectrum Disorder. *Evaluation & the Health Professions, 34*(1), 57-80.

Peadon, E., Payne, J., Henley, N., D'Antoine, H., Bartu, A., O'Leary, C.,…Elliott, E. J. (2010). Women's knowledge and attitudes regarding alcohol consumption in pregnancy: A national survey. *BMC Public Health, 10*, 510.

Pease, T., & Frantz, B. (1994). *Your rights and personal safety: An abuse prevention education program to empower adults with disabilities and train service providers.* Doylestown, PA: Network of Victim Assistance.

Pei, J., Denys, K., Hughes, J., & Rasmussen, C. (2011). Mental health issues in Fetal Alcohol Spectrum Disorder. *Journal of Mental Health, 20*(5), 438-448.

Premji, S., Benzies, K., Serrett, K., & Hayden, K. A. (2006). Research-based interventions for children and youth with a Fetal Alcohol Spectrum Disorder: Revealing the gap. *Child: Care, Health and Development, 33*, 389-397.

Prochaska, J., & DiClemente, C. (1986). Toward a comprehensive model of change. In W. R. Miller, & N. Heather (Eds.), *Treating Addictive Behaviors: Processes of Change* (pp. 3-27). New York: Plenum Press.

Project CHOICES Intervention Research Group. (2003). Reducing the risk of alcohol-exposed pregnancies: A study of motivational intervention in community settings. *Pediatrics, 111*, 1131-1135.

Project CHOICES Research Group. (2002). Alcohol-exposed pregnancy: Characteristics associated with risk. *American Journal of Preventive Medicine, 23*(3), 166-173.

Rasmussen, C. (2005). Executive functioning and working memory in fetal alcohol spectrum disorder. *Alcoholism: Clinical and Experimental Research, 29*, 1359–1367.

Riggins, T., Cacic, K., Buckingham-Howes, S., Scaletti, L. A., Salmeron, B.J., & Black, M. M. (2012). Memory ability and hippocampal volume in adolescents with prenatal drug exposure. *Neurotoxicology and Teratology, 34*(4), 434-441.

Roberts, G., & Nanson, J. (2000). *Best practices: Fetal Alcohol Syndrome/ Fetal Alcohol Effects and the effects of other substance use during pregnancy.* Ontario: Health Canada.

Royal College of Physicians of London. (1726). Annals of Royal College of Physicians, London, England (p. 253).

Russell, M. (1994). New assessment tools for risk drinking during pregnancy. *Alcohol Health & Research World, 18*(1), 55-61.

Russell, M., Czarnecki, D. M., Cowan, R., McPherson, E., & Mudar, P.J. (1991). Measures of maternal alcohol use as predictors of development in early childhood. *Alcoholism: Clinical & Experimental Research, 15*(6), 991–1000.

Russell, M., Martier, S. S., Sokol, R. J., Mudar, P., Jacobson, S., & Jacobson, J. (1996). Detecting risk drinking during pregnancy: A comparison of four screening questionnaires. *American Journal of Public Health, 86*(10), 1435– 1439.

Rutman, D. (2011). *Substance using women with FASD and FASD prevention: Service providers' perspectives on promising approaches in substance use treatment and care for women with FASD.* Victoria, British Columbia: University of Victoria.

Salmon, J. (2008). Fetal Alcohol Spectrum Disorder: New Zealand birth mothers' experiences. *Canadian Journal of Clinical Pharmacology, 15*(2), e191-e213.

Sampson, P. D., Bookstein, F. L., Barr, H. M., & Streissguth, A. P. (1994). Prenatal alcohol exposure, birthweight, and measures of child size from birth to age 14 years. *American Journal of Public Health, 84*(9), 1421-1428.

Sampson, P. D., Streissguth, A. P., Bookstein, F. L., Little, R. E., Clarren, S. K., Dehaene, P.,... Graham, J. M. (1997). Incidence of Fetal Alcohol Syndrome and prevalence of Alcohol-Related Neurodevelopmental Disorder. *Teratology, 56*(5), 317-326.

Sarkar, M., Burnett, M., Carriere, S., Cox, L. V., Dell, C. A., Gammon, H.,...Wood, R. (2009). Screening and recording of alcohol use among women of child-bearing age and pregnant women. *The Canadian Journal of Clinical Pharmacology, 16*(1), e242-e263.

Savage, C., Wray, J., Ritchey, P. N., Sommers, M., Dyehouse, J., & Fulmer, M. (2003). Current screening instruments related to alcohol consumption in pregnancy and a proposed alternative method. *Journal of Obstetric, Gynecologic, & Neonatal Nursing, 32*(4), 437-446.

Schmucker, C. A. (1997). Case managers and independent living instructors: Practical hints and suggestions for adults with FAS. In A. Streissguth, & J. Kanter (Eds.), *The Challenge of Fetal Alcohol Syndrome: Overcoming Secondary Disabilities* (pp. 96-101). Seattle: University of Washington Press.

Schonfeld, A. M., Mattson, S. N., & Riley, E. P. (2005). Moral maturity and delinquency after prenatal alcohol exposure. *Journal of Studies on Alcohol and Drugs, 66*(4), 545-554.

Schonfeld, A. M., Paley, B., Frankel, F., O'Connor, M. H. (2006). Executive functioning predicts social skills following prenatal alcohol exposure. *Child Neuropsychology, 12*(6), 439-452.

Seale, J. P., Boltri, J. M., Shellenberger, S., Velasquez, M. M., Cornelius, M., Guyinn, M., Okosun, I., & Sumner, H. (2006). Primary care validation of a single screening question for drinkers. *Journal of Studies on Alcohol and Drugs, 67*(5), 778-784.

Shor, S., Nulman, I., Kulaga, V., & Koren, G., (2010). Heavy in utero ethanol exposure is associated with the use of other drugs of abuse in a high-risk population. *Alcohol, 44*(7), 623-627.

Shults, R. A., Elder, R. W., Sleet, D. A., Nichols, J. L., Alao, M. O., Carande-Kulis, V. G.,... the Task Force on Community Preventive Services. (2001). Reviews of evidence regarding interventions to reduce alcohol-impaired driving. *American Journal of Preventive Medicine, 21*(4S), 66-88.

Silverman, A. B., Reinherz, H. Z., & Giaconia, R. M. (1996). The long-term sequelae of child and adolescent abuse: A longitudinal community study. *Child Abuse and Neglect, 20*(8), 709-723.

Sokol R. J., & Clarren, S. K. (1989). Guidelines for use of terminology describing the impact of prenatal alcohol on the offspring. *Alcoholism: Clinical and Experimental Research, 13*(4), 597-598.

Sokol, R. J., Delaney-Black, V., & Nordstrom, B. (2003). Fetal Alcohol Spectrum Disorder. *JAMA, 290*(22), 2996-2999.

Sokol, R. J., Martier, S. S., & Ager, J. W. (1989). The T-ACE questions: Practical prenatal detection of risk drinking. *American Journal of Obstetrics and Gynecology, 160*(4), 863-870.

Spohr, H. L., Willms, J., & Steinhausen, H. C. (2007). Fetal Alcohol Spectrum Disorders in young adulthood. *Journal of Pediatrics, 150*(2), 175-179.

Springer, F., & Phillips, J. L. (2006). The IOM Model: A tool for prevention planning and implementation. *Prevention Tactics, 8*(13), 1-7.

Springer, J. F., & Phillips, J. L. (2007). *The Institute of Medicine framework and its implication for the advancement of prevention policy, programs and practice.* Prevention Policy Paper Series. EMT Associates, Inc: Folsom, CA. Accessed January 18, 2012 at **http://www.ca-sdfsc.org/docs/resources/SDFSC_IOM_Policy.pdf**.

Springer, K. W., Sheridan, J., Kuo, D., & Carnes, M. (2007). Long-term physical and mental health consequences of childhood physical abuse: Results from a large population-based sample of men and women. *Child Abuse & Neglect, 31*, 517-530.

Stratton, K., Howe, C., Battaglia, F., & the Committee to Study Fetal Alcohol Syndrome. (1996). *Fetal Alcohol Syndrome: Diagnosis, epidemiology, prevention and treatment.* Washington, DC: National Academy Press.

Streissguth, A. (1997). *Fetal Alcohol Syndrome: A guide for families and communities.* Baltimore: Paul H. Brookes Publishing Co.

Streissguth, A. P., Barr, J. K., & Bookstein, F. L. (1996). *Understanding the occurrence of secondary disabilities in clients with Fetal Alcohol Syndrome (FAS) and Fetal Alcohol Effects (FAE).* University of Washington: Seattle, WA.

Streissguth A. P., Bookstein, F. L., Barr, H. M., Sampson, P. D., O'Malley, K., & Young, J. K. (2004). Risk factors for adverse life outcomes in Fetal Alcohol Syndrome and Fetal Alcohol Effects. *Journal of Developmental Behavioral Pediatrics, 25*(4), 228-238.

Streissguth, A. P., & O'Malley, K. (2000). Neuropsychiatric implications and long-term consequences of fetal alcohol spectrum disorders. *Seminars in Clinical Neuropsychiatry, 5*(3), 177–190.

Sullivan, W. C. (1899). A note on the influence of maternal inebriety on the offspring. *Journal of Mental Science, 45*, 489-503.

Taylor, P., Bailey, D., Peters, R., & Stein, B. (2009). *Substance abuse during pregnancy: Guidelines for screening.* Olympia, WA: Washington State Department of Health.

Teicher, M. D. (2000). Wounds that time won't heal: The neurobiology of child abuse. *Cerebrum: The Dana Forum on Brain Science, 2*(4), 50-67.

Ulleland, C. (1972). The offspring of alcoholic mothers. *Annals New York Academy of Sciences, 197*, 167-169. Accessed July 1, 2012 at **http://depts.washington.edu/fasdpn/htmls/literature.htm**.

Ulleland, C., Wennberg, R., Igo, R., & Smith, N. (1970). *The offspring of alcoholic mothers.* Jersey City, New Jersey: American Pediatric Society and Society for Pediatric Research. Accessed July 1, 2012 at **http://depts.washington.edu/fasdpn/htmls/literature.htm**.

U.S. Department of Health and Human Services. (2003). *Developing cultural competence in disaster mental health programs: Guiding principles and recommendations.* (DHHS Pub. No. (SMA) 3828). Rockville, MD: Center for Mental Health Services, Substance Abuse and Mental Health Services Administration.

Vallone, D. M., Duke, J. C., Cullen, J., McCausland, K. L., & Allen, J. A. (2011). Evaluation of EX: A national mass media smoking cessation campaign. *Research and Practice, 101*(2), 302-309.

Voas, R. B., & Fell, J. C. (2010). Preventing alcohol-related problems through health policy research. *Alcohol Research & Health, 33*(1-2), 18-28.

Vogel, H., Knight, E., Lauded, A., & Maura, S. (1998). Double Trouble in recovery: Self-help for people with dual diagnoses. *Psychiatric Rehabilitation Journal, 21*(4), 356-364.

Wagenaar, A. C., Murray, D. M., & Toomey, T. L. (2000). Communities Mobilizing for Change on Alcohol (CMCA): Effects of a randomized trial on arrests and traffic crashes. *Addiction, 95*(2), 209-217.

Wagenaar, A. C., Salois, M. J., & Komro, K. A. (2009). Effects of beverage alcohol price and tax levels on drinking: A meta-analysis of 1003 estimates from 112 studies. *Addiction, 104*, 179-190.

Wilkinson, G. S., & Robertson, G. J. (2006). *WRAT4 Wide Range Achievement Test professional manual.* Lutz, FL: Psychological Assessment Resources, Inc.

Williams, M. S., & Shwellenberger, S. (1996). *How does your engine run? A Leader's guide to the alert program for self-regulation.* Albuquerque, NM: Therapy Works Inc.

Williams, R., & Vinson, D. C. (2001). Validation of a single screening question for problem drinking. *The Journal of Family Practice, 50*(4), 307-312.

Winn, S., & Hay, I. (2009). Transition from school for youths with a disability: Issues and challenges. *Disability & Society, 24*(1), 103-115.

Zlotnick, C., Johnson, D. M., Stout, R. L., Zywiak, W. H., Johnson, J. E., & Schneider, R. J. (2006). Childhood abuse and intake severity in alcohol disorder patients. *Journal of Traumatic Stress, 19*(6), 949-959.

Appendix B—Selected Screening Instruments for Identifying Alcohol Use Among Women

[NOTE: Part 3 of this TIP, the online Literature Review, contains a full discussion of these and other alcohol screening instruments for use with women.]

T-ACE

The T-ACE is a 4-item instrument appropriate for detecting heavy alcohol use in pregnant women (Sokol, Martier, & Ager, 1989). T-ACE uses the **A**, **C**, and **E** questions from the CAGE screening tool and adds one on **T**olerance for alcohol. The first question assesses tolerance by asking if it takes more than it used to, to get "high" (i.e., intoxicated). T-ACE has sensitivity equal to the longer Michigan Alcohol Screening Test (MAST) and greater than the CAGE (Bradley, Bush, McDonell, Malone, & Fihn, 1998). It has been validated only for screening pregnant women with risky drinking (Russell, 1994).

1. How many drinks does it take for you to feel high? (**T**olerance)
2. Have people **A**nnoyed you by criticizing your drinking?   A) Yes   B) No
3. Have you ever felt you ought to **C**ut down on your drinking?   A) Yes   B) No
4. Have you ever had a drink first thing in the morning to steady your nerves or get rid of a hangover? (**E**ye-opener)   A) Yes   B) No

Scores

Any woman who answers more than two drinks on question 1 is scored 2 points. Each "yes'" to the additional 3 questions scores 1. Scoring 2 or more is considered a positive screen (Chang, Wilkins-Haug, Berman, & Goetz, 1999), and the woman should receive—or be referred to a specialist for—further assessment. At the same time, a woman could drink 2 drinks per day during pregnancy and not get a positive screen using this tool. She may not be at risk for alcoholism, but because of her pregnancy she's drinking at an unsafe level.

Sources:
- Bradley, K. A., Bush, K. R., McDonell, M. B., Malone, T., & Fihn, S. D. (1998). Screening for problem drinking: Comparison of CAGE and AUDIT. Ambulatory Care Quality Improvement Project (ACQUIP). Alcohol Use Disorders Identification Test. *Journal of General Internal Medicine, 13*(6), 379–388.
- Chang, G., Wilkins-Haug, L., Berman, S., & Goetz, M. A. (1999). The TWEAK: Application in a prenatal setting. *Journal of Studies on Alcohol, 60*(3), 306–309.
- Russell, M. (1994). New assessment tools for risk drinking during pregnancy: T-ACE, TWEAK, and others. *Alcohol Health and Research World, 18*(1), 55–61.
- Sokol, R. J., Martier, S. S., & Ager, J. W. (1989). The T-ACE questions: Practical prenatal detection of risk drinking. *American Journal of Obstetrics and Gynecology, 160*(4), 863-870.

TWEAK

TWEAK (Russell, Czarnecki, Cowan, McPherson, & Mudar, 1991) identifies pregnant women who are at risk for alcohol use. It consists of five items and uses a 7-point scoring system. In a study of more than 3,000 women at a prenatal clinic, the TWEAK was found to be more sensitive than the CAGE and Michigan Alcohol Screening Test (MAST), and more specific than the T-ACE (Russell et al., 1996). The tolerance question scores 2 points for an answer of three or more drinks. However, if the criterion for the tolerance question is reduced to two drinks for women, the sensitivity of TWEAK increases, and the specificity and predictive ability decrease somewhat (Chang et al., 1999).

1. (**T** – Tolerance) How many drinks does it take for you to feel high?
2. (**W** – Worried) Does your partner (or do your parents) ever worry or complain about your drinking? A) Yes   B) No
3. (**E** – Eye-Opener) Have you ever had a drink first thing in the morning to steady your nerves or get rid of a hangover? (Eye-opener) A) Yes   B) No
4. (**A** – Amnesia) Have you ever awakened the morning after some drinking the night before and found that you could not remember part of the evening before? A) Yes   B) No
5. (**K** – K/Cut down) Have you ever felt that you ought to cut down on your drinking? A) Yes   B) No

Scores

A woman receives 2 points on question 1 if she reports that she can hold more than 5 drinks without falling asleep or passing out. A positive response to question 2 scores 2 points, and a positive response to each of the last 3 questions scores 1 point each. A total score of 2 or more indicates that the woman is a risky drinker and requires further assessment. At the same time, drinking at any level during pregnancy is unsafe, even if the woman scores negative with this tool.

Sources:
- Chang, G., Wilkins-Haug, L., Berman, S., & Goetz, M. A. (1999). The TWEAK: Application in a prenatal setting. *Journal of Studies on Alcohol, 60*(3), 306–309.
- Russell, M., Czarnecki, D. M., Cowan, R., McPherson, E., & Mudar, P.J. (1991). Measures of maternal alcohol use as predictors of development in early childhood. *Alcoholism: Clinical & Experimental Research, 15*(6), 991–1000.
- Russell, M., Martier, S. S., Sokol, R. J., Mudar, P., Jacobson, S., & Jacobson, J. (1996). Detecting risk drinking during pregnancy: A comparison of four screening questionnaires. *American Journal of Public Health, 86*(10), 1435– 1439.

The CRAFFT Screening Interview

The CRAFFT is a behavioral health screening tool for use with children under the age of 21 and is recommended by the American Academy of Pediatrics' Committee on Substance Abuse for use with adolescents. It consists of a series of six questions developed to screen adolescents for high-risk alcohol and other drug use disorders simultaneously. It is a short, effective screening tool meant to assess whether a longer conversation about the context of use, frequency, and other risks and consequences of alcohol and other drug use is warranted. The questions should be asked exactly as written.

Begin: "I'm going to ask you a few questions that I ask all my patients. Please be honest. I will keep your answers confidential."

Part A

During the PAST 12 MONTHS, did you:	No	Yes
1. Drink any <u>alcohol</u> (more than a few sips)? (Do not count sips of alcohol taken during family or religious events.)		
2. Smoke any <u>marijuana</u> or <u>hashish</u>?		
3. Use <u>anything else</u> to <u>get high</u>? ("anything else" includes illegal drugs, over the counter and prescription drugs, and things that you sniff or "huff")		

For clinic use only: Did the patient answer "yes" to any questions in Part A?
No: Ask CAR question only, then stop.   **Yes: Ask all 6 CRAFFT questions.**

Part B	No	Yes
1. Have you ever ridden in a <u>CAR</u> driven by someone (including yourself) who was "high" or had been using alcohol or drugs?		
2. Do you ever use alcohol or drugs to <u>RELAX</u>, feel better about yourself, or fit in?		
3. Do you ever use alcohol or drugs while you are by yourself, or <u>ALONE</u>?		
4. Do you ever <u>FORGET</u> things you did while using alcohol or drugs?		
5. Do your <u>FAMILY</u> or <u>FRIENDS</u> ever tell you that you should cut down on your drinking or drug use?		
6. Have you ever gotten into <u>TROUBLE</u> while you were using alcohol or drugs?		

CONFIDENTIALITY NOTICE:

The information recorded on this page may be protected by special federal confidentiality rules (42 CFR Part 2), which prohibit disclosure of this information unless authorized by specific written consent. A general authorization for release of medical information is NOT sufficient for this purpose.

© CHILDREN'S HOSPITAL BOSTON, 2009. ALL RIGHTS RESERVED.
Reproduced with permission from the Center for Adolescent Substance Abuse Research, CeASAR, Children's Hospital Boston. (**www.ceasar.org**)

Scores
Each "yes" response in Part B scores 1 point. A total score of 2 or higher is a positive screen, indicating a need for additional assessment.

© Children's Hospital Boston, 2009. This form may be reproduced in its exact form for use in clinical settings, courtesy of the Center for Adolescent Substance Abuse Research, Children's Hospital Boston, 300 Longwood Ave, Boston, MA 02115, U.S.A., (617) 355-5433, **www.ceasar. org.**

Sources:
- American Psychiatric Association. (2000). *Diagnostic and statistical manual of mental disorders, fourth edition, text revision.* Washington DC: American Psychiatric Association.
- Knight, J. R., Sherritt, L., Shrier, L. A., Harris, S. K., & Chang, G. (2002). Validity of the CRAFFT substance abuse screening test among adolescent clinic patients. *Archives of Pediatrics & Adolescent Medicine, 156*(6), 607-614.
- Knight, J. R., Shrier, L. A., Bravender, T. D., Farrell, M., Vander Bilt. J., & Shaffer, H. J. (1999). A new brief screen for adolescent substance abuse. *Archives of Pediatrics & Adolescent Medicine, 153*(6), 591-596.

AUDIT-C

The AUDIT-C comprises the first three questions of the World Health Organization (WHO) AUDIT. The AUDIT-C was first described in VA patients (Bush, Kivlahan, McDonell, Fihn, & Bradley, 1998; Bradley et al., 2003), but has now been validated in other U.S. clinical populations (Bradley et al., 2007; Frank et al., 2008; Seale et al., 2006; Williams & Vinson, 2001).

Q1: How often did you have a drink containing alcohol in the past year?	Points
Never - 0 Monthly or less - 1 Two to four times a month - 2 Two to three times a week - 3 Four or more times a week - 4	
Q2: How many drinks did you have on a typical day when you were drinking in the past year?	**Points**
None, I do not drink - 0 1 or 2 - 0 3 or 4 - 1 5 or 6 - 2 7 to 9 - 3 10 or more - 4	
Q3: How often did you have six or more drinks on one occasion in the past year?	**Points**
Never - 0 Less than monthly - 1 Monthly - 2 Weekly - 3 Daily or almost daily - 4	

Scores

The AUDIT-C is scored on a scale of 0–12 (scores of 0 reflect no alcohol use). In women, a score of 3 or more is considered positive.

Sources:
- Bradley, K. A., Bush, K. R., Epler, A. J., Dobie, D. J., Davis, T. M., Sporleder, J. L., Maynard, C., Burman, M. L., & Kivlahan, D. R. (2003). Two brief alcohol-screening tests From the Alcohol Use Disorders Identification Test (AUDIT): Validation in a female Veterans Affairs patient population. *Archives of Internal Medicine, 163*(7), 821-829.

- Bradley, K. A., DeBenedetti. A. F., Volk, R. J., Williams, E. C., Frank, D., & Kivlahan, D. R. (2007). AUDIT-C as a brief screen for alcohol misuse in primary care. *Alcoholism: Clinical and Experimental Research, 31*(7), 1-10.

- Bush, K., Kivlahan, D. R., McDonell, M. B., Fihn, S. D., & Bradley, K. A. (1998). The AUDIT alcohol consumption questions (AUDIT-C): An effective brief screening test for problem drinking. *Archives of Internal Medicine, 158*(16), 1789-195.

- Frank, D., Debenedetti, A. F., Volk, R. J., Williams, E. C., Kivlahan, D. R., & Bradley, K. A. (2008). Effectiveness of the AUDIT-C as a screening test for alcohol misuse in three racial/ethnic groups. *Journal of General Internal Medicine, 23*(6), 781-787.

- Seale, J. P., Boltri, J. M., Shellenberger, S., Velasquez, M. M., Cornelius, M., Guyinn, M., Okosun, I., & Sumner, H. (2006). Primary care validation of a single screening question for drinkers. *Journal of Studies on Alcohol and Drugs, 67*(5), 778-784.

- Williams, R., & Vinson, D. C. (2001). Validation of a single screening question for problem drinking. *The Journal of Family Practice, 50*(4), 307-312.

Appendix C—Public and Professional Resources on FASD

The SAMHSA FASD Center for Excellence

SAMHSA FASD Center for Excellence
www.fasdcenter.samhsa.gov

The official site of the SAMHSA FASD Center for Excellence provides information and resources about FASD, as well as awareness materials, a fully searchable database, and access to training, technical assistance, and conference/event speakers.

National Association of FASD State Coordinators
http://fasdcenter.samhsa.gov/statesystemsofcare/nafsc.aspx

The SAMHSA FASD Center for Excellence helped to establish the National Association of FASD State Coordinators (NAFSC) in 2003 to support state-based efforts to increase the system of care available to individuals with an FASD and their families. NAFSC's mission is to promote prevention, treatment, and care systems for FASD, nationwide, through collaboration with systems within their respective states and among member states. The site provides updates on current activities, a roster of current members, and full contact information.

Assessment and Diagnosis

National Organization on FAS (NOFAS)
www.nofas.org

NOFAS is a leading voice and resource for the FASD community, and was one of the first. Founded in 1990, NOFAS is still the only international non-profit organization committed solely to FASD primary prevention, advocacy, and support. NOFAS has 30 affiliate programs around the country, and provides a Resource Directory to help locate FASD-related services. Also see *Information and Training*, below.

University of Washington: FAS Diagnostic & Prevention Network
http://depts.washington.edu/fasdpn/

The Washington State FAS Diagnostic & Prevention Network (FAS/DPN) is a network of four WA State community-based interdisciplinary FASD diagnostic clinics linked by the core clinical/research/training clinic at the Center on Human Development and Disability at the University of Washington in Seattle. The network was established in 1993. Each clinic in the network uses the same interdisciplinary approach to diagnosis and the same systematic diagnostic method; the *4-Digit Diagnostic Code*. The mission of the FAS DPN is primary and secondary prevention of FAS through screening, diagnosis, intervention, training, education, and research. The FAS DPN began diagnosing patients in 1993, and has diagnosed over 2,000 patients to date. See also *Information and Training*, below.

Grant Opportunities

SAMHSA Grant Opportunities
http://www.samhsa.gov/grants/

SAMHSA's grant management site allows applicants and prospective applicants to review Requests for Application (RFA's) from each of SAMHSA's sub-agencies, submit applications online, track application status, review reporting requirements, and manage the activity of awarded grants.

Grants.gov
www.grants.gov

Grants.gov was established as a governmental resource named the E-Grants Initiative, part of the President's 2002 Fiscal Year Management Agenda to improve government services to the public. Today, Grants.gov is a central storehouse for information on over 1,000 grant programs and provides access to approximately $500 billion in annual awards. The site is searchable by agency, keyword, and a variety of other variables.

Information and Training

Families Moving Forward
http://depts.washington.edu/fmffasd/

The *Families Moving Forward Program* intervention is a scientifically validated behavioral consultation program tailored for families raising preschool and school-aged individuals with FASD or confirmed prenatal alcohol exposure. The intervention includes methods and materials that appropriately trained counselors can use when working with families of a client who has an FASD. Training on FASD intervention, and on the *Families Moving Forward Program*, is regularly available through the East Coast (Florida) or West Coast (Seattle) training centers, or on-site at an agency location in the United States, Canada, or elsewhere. Once training is completed, all materials are freely available on a Web site to be downloaded.

The FASD Information Page of the Centers for Disease Control and Prevention (CDC)
http://www.cdc.gov/ncbddd/fasd/

The CDC's FASD page offers extensive information on the background of FASD, diagnosis and treatment, and training and educational materials, as well as access to articles, print materials, and multimedia tools for raising awareness.

FASD Regional Training Centers
http://www.cdc.gov/ncbddd/fasd/index.html

The CDC's FASD Regional Training Centers (RTCs) develop, implement, and evaluate educational curricula regarding FASD prevention, identification, and care, and incorporate the curricula into training programs at each grantee's university or college, into other schools throughout their regions, and into the credentialing requirements of professional boards. Check the site for links to specific, currently-active regional sites. Currently funded regional sites include the following:

- **Southeastern FASD Regional Training Center**
- **Arctic FASD Regional Training Center**
- **Frontier FASD Regional Training Center**

The National Institute on Alcohol Abuse and Alcoholism
http://www.niaaa.nih.gov

The National Institute on Alcohol Abuse and Alcoholism (NIAAA) is one of the 27 Institutes and Centers that comprise the National Institutes of Health (NIH), a component of HHS. NIAAA is the primary U.S. agency for conducting and supporting research on the causes, consequences, prevention, and treatment of alcohol abuse, alcoholism, and alcohol problems, including health effects such as FASD. NIAAA disseminates research findings to general, professional, and academic audiences. The Web site has links to relevant NIAAA publications. The FASD-specific **Web link** at NIAAA is **http://www.niaaa.nih.gov/research/major-initiatives/fetal-alcohol-spectrum-disorders**. This page also links to overviews of the activities of NIAAA's Interagency Coordinating Committee on FASD (ICCFASD).

National Organization on FAS (NOFAS)
www.nofas.org

NOFAS is a leading voice and resource for the FASD community, and was one of the first. Founded in 1990, NOFAS is still the only international non-profit organization committed solely to FASD primary prevention, advocacy, and support. The official site provides access to materials for educators, healthcare professionals, expectant mothers, and individuals and families living with an FASD. Also see *Assessment and Diagnosis*, above.

University of Washington FAS/DPN Training
http://depts.washington.edu/fasdpn/htmls/training.htm

In addition to assessment and diagnostic services, the University of Washington's FAS/DPN offers 1-day trainings on screening, diagnosis, treatment planning, and primary prevention of FASD, and also 2-day and online trainings for interdisciplinary clinical teams (or individual clinical team members) seeking to establish a FASD Diagnostic Clinic in their community.

Research and Journal Articles

Appendix A of this TIP contains an extensive bibliography for further reading on FASD, and Part 3 of this TIP, the online Literature Review (**http://store.samhsa.gov/home**), contains its own bibliography. In addition, the following Web sites and journals are excellent resources for further literature on FASD and related issues.

Alcohol
http://www.sciencedirect.com/science/journal/07418329/44/7-8

In 2010, the journal *Alcohol* published two issues devoted entirely to FASD diagnosis and intervention (Volume 44, issues 7-8). Together, these issues contain 16 articles, all of which can be accessed via the link above. Note: There is a cost for each article.

The Collaborative Initiative on FASD (CIFASD)
http://cifasd.org/

The Collaborative Initiative on FASD (CIFASD) is a consortium dedicated to informing and developing effective interventions and treatment approaches for FASD through multidisciplinary research involving basic, behavioral, and clinical investigators and projects. The Web site contains an extensive bibliography of recent FASD-related literature (2004 to the present). Many of the bibliographic items link to full abstracts through PubMed, but full articles must be purchased.

The Journal of Psychiatry & Law
http://www.federallegalpublications.com/journal-of-psychiatry-law/

The Winter 2010 (**Volume 38, issue 4**) and Spring 2011 (**Volume 39, issue 1**) issues of *The Journal of Psychiatry & Law* are devoted entirely to FASD-related issues, ranging from intervention approaches, to addressing FASD in the criminal justice system, to FASD as an adoption disclosure issue. A full listing of the articles is contained at the Volume links above. Note: There is a cost for each full issue.

Research Search Engines

Both the SAMHSA FASD Center for Excellence and NOFAS offer free online search engines that can be used to access FASD-related literature by author, title, keywords, or topic area.

Support Networks for Individuals with an FASD and Their Families

Birth Mothers Network
http://www.nofas.org/join-the-circle-of-hope/

The Birth Mothers Network, also known as the Circle of Hope, was founded through NOFAS in 2004. It is a network of women who have consumed alcohol during pregnancy and may have a child or children with an FASD. Members are lovingly referred to as "Warrior Moms" because of their incredible strengths. Many of the women are in recovery from alcoholism, or alcohol and drug addiction. However, the network also includes women without the disease of addiction, but who drank alcohol during pregnancy. The women of the Birth Mothers Network serve as mentors to one another, help each other cope with the challenges of parenting a child with an FASD, and provide caring, non-judgmental support to members who are in recovery.

Living With FASD
http://www.nofas.org/living

The Living With FASD page is provided by NOFAS, and contains links to financial assistance programs such as Supplemental Security Income (SSI) and Social Security Disability Insurance (SSDI) (both can be contacted at 1-800-772-1213), and <u>Medicaid</u>, as well as family and mother support programs such as **Women, Infants and Children** (WIC).

Additional Support Sites

In addition to research and general information, each of the following sites provides access to other members of the FASD community, as well as parenting guidance, personal stories from others who are coping with FASD, and guides to services.

• The FAS Community Resource Center

http://www.come-over.to/FASCRC/

• FASlink

http://www.faslink.org/

• One-Stop Centers

http://www.careeronestop.org/

One-Stop Centers are Internet job sites that can provide links to your state Department of Labor and Workforce Development, the local division for vocational rehabilitation services, and/or specific state initiatives for development of customized employment for people with disabilities.

Appendix D—The FASD 4-Digit Code Caregiver Interview Checklist: Profiles of FASD

The form below was developed by the Washington State FAS Diagnostic and Prevention Network (FAS DPN), and is part of the *4-Digit Diagnostic Code* (Astley, 2004). The caregivers of all patients receiving an FASD diagnostic evaluation in the Washington State FAS DPN clinics participate in a 2-hour interview with the pediatrician and psychologist. The purpose of the interview is to identify areas of significant delay/impairment across a wide array of functional domains.

The article *Profile of the First 1,400 Patients Receiving Diagnostic Evaluations for Fetal Alcohol Spectrum Disorder at the Washington State Fetal Alcohol Syndrome Diagnostic & Prevention Network*, by Dr. Susan Astley (2010), provides a graphical summary of the first 1,400 caregiver interviews conducted by the FAS DPN clinics. Presented is the proportion of patients classified by the pediatrician as "significantly delayed/impaired" in behaviors addressed in a 2-hour, structured caregiver interview administered jointly by the pediatrician and psychologist during the FASD diagnostic evaluation. This graphical presenta-tion illustrates the cumulative increase in impairment as one advances across the FASD diagnostic groups. The illustration is color-dependent and too complex to present in this TIP. However, readers are encouraged to access the article at the following link: **http://depts.washington.edu/fasdpn/pdfs/astley-profile-2010.pdf**

The FASD 4-Digit Code Caregiver Interview Checklist

Severity Score: Severity of Delay/Impairment (Displayed along left margin)

Circle: **0** = Unknown, Not Assessed, Too Young **1** = Within Normal Limits **2** = Mild to Moderate **3** = Significant

Severity	Caregiver Observations
	Planning/Temporal Skills
0 1 2 3	Needs considerable help organizing daily tasks _____
0 1 2 3	Cannot organize time _____
0 1 2 3	Does not understand concept of time _____
0 1 2 3	Difficulty in carrying out multi-step tasks _____
0 1 2 3	Other _____

	Behavioral Regulation/Sensory Motor Integration
0 1 2 3	Poor management of anger/tantrums _____
0 1 2 3	Mood swings _____
0 1 2 3	Impulsive _____
0 1 2 3	Compulsive _____
0 1 2 3	Perseverative _____
0 1 2 3	Inattentive _____
0 1 2 3	Inappropriately [high or low] activity level _____
0 1 2 3	Lying/stealing _____
0 1 2 3	Unusual [high or low] reactivity to [sound touch light] _____
0 1 2 3	Other _____
	Abstract Thinking/Judgment
0 1 2 3	Poor judgment _____
0 1 2 3	Cannot be left alone _____
0 1 2 3	Concrete, unable to think abstractly _____
0 1 2 3	Other _____
	Memory/Learning/Information Processing
0 1 2 3	Poor memory, inconsistent retrieval of learned information _____
0 1 2 3	Slow to learn new skills _____
0 1 2 3	Does not seem to learn from past experiences _____
0 1 2 3	Problems recognizing consequences of actions _____
0 1 2 3	Problems with information processing speed and accuracy _____
0 1 2 3	Other _____
	Spatial Skills and Spatial Memory
0 1 2 3	Gets lost easily, has difficulty navigating from point A to point B __
0 1 2 3	Other _____
	Social Skills and Adaptive Behavior
0 1 2 3	Behaves at a level notably younger than chronological age _____
0 1 2 3	Poor social/adaptive skills _____
0 1 2 3	Other _____
	Motor/Oral Motor Control
0 1 2 3	Poor/delayed motor skills _____
0 1 2 3	Poor balance _____
0 1 2 3	Other _____

Source: Astley, S. J. (2004). *Diagnostic guide for Fetal Alcohol Spectrum Disorders: The 4-Digit Diagnostic Code*, Third Edition. Seattle, WA: University of Washington. Accessed June 1, 2012 at **http://depts.washington.edu/fasdpn/pdfs/FASD-2004-Diag-Form-08-06-04.pdf**. Used with permission from the author.

Appendix E—Comparison of Current FASD Diagnostic Systems

Fetal Alcohol Syndrome (FAS) is a permanent birth defect syndrome caused by maternal consumption of alcohol during pregnancy. Almost four decades have passed since the term FAS was first coined. The condition is now recognized as a spectrum of disorders: Fetal Alcohol Spectrum Disorders (FASD). Substantial progress has been made in developing specific criteria for delineating diagnoses under the umbrella of FASD. In the 14 years since the publication of the seminal report on FAS by the Institute of Medicine in 1996, clear consensus has been reached on two fundamental issues: 1) an FASD diagnostic evaluation is best conducted by a team of professionals from multiple disciplines (medicine, psychology, speech-language, occupational therapy) and 2) the team should use rigorously case-defined and validated FASD diagnostic guidelines.

In 2011, Dr. Susan Astley wrote a chapter on Diagnosing FASD in a book entitled *Prenatal Alcohol Use and Fetal Alcohol Spectrum Disorders: Diagnosis, Assessment and New Directions in Research and Multimodal Treatment* (Astley, 2011). This chapter provided a brief overview of the discovery of FASD, diagnostic challenges, how diagnostic guidelines and clinical models have evolved over time to address these challenges, and how new technology may influence the future of FASD diagnosis. The tables below come from that chapter, and provide a side-by-side comparison of the five most commonly used diagnostic guidelines for forms of FASD; the 4-Digit Diagnostic Code (Astley, 2004b), the guidelines developed by the Centers for Disease Control and Prevention (Bertrand et al., 2004), the Canadian guidelines (Chudley et al., 2005), the revised guidelines of the Institute of Medicine (IOM) (Hoyme et al., 2005), and the original IOM guidelines (Stratton et al., 1996). Table 1 compares diagnostic criteria for FAS; Table 2, pFAS; Table 3, ARND; and Table 4, ARBD. These tables are reprinted here with the permission of the author.

It is important to note that, for the purposes of this Appendix, the 4-Digit Diagnostic Code has been translated, as best as possible, into a text (rather than numeric) format. This was done to facilitate comparison to the other guidelines that publish their diagnostic criteria in text format. Diagnostic teams should not use the textual translations of the 4-Digit Code presented in Tables 1-4 to derive a 4-Digit Code, but rather the numeric format presented in the *Diagnostic Guide for Fetal Alcohol Spectrum Disorders: The 4-Digit Diagnostic Code*, Third Edition (Astley, 2004a).

Table 1. FAS Diagnostic Criteria: Comparison Across the Five Most Current FASD Diagnostic Guidelines

	4-Digit Code (2004)	CDC (2004)	Canadian (2005)	Revised IOM (2005)	IOM (1996)
Growth	Prenatal and/or postnatal height or weight ≤ 10th percentile (Growth Ranks 2-4)	Prenatal and/or postnatal height or weight ≤ 10th percentile	At least 1 of the following: • Prenatal and/or postnatal height or weight ≤ 10th percentile • Weight-to-height ratio (≤10th percentile)	Prenatal and/or postnatal height or weight ≤ 10th percentile	At least 1 of the following: • Low birth weight • Low weight for height • Decelerating weight
Face	All 3 of the following at any age: • PFL ≤ 3rd percentile • Smooth philtrum Rank 4 or 5 • Thin upper lip Rank 4 or 5 (Face Rank 4)	All 3 of the following: • PFL ≤ 10th percentile • Smooth philtrum Rank 4 or 5 • Thin upper lip Rank 4 or 5	All 3 of the following at any age: • PFL ≤ 3rd percentile • Smooth philtrum Rank 4 or 5 • Thin upper lip Rank 4 or 5	2 or more of the following: • PFL ≤ 10th percentile • Smooth philtrum Rank 4 or 5 • Thin upper lip Rank 4 or 5	Characteristic pattern that includes features such as short PFL, flat upper lip, flattened philtrum, and flat midface.

CNS	At least 1 of the following:
	• Structural/Neurological: (e.g., OFC ≤ 3rd percentile, abnormal structure, seizure disorder, hard signs)
	• Severe Dysfunction: (3 or more domains[a] of function with impairment 2 or more SDs below the mean)
		At least 1 of the following:
		• Structural/Neurological: (e.g., OFC ≤ 10th percentile, abnormal structure, seizure disorder, hard/soft signs)
		• Dysfunction[b]:
		  • 3 or more domains of function with impairment 1 or more
			At least 3 of the following Structure/Neurological/Functional domains with impairment[c]:
			• Hard/soft signs, structure, cognition, communication, academic achievement, memory, executive functioning, abstract reasoning, ADD,
				At least 1 of the following:
				• Structural
				  • OFC ≤ 10th percentile
				  • Abnormal structure
					At least 1 of the following:
					• Structural/Neurological:
					  • Decreased cranial size at birth
					  • Abnormal structure (e.g., microcephaly, partial/complete agenesis of the corpus callosum, cerebellar hypoplasia)
					  • Neurological hard/soft signs

	(CNS Rank 3 and/or 4)	SDs below the mean • Global deficit (2 or more SDs below the mean)	adaptive behavior, social skills, or communication		
Alcohol	Confirmed or Unknown (Alcohol Ranks 2,3 or 4)	Confirmed or Unknown	Confirmed or Unknown	Confirmed-excessive or Unknown	Confirmed-excessive or Unknown

a. 4-Digit Code: Domains may include, but are not limited to: executive function, memory, cognition, social/adaptive skills, academic achievement, language, motor, attention, or activity level.

b. CDC: Performance substantially below that expected for an individual's age, schooling, or circumstances, as evidenced by: 1) Global cognitive or intellectual deficits representing multiple domains of deficit (or significant developmental delay in younger children) with performance below the 3rd percentile (2 standard deviations below the mean for standardized testing) or 2) Functional deficits below the 16th percentile (1 standard deviation below the mean for standardized testing) in at least three of the following domains: a) cognitive or developmental deficits or discrepancies b) executive functioning deficits c) motor functioning delays d) problems with attention or hyperactivity e) social skills f) other, such as sensory problems, pragmatic language problems, memory deficits, etc.

c. Canadian: Impairment indicates scores $\geq$ 2 SDs below the mean, discrepancies of 1.5-2 SDs among subtests, or $\geq$ 1 SD discrepancy between subdomains.

Table 2: Partial FAS Diagnostic Criteria: Comparison Across the Five Most Current FASD Diagnostic Guidelines

	4-Digit Code (1997-2004)	CDC[a] (2004)	Canadian (2005)	Revised IOM (2005)	IOM (1996)
Growth	Prenatal or postnatal height or weight $\leq$ 10th percentile (Growth Ranks 1-4)	--	No growth deficiency	Prenatal and/or postnatal height or weight $\leq$ 10th percentile	At least 1 of the following: • Low birth weight • Low weight for height • Decelerating weight
Face	All 3 of the following at any age: • PFL $\leq$ 3rd percentile	--	2 of the following at any age: • PFL $\leq$ 3rd percentile	2 or more of the following: • PFL $\leq$ 10th percentile	Some components of the pattern of FAS characteristic facial anomalies.

	• Smooth philtrum Rank 4 or 5 • Thin upper lip Rank 4 or 5 (Face Ranks 3 or 4)*		• Smooth philtrum Rank 4 or 5 • Thin upper lip Rank 4 or 5	• Smooth philtrum Rank 4 or 5 • Thin upper lip • Rank 4 or 5	

CNS	At least 1 of the following:
	• Structural/ Neurological: (e.g., OFC ≤ 3rd percentile, abnormal structure, seizure disorder, hard signs)
	• Severe Dysfunction: (3 or more domains[b] of function with impairment 2 or more SDs below the mean)
	(CNS Rank 3 and/or 4)
		--	At least 3 of the following Structure/ Neurological/ Functional domains with significant impairment[c]:
			• Hard/soft signs, structure, cognition, communication, academic achievement, memory, executive functioning, abstract reasoning, ADD, adaptive behavior, social skills, or communication
				At least 1 of the following:
				• Structural
				  • OFC ≤ 10th percentile
				  • Abnormal structure
				• Dysfunction
				  • Complex pattern[d] of behavior/ cognitive abnorm-alities
					At least 1 of the following:
					• Structural/ Neurological:
					  • Decreased cranial size at birth
					  • Abnormal structure
					  • Hard/soft signs
					• Dysfunction
					  • Complex pattern[e] of behavior/ cognitive abnormalities

Additional Criteria	PFAS requires the CNS and Alcohol criteria to be met and allows either the Growth or the Face criteria to be relaxed just slightly. • *If the growth deficiency criteria above are met, one facial feature may be relaxed as follows: (PFL ≤ 1 SD, or Philtrum Rank 3, or Lip Rank 3) or	--	None	PFAS requires the Face and Alcohol criteria to be met and only one of the following additional criteria: • Growth • CNS Structural • CNS dysfunction	PFAS requires the Face and Alcohol criteria to be met and only one of the following additional criteria: • Growth • CNS Structural/ Neurological • CNS dysfunction

	• If the FAS face criteria are met, growth can be relaxed to normal.				
Alcohol	Confirmed (Alcohol Ranks 3 or 4)	--	Confirmed	Confirmed-excessive or Unknown	Confirmed-excessive

a. The CDC Guidelines only address FAS.

b. 4-Digit Code: Domains may include, but are not limited to: executive function, memory, cognition, social/adaptive skills, academic achievement, language, motor, attention, or activity level.

c. Canadian: Impairment indicates scores ≥ 2 SDs below the mean, discrepancies of 1.5 to 2 SDs among subtests, or ≥ 1 SD discrepancy between subdomains.

d. Hoyme: Marked impairment in the performance of complex tasks (complex problem solving, planning, judgment, abstraction, metacognition, and arithmetic tasks); higher-level receptive and expressive language deficits; and disordered behavior (difficulties in personal manner, emotional lability, motor dysfunction, poor academic performance, and deficient social interaction).

e. IOM: Complex pattern of behavior or cognitive abnormalities that are inconsistent with developmental level and cannot be explained by familial background or environment alone: e.g., learning difficulties; deficits in school performance; poor impulse control; problems in social perception; deficits in higher level receptive and expressive language; poor capacity for abstraction or metacognition; specific deficits in mathematical skills; or problems in memory, attention or judgment.

Table 3. ARND (or its equivalent: Static Encephalopathy/Alcohol Exposed or Neurobehavioral Disorder/Alcohol Exposed) Diagnostic Criteria: Comparison Across the Five Most Current FASD Diagnostic Guidelines

	4-Digit Code (1997-2004)	CDC[a] (2004)	Canadian (2005)	Revised IOM (2005)	IOM (1996)
Growth	Normal to deficient (Growth Ranks 1-4)	--	No growth deficiency	No growth deficiency	No growth deficiency
Face	No more than 1 of the following: • PFL ≤ 3rd percentile • Philtrum Rank 4 or 5 • Lip Rank 4 or 5 (Face Ranks 1-2)	--	No FAS facial phenotype	No FAS facial phenotype	Presumably no components of the pattern of FAS characteristic facial anomalies.

CNS	Criteria for "Static Encephalopathy" At least 1 of the following:
	• Structural/ Neurological: (e.g., OFC ≤ 3rd percentile, abnormal structure, seizure disorder, hard signs)
	• Severe Dysfunction: (3 or more domains[b] of function with impairment 2 or more SDs below the mean)
	(CNS Rank 3 and/or 4)
	
	Criteria for "Neurobehavioral Disorder"[c]
	• No Structural/ Neurological abnormalities.
	• Moderate Dysfunction: 1-2 domains[b] of function with impairment ≥ 1.5 SDs below the mean)
		--	At least 3 of the following Structure/ Neurological/ Functional domains with significant impairment[c]:
			• Hard/soft signs, structure, cognition, communication, academic achievement, memory, executive functioning, abstract reasoning, ADD, adaptive behavior, social skills, or communication
				At least 1 of the following:
				• Structural
				  • OFC ≤ 10th percentile
				  • Abnormal structure
				• Dysfunction
				  • Complex pattern[d] of behavior/ cognitive abnormalities
					At least 1 of the following:
					• Structural/ Neurological:
					  • Decreased cranial size at birth
					  • Abnormal structure
					  • Hard/soft signs
					• Dysfunction
					  • Complex pattern[e] of behavior/cognitive abnormalities

Additional Criteria	The term ARND is not used. The following terms are used in lieu of ARND: Static Encephalopathy (Severe dysfunction) Neurobehavioral Disorder	--	--	--	--

	(Moderate dysfunction)				
Alcohol	Confirmed (Alcohol Ranks 3 or 4)	--	Confirmed	Confirmed-excessive	Confirmed-excessive

a. The CDC Guidelines only address FAS.

b. 4-Digit Code: Domains may include, but are not limited to: executive function, memory, cognition, social/adaptive skills, academic achievement, language, motor, attention, or activity level. MRI research confirms Neurobehavioral Disorder/Alcohol Exposed is a distinct, clinically meaningful subclassification under the umbrella of FASD [6].

c. Canadian: Impairment indicates scores $\geq$ 2 SDs below the mean, discrepancies of 1.5-2 SDs among subtests, or $\geq$ 1 SD discrepancy between subdomains.

d. Hoyme: Marked impairment in the performance of complex tasks (complex problem solving, planning, judgment, abstraction, metacognition, and arithmetic tasks); higher-level receptive and expressive language deficits; and disordered behavior (difficulties in personal manner, emotional lability, motor dysfunction, poor academic performance, and deficient social interaction).

e. IOM: Complex pattern of behavior or cognitive abnormalities that are inconsistent with developmental level and cannot be explained by familial background or environment alone: e.g., learning difficulties; deficits in school performance; poor impulse control; problems in social perception; deficits in higher level receptive and expressive language; poor capacity for abstraction or metacognition; specific deficits in mathematical skills; or problems in memory, attention or judgment.

Table 4. ARBD Diagnostic Criteria: Comparison Across the Five Most Current FASD Diagnostic Guidelines

	4-Digit Code[a] (1997-2004)	CDC[b] (2004)	Canadian[a] (2005)	Revised IOM (2005)	IOM (1996)
Growth	--	--	--	Not specified	Not specified
Face	--	--	--	2 or more of the following: • PFL $\leq$ 10th percentile • Philtrum Rank 4 or 5 • Lip Rank 4 or 5	Not specified
CNS	--	--	--	Not specified	Not specified

Congenital Defects	--	--	--	1 or more of the following: • Cardiac: Atrial septal defects, Ventricular septal defects, Aberrant great vessels, Tetralogy of Fallot. • Skeletal: Hypoplastic nails, Shortened fifth digits, Radioulnar synostosis, Flexion contractures, Camptodactyly, Clinodactyly, Pectus excavatum and carinatum, Klippel-Feil syndrome, Hemivertebrae, Scoliosis. • Renal: Aplastic/dysplastic/hypoplastic kidneys, Horseshoe kidneys, Ureteral duplications, Hydronephrosis. • Ocular: Strabismus, Retinal vascular anomalies, Refractive problems secondary to small globes. • Auditory: Conductive hearing loss, Neurosensory hearing loss. • Other: Virtually every malformation has been described in some patient with FAS.	Congenital structural defects in 1 of the following categories, including malformations and dysplasias (if the patient displays minor anomalies only, 2 must be present): • Cardiac: Atrial septal defects, Ventricular septal defects, Aberrant great vessels, conotruncal heart defects. • Skeletal: Radioulnar synostosis, Vertebral segmentation defects, Large joint contractures, Scoliosis. • Renal: Aplastic/dysplastic/hypoplastic kidneys, "Horseshoe" kidney/ureteral duplications. • Eyes: Strabismus, Ptosis, Retinal vascular anomalies, Optic nerve hypoplasia. • Ears: Conductive hearing loss, Neurosensory hearing loss. • Minor Anomalies: Hypoplastic nails, Short fifth digits, Clinodactyly of fifth fingers, Pectus carinatum/excavatum, Camptodactyly, "Hockey stick" palmar creases, Refractive errors,

	--	--	--	The etiologic specificity of most of these anomalies to alcohol teratogenesis remains uncertain.	"Railroad track" ears.
Alcohol	--	--	--	Confirmed-excessive	Confirmed-excessive

a. The 4-Digit Code and Canadian Guidelines do not recognize ARBD as a FASD diagnostic classification.
b. The CDC Guidelines only address FAS.

Appendix F—Sample Crisis/ Safety Plan

The following is a suggested Crisis/Safety Plan that can be used with a client who has or may have an FASD, or with a family member or caregiver of the client. The plan is designed to help identify safety concerns for the client, actions that can be taken to prevent or address those concerns, and support persons that can assist.

If you have access to an electronic version of this TIP, consider printing this and the following page back-to-back as a way to reproduce the form for your use. This form has been adapted from materials in the *Families Moving Forward Program* (**http://depts.washington.edu/fmffasd/**). Check their Web site for additional resources.

Client Crisis/Safety Plan

Client's Name: _____ Date: _____

Caregiver(s): _____

Legal Guardian(s): _____

Provider/Counselor: _____

1. List the crisis or safety concerns for the client and other family members/ caregivers.

    _____

    _____

    _____

    _____

☐   *No crisis or safety concerns were identified. Clients were given appropriate resources. Item #2 below was filled out.*

2. List formal and informal supports. These can be family, friends, respite providers, social workers, community supports such as faith-based organizations (and so on). These are people available to help with crisis/ safety concerns. *(Fill out even if there are no current concerns.)*

    _____

    _____

    _____

---

3. How can these support people help during a crisis?

Name: _____ Phone: _____

    Action: _____

    _____

Name: _____ Phone: _____

    Action: _____

    _____

Name: _____ Phone: _____

    Action: _____

    _____

Name: _____ Phone: _____

    Action: _____

    _____

4. Steps for the crisis plan. *(Use if safety concerns are immediate or the situation could get out of hand. Describe what might happen and what you'd do. Include phone numbers of people you would call.)*

_____

_____

_____

IF THERE IS A MEDICAL EMERGENCY, CALL 911.

5. Local Crisis Line number: _____

This is only a suggested action plan. Input from other service providers should be taken into account. This can include therapists, doctors, and emergency services.

This sample Crisis/Safety Plan was developed as part of the *Families Moving Forward Program* and adapted for this TIP with permission of the authors.

Appendix G—Services and Supports Checklist

Counselors can provide invaluable assistance to the family/caregivers of an individual who has or may have an FASD, or to their client with FASD, by helping them access appropriate services and supports. Below is a comprehensive checklist that can help a counselor and client identify what supports are needed, and choose what community resources are realistic as linkages.

If you have access to an electronic version of the TIP, consider printing this and the following page back-to-back to use with clients as an efficient worksheet. This form has been adapted from materials in the *Families Moving Forward Program* (**http://depts.washington.edu/fmffasd**). Check their Web site for more resources.

Services and Supports Checklist

Client's Name: _____ Date: _____

Which of the following would you like to look into?

Material and Financial Assistance and Resources
_____Government/financial assistance (SSI, WIC, etc.)

_____Low-cost housing

_____Adoption funding

_____Developmental disabilities funding

Information and Advocacy Resources
_____Advocacy services

_____Case management services

_____Diagnostic and evaluation services (FASD/non-FASD)

_____Guardian/future planning services

_____Information and referral services

_____Parent/family training, parenting classes

_____Legal services/assistance

Health and Mental Health Resources
_____Health/mental health care financial support

_____Medication evaluation

_____Mental health services

_____Alcohol and drug treatment/recovery programs

_____Family planning/contraceptive resources

_____Substance abuse education for children

Childcare and Respite Resources

_____In-home respite/sitter services

_____Out-of-home respite services

_____Daycare

Crisis Lines and Response Teams

_____Crisis lines/response teams

_____Crisis response teams

_____Child protective services

_____Other crisis resources

Mentor and Support Groups and Resources

_____FASD caregiver/family support groups

_____FASD self-advocacy resources

_____Birth mother network

_____Other types of support groups

_____Sibling support groups

_____Parent-to-parent support (formal and informal)

_____Mentor programs

_____Recreational activities

_____Recovery supports

_____Other support resources

Educational Services and Job Resources

_____Special education and other accommodation programs

_____School-based treatment/therapeutic services

_____Behavior management assistance

_____Tutoring

_____Educational advocacy services

_____Vocational rehabilitation

_____Vocational or job counseling/coaching

Internet and Educational Resources

_____Information on FASD and FASD supports

_____E-mail lists (for? _____)

_____Internet sites (about? _____)

_____Other brochures, books (about? _____)

OTHER

_____Juvenile justice services

_____Representative (or protective) payee services

_____ _____

This checklist was developed as part of the _Families Moving Forward Program_, and is adapted for this TIP with permission of the authors.

Appendix H—Operational Standards for Fetal Alcohol Spectrum Disorders (FASD): A Model

The state of Mississippi has developed operational standards addressing FASD that can potentially help define and inform other state reimbursement systems. The following selected standards are taken from the Mississippi Department of Mental Health's *Operational Standards for Mental Health, Intellectual/Developmental Disabilities, and Substance Abuse Community Service Providers*, published January 2011.

- **XVI.D.1.** Fetal alcohol spectrum disorders (FASD) is an umbrella term describing the range of effects that can occur in an individual whose mother drank alcohol during pregnancy. These effects may include physical, mental, behavioral, and/or learning disabilities with possible lifelong implications. Behavioral or cognitive problems may include intellectual disability, learning disabilities, attention deficits, hyperactivity, poor impulse control, and social, language, and memory deficits. FASD occurs in about 1% of all live births, or about 450 to 500 new cases in Mississippi per year. The damage caused by prenatal alcohol exposure is permanent. The effects cannot be reversed, but many of them can be treated with the appropriate combination of interventions and support. Secondary disabilities of FASD include mental health issues (90%), school problems (60%), trouble with the law (60%) and attempted suicide (23%). Early identification and diagnosis of children with an FASD can help ensure appropriate treatment which in turn will help reduce the occurrence and impact of these secondary disabilities.

- **XVI.D.2.** Children ages birth to age 18 must be screened within six (6) months of Intake to determine if there is a need for a Fetal Alcohol Spectrum Disorders (FASD) diagnostic evaluation. Youth ages 18 to 24 may be screened for an FASD if the provider has reason to believe that there was prenatal alcohol exposure.

- **XVI.D.3.** The FASD screening tool1 will be provided by the Division of Children and Youth Services (see the DMH Record Guide). The screening may be conducted by a case manager, a therapist, or other children's mental health professional.

- **XVI.D.5.** Results of the FASD screening and FASD diagnostic evaluations, if indicated, must be reflected in the child's Individual Service Plan and/or

Case Management Service 185 Plan. If a child receives a fetal alcohol-related diagnosis, it should be recorded on the appropriate Axis.

- **XVI.D.6.** If a child's initial FASD screening result is negative and if additional information regarding maternal alcohol history is obtained that might change the results of the initial FASD screen from negative to positive for possible prenatal alcohol exposure, the result of the initial screening must be revised on the FASD Screening Form to reflect this change and a diagnostic evaluation must be sought.

- **XVI.D.7.** With consent obtained from the parent/legal guardian, children who receive a positive FASD screen should be referred to the Child Development Clinic at the University of Mississippi Medical Center or other multi-disciplinary children's clinic qualified to diagnose FASD for a diagnostic evaluation. With consent obtained from the parent/legal guardian, best practice requires a provider staff person to accompany the child and parent/ guardian to the diagnostic appointment in order to participate in the child's history interview and the informational interview. If this best practice is not followed, the child's record must be documented to show the effort put forth by the staff person to attend the diagnostic appointment and the reason this did not occur. A copy of the full diagnostic report must be placed in the child's record.

- **XVI.D.8.** Treatments and interventions recommended by the FASD multi-disciplinary diagnostic team must be either provided or facilitated by the CMHC. Referral to the local MAP Team should be made when appropriate.

- **XVI.D.9.** Because children with an FASD often are not able to respond to traditional mental health services and/or treatments, children's mental health services may need to be modified in order to be more effective for children with an FASD. FASD services and service modifications must be documented in the child's record.

[1] The FASD screening tool referred to in operational standard **XVI.D.3** is available on pp. 129-131 of the *Department of Mental Health Record Guide for Mental Health, Intellectual and Developmental Disabilities, and Substance Abuse Community Providers, 2012 Revision* (**http://www.dmh.state.ms.us/pdf/DMH%20Record%20Guide%202012%20Revision.pdf**), published by the Mississippi Department of Mental Health. The tool is less extensive than the *FASD 4-Digit Code Caregiver Interview Checklist* included in Part 1, Chapter 2 of this TIP, and is intended primarily for use with children (although it is suggested for limited use with individuals ages 18-24).

Appendix I—Stakeholders Meeting Participants

Sally Anderson, Ph.D.
Special Assistant to Deputy Director, National Institute on Alcohol Abuse and Alcoholism

Jacquelyn Bertrand, Ph.D.
Behavioral Scientist, Centers for Disease Control and Prevention

Sterling K. Clarren, M.D., FAAP
Chief Executive Officer and Scientific Director, Canada NW FASD Research Network; Clinical Professor of Pediatrics, University of British Columbia; Clinical Professor of Pediatrics, University of Washington; TIP Co-Chair

Carolyn Hartness
FASD Project Specialist, Northwest Portland Area Indian Health Board

Lynne Haverkos, M.D., M.P.H.
Medical Officer, National Institute of Child Health and Human Development

John H. McGovern, M.G.A.
Senior Public Health Analyst, Health Resources and Services Administration

Sara Messelt
Executive Director, Minnesota Organization on Fetal Alcohol Syndrome

Kathleen Mitchell, M.H.S., LCADC
Vice President and National Spokesperson, National Organization on Fetal Alcohol Syndrome

Melinda M. Ohlemiller, M.A.
Chief Executive Officer, Nurses for Newborns Foundation; TIP Co-Chair

Feng Zhou, Ph.D.
Past President, FASD Study Group; Professor, Indiana University School Medicine

Center for Substance Abuse Treatment

Sharon Amatetti, M.P.H.
Public Health Analyst, Division of Services Improvement, Center for Substance Abuse Treatment

Christina Currier
Project Officer, CSAT Knowledge Application Program, Division of Services Improvement, Center for Substance Abuse Treatment

Richard T. Kopanda, M.A.
CSAT Deputy Director, Center for Substance
Abuse Treatment

Linda White-Young, M.S.W., LC SW
Public Health Advisor, Division of Services
Improvement, Center for Substance Abuse
Treatment

Center for Substance Abuse Prevention

Jon Dunbar-Cooper, M.A., CPP
Task Order Officer, SAMHSA FASD Center
for Excellence, Division of Systems
Development, Center for Substance Abuse
Prevention

Patricia Getty, Ph.D.
Deputy Task Order Officer, SAMHSA FASD
Center for Excellence, Division of Systems
Development, Center for Substance Abuse
Prevention

CDR Josefine Haynes-Battle, R.N., B.S.N., M.S.N.
Past Deputy Task Order Officer, SAMHSA
FASD Center for Excellence, Division
of Systems Development, Center for
Substance Abuse Prevention

Mike Lowther, M.A.
Acting Deputy Director, Center for Substance
Abuse Prevention

Virginia Mackay-Smith, M.P.H.
Director, Division of Systems Development,
Center for Substance Abuse Prevention

Center for Mental Health Services

Anna Marsh, Ph.D.
Deputy Director, Center for Mental Health
Services

Deborah Stone, Ph.D.
Social Science Analyst, Center for Mental
Health Services (Retired)

Appendix J—Field Reviewers

Susan Adubato, Ph.D.
Director, Northern New Jersey FAS
   Diagnostic Center
Director, New Jersey/North East
   FASD Education and Research
   Center, University of Medicine
   and Dentistry of New Jersey, New
   Jersey Medical School
Newark, NJ

Sally Anderson, Ph.D.
Special Assistant to Deputy Director
National Institute on Alcohol Abuse
   and Alcoholism
Rockville, MD

Susan Astley, Ph.D.
Professor of Epidemiology/Pediatrics,
   University of Washington
Director, WA State FAS Diagnostic &
   Prevention Network
Seattle, WA

Michael Baldwin, M.N.S.
Alaska Mental Health Trust Authority
Anchorage, AK

Jacqueline Bertrand, Ph.D.
Psychologist
Centers for Disease Control and
   Prevention
Atlanta, GA

Eileen B. Bisgard, J.D.
Project Director
Seventeenth Judicial FASD Project
Brighton, CO

Anthony Bullock
Hattiesburg, MS

Janet S. Burtt, M.A.
Southern California Alcohol & Drug
   Programs, Inc.
Downey, CA

Melissa Clarke
Lissie's Luv Yums
Great Falls, MT

Deborah E. Cohen, Ph.D.
Director, Office for Prevention
   of Mental Retardation and
   Developmental Disabilities, State
   of New Jersey (Retired)
Longboat Key, FL

Randolph Crawford
Norman, OK

Leah Davies
TOPDD
Austin, TX

Mary DeJoseph, D.O.
Doctor
New Jersey FASD Education and Research
    Center
Palmyra, NJ

Thomas Ebert, M.S.S.W., Ph.D.
ARC Community Services, Inc.
Madison, WI

Louise Floyd, R.N., D.S.N.
Team Leader/Behavioral Scientist
Fetal Alcohol Syndrome Prevention Team
National Center for Birth Defects and
    Developmental Disabilities
Centers for Disease Control and Prevention
Atlanta, GA

Sid Gardner, M.P.A.
President
Children and Family Futures
Irvine, CA

Julie Gelo
Trainer/Consultant/Advocate/Parent
Executive Director, NOFAS Washington
Support Person, Self Advocates with FASD in
    Action
Bothell, WA

Linda Grant
Evergreen Manor
Everett, WA

Therese Grant, Ph.D.
Ann Streissguth Endowed Professor in Fetal
    Alcohol Spectrum Disorders Director,
    Fetal Alcohol and Drug Unit
University of Washington School of Medicine
Seattle, WA

Cecily Hardin, M.S.W.
FASD Project Coordinator
Child Guidance Center
Jacksonville, FL

Patricia A. Harrison, Ph.D.
Research Director
Minneapolis, MN

Trisha Hinson, M.Ed., CMHT
FASD State Coordinator/Project Director
Mississippi Department of Mental Health
Brandon, MS

Sr. Johnelle Howanach
Lissie's Luv Yums
Great Falls, MT

Catherine Hutsell, M.P.H.
Health Education Specialist
FAS Prevention Team
National Center on Birth Defects and
    Development Disorders
Centers for Disease Control and Prevention
Atlanta, GA

Wendy O. Kalberg, M.A., CED
Senior Program Manager
UNM CASAA
Albuquerque, NM

**Judith King, M.S.W., LCSW, LCADC,
    CPAS**
Coordinator, Perinatal Addictions Prevention
    Project
Hudson Perinatal Consortium, Inc.
Jersey City, NJ

Suzie Kuerschner, M.Ed.
FASD Consultant and Trainer
Northwest Portland Area Indian Health
    Board
Rhododendron, OR

John H. McGovern, M.G.A.
Senior Public Health Analyst
Health Resources and Services Administration
Rockville, MD

Sara Messelt
Executive Director
Minnesota Organization on FAS (MOFAS)
St. Paul, MN

Violet Mitchell-Enos, M.S.W.
Scottsdale, AZ

Patricia Moran
Program Manager
White Earth Substance Abuse Program
Ponsford, MN

Jeri Museth
Wellness Coordinator, Tribal Family and
    Youth Services
Central Council of the Tlingit and Haida
    Indian Tribes of Alaska
Juneau, AK

Raquelle Myers
Santa Rosa, CA

Diane O'Connor
FASD Prevention Initiative, Research
    Foundation of Mental Hygiene
Support Person, Self Advocates with FASD in
    Action (SAFA)
Albany, NY

Heather Carmichael Olson, Ph.D.
Department of Psychiatry and Behavioral
    Sciences
University of Washington School of Medicine
    and Seattle Children's Research Institute
Seattle, WA

Carol Rangel
FASD Project Director
Division of Health and Human Services
Arkansas Division of Child and Family
    Services
Little Rock, AR

Jamie Reinebold, M.S.W.
Supervisor, FACES
Memorial Health System
South Bend, IN

Julia Robbins
Institute for Health and Recovery
Cambridge, MA

Paulette Romashko, M.S.W., LCSW
Director of Program Development and
    Evaluation
FASD Project Director
ARC Community Services, Inc.
Madison, WI

Iris Smith, Ph.D., M.P.H.
Clinical Associate Professor
Department of Behavioral Sciences and
    Health Education
Rollins School of Public Health
Atlanta, GA

Brenda Stoneburner, M.A., LPC
Communicable Disease Specialist
Michigan Department of Health
Bureau of Substance Abuse and Addiction
Lansing, MI

Sue Taylor, M.S.
Manager Early Childhood Services
Memorial Health System
South Ben, IN

Tracey Waller, M.B.A., RD, LD
Bellbrook, OH

Mary Kate Weber, M.P.H.
Behavioral Scientist
Fetal Alcohol Syndrome Prevention Team
National Center on Birth Defects and
    Developmental Disabilities
Centers for Disease Control and Prevention
Atlanta, GA

Nancy Whitney, M.S., LMHC
Clinical Director, King County Parent Child
    Assistant Program
University of Washington
Seattle, WA

Georgiana Wilton, Ph.D.
Associate Scientist, Family Medicine
University of Wisconsin
Madison, WI

Barbara Wybrecht, R.N.
FASD Clinical Nurse Specialist
Advocate/Trainer
Support Person, Self Advocates with FASD in
    Action
Grand Rapids, MI

Rob Wybrecht
Lifelong Expert on FASD
Arc of Kent County
Network Coordinator, Self Advocates with
    FASD in Action (SAFA)
Grand Rapids, MI

Appendix K— Acknowledgments

Numerous people contributed to the development of this TIP, including the TIP Consensus Panelists (see pp. ix-x), Stakeholder meeting attendees (see Appendix I) and field reviewers (see Appendix J).

This publication was produced under the Fetal Alcohol Spectrum Disorders (FASD) Center for Excellence contract with the Northrop Grumman Corporation, for the Substance Abuse and Mental Health Services Administration, Center for Substance Abuse Prevention.

Callie B. Gass served as the FASD Center for Excellence Project Director, and Sharon James Ackah, J.D., M.P.H., served as the Deputy Project Director. Other Northrop Grumman-FASD Center for Excellence personnel included Dan Dubovsky, M.S.W., LCSW, Senior FASD Specialist; Vinitha Meyyur, Ph.D., Senior Evaluator and TIP Task Manager; Susan Kimner, Manager for Product Development; Jason P. Merritt, M.A., Senior Writer; Barbara Kosogof, M.P.A., and Katie Chan, Health Research Analysts and Literature Review Authors; Sharon J. Lytle, Quality Assurance Editor; and Jennifer Aggelis, Graphic Designer.

Index

CSAT TIPs and Publications Based on TIPs

What Is a TIP?

Treatment Improvement Protocols (TIPs) are the product of a systematic and innovative process that brings together clinicians, researchers, program managers, policymakers, and other Federal and non-Federal experts to reach consensus on state-of-the-art treatment practices. TIPs are developed by SAMHSA to improve the treatment capabilities of the nation's behavioral health service system.

What Is a Quick Guide?

A Quick Guide clearly and concisely presents the primary information from a TIP in a pocket-sized booklet. Each Quick Guide is divided into sections to help readers quickly locate relevant material. Some contain glossaries of terms or lists of resources. Page numbers from the original TIP are referenced so providers can refer back to the source document for more information.

What Are KAP Keys?

Also based on TIPs, KAP Keys are handy, durable tools. Keys may include assessment or screening instruments, checklists, and summaries of treatment phases. Printed on coated paper, each KAP Keys set is fastened together with a key ring and can be kept within a treatment provider's reach and consulted frequently. The Keys allow you, the busy clinician or program administrator, to locate information easily and to use this information to enhance treatment services.

Ordering Information

Publications may be ordered or downloaded for free at http://store.samhsa.gov/. To order by phone, please call 1-877-SAMHSA-7 (1-877-726-4727) (English and Español).

TIP 1 State Methadone Treatment Guidelines—*Replaced by TIP 43*

TIP 2* Pregnant, Substance-Using Women—BKD107

TIP 3 Screening and Assessment of Alcohol- and Other Drug-Abusing Adolescents—*Replaced by TIP 31*

TIP 4 Guidelines for the Treatment of Alcohol- and Other Drug-Abusing Adolescents—*Replaced by TIP 32*

TIP 5 Improving Treatment for Drug-Exposed Infants—BKD110

TIP 6* Screening for Infectious Diseases Among Substance Abusers—BKD131
Quick Guide for Clinicians QGCT06
KAP Keys for Clinicians KAPT06

TIP 7 Screening and Assessment for Alcohol and Other Drug Abuse Among Adults in the Criminal Justice System—*Replaced by TIP 44*

TIP 8 Intensive Outpatient Treatment for Alcohol and Other Drug Abuse—*Replaced by TIPs 46 and 47*

TIP 9 Assessment and Treatment of Patients With Coexisting Mental Illness and Alcohol and Other Drug Abuse—*Replaced by TIP 42*

TIP 10 Assessment and Treatment of Cocaine-Abusing Methadone-Maintained Patients—*Replaced by TIP 43*

TIP 11* Simple Screening Instruments for Outreach for Alcohol and Other Drug Abuse and Infectious Diseases—BKD143
Quick Guide for Clinicians QGCT11
KAP Keys for Clinicians KAPT11

TIP 12 Combining Substance Abuse Treatment With Intermediate Sanctions for Adults in the Criminal Justice System—*Replaced by TIP 44*

TIP 13 Role and Current Status of Patient Placement Criteria in the Treatment of Substance Use Disorders—BKD161
Quick Guide for Clinicians QGCT13
Quick Guide for Administrators QGAT13
KAP Keys for Clinicians KAPT13

*Under revision

*Under revision

*Under revision